Symbolic Logic and Language

A Programmed Text

SYMBOLIC LOGIC AND LANGUAGE

A Programmed Text

by

James Dickoff
Patricia James

Yale University

McGraw-Hill Book Company
New York   St. Louis   San Francisco
Toronto   London   Sydney

Preface

Symbolic Logic and Language is a learning program whose aim is to introduce logic in a readily understandable manner. The presentation presumes no prior knowledge or training in logic, but nonetheless makes no compromise in rigor or sophistication. System F, the system of logic developed here, is equivalent to classical propositional logic; but in preference to an axiomatic or truth-table formulation, system F is formulated essentially in terms of Professor Fitch's subordinate-proof method for natural deduction. The present formulation is akin to Gentzen's, however, in using not rules of deduction but LAFs (logical argument formulas)—the counterparts of Gentzen's figures of deduction—and in explicitly specifying the elements of the system to be expressions taken as spatial configurations.

Symbolic Logic and Language gives detailed training toward a mastery not only of automatic symbol manipulation but also of the more difficult and more significant task of discovering proofs in logic. This training is given in such a way that the reader is at the same time presented with an elementary case of systematic problem solving. The subordinate-proof formulation gives rise quite naturally to reducing a problem to subordinate problems and to the introduction of general strategies for such reduction. Moreover, a careful reader can become notationally bilingual and can see the existence of more than one notation as something other than mere perversity on the part of logicians; for though the parenthesis-free Lukasiewicz notation was especially convenient for developing and stating strategies for proof discovery, this notation is introduced through a consideration of notation in the *Principia* tradition, and account is taken of the reasoned move from the one notation to the other. Exercise in translation of notation are provided, as elsewhere exercises are supplied to allow applications of skill and knowledge in a context less structured than the text itself.

But *Symbolic Logic and Language* is not content to teach mere symbol manipulation. Care is taken to give a notion of a formal system as such, not just as a computing device, and to show how, why, and to what extent the system of logic can serve as a device for computing validity of arguments. Classroom experience with early versions of *Symbolic Logic and*

Language revealed that after mastery of system F through this text a reader was remarkably capable of mastering with minimal effort alternative formal systems. Therefore the appendixes contain axiomatic and truth-table formulations of classical propositional calculus along with exercises in the use of these systems.

Further, an attempt is made to show the relation of logic not only to arguments but to language in general. Emphasis on the logical or argumentive force of language, the structure of arguments, and their evaluation with respect to validity is calculated, on the one hand, to give a sensitivity to the logical or argumentive force of language as this force is imparted by connecting words and, on the other hand, indirectly to urge that language has other than logical function and force.

In a companion volume, *Symbolic Logic and Systems*, we treat logical form as imparted by linguistic devices other than connecting words, traditional syllogistics as a formal system, and then a natural-deduction formulation of predicate calculus; explicit attention is directed also to properties of formal systems and to their comparison and evaluation.

How to Use This Book

Symbolic Logic and Language is a learning program—that is, a carefully constructed sequence of items. The sequence of items that constitutes *Symbolic Logic and Language* is designed not to bring the learner a mere awareness of symbols, logic, language, and their interrelations but to bring him to a significant understanding of and respectable skill in each topic treated, as well as to an appreciation of how the topics are related to each other and to the whole of which they are parts.

For best results we suggest that the program be used in this way: Use a blank sheet of paper to cover all but the first item. Read the first item and then write a response on a piece of paper placed alongside the program. Then slide the piece of paper down to expose on the right the correct response to the first item and on the left the second item. Compare the response you wrote with the indicated response. Read the second item, respond in writing, slide the paper down, compare your response, and then read the next item. Continue this procedure during your work time. It is important to write responses or at least to formulate them before exposing the suggested response.

In general, it is recommended that a learner work at most from thirty to forty-five minutes at a single sitting and that preferably work should stop at the end of a section. A longer work period makes difficult the appropriately careful and attentive reading needed to profit most fully from the program's attempt to summarize old and integrate new material as the learner proceeds—making other review unnecessary and integration almost automatic. For the learner's convenience exercises and an achievement test are included after each chapter; answers to the achievement tests are to be found at the back of this book.

Acknowledgments

We gratefully acknowledge the many suggestions, comments, and contributions offered by Prof. Layman Allen, Director, and Mr. Robin Brooks, our colleagues in the ALL Project sponsored by the Carnegie Corporation. Work on this learning program was begun during the course of that project. We are grateful also for the kind cooperation of persons at the Mary L. Tracy School, Yale College, and the Yale School of Nursing. But our debt is of course greatest to Prof. Frederic Fitch, whose method of subordinate proof is essentially incorporated into this program and whose encouragement and guidance in theoretic matters have meant much to us.

James Dickoff
Patricia James

Contents

Symbolic Logic and Language

A Programmed Text

Part **1**

Sentences: Their Representation and Formalization

unit **1**

Well-formed Sentences

1-1 *(1) When Socrates was in prison he drank poison at the command of the Athenian government.*
(2) When Socrates was in prison.

We would call (1) a sentence. But since the string of words (2) makes no complete sense, clearly we would not call (2) a _____ .

sentence

1-2 *(1) Socrates was a famous teacher.*
(2) Thinker Greek poison Athens.

(1) is a sentence. But since (2) makes no sense, (2) is not a _____ .

sentence

1-3 *(1) Socrates taught Plato, and Plato founded a school.*
(2) Socrates taught Plato and.

Which of the above is not a sentence? _____

2

1-4 *(1) Socrates taught Plato, and thinker Greek poison Athens.*
(2) Socrates taught by asking questions, and Socrates claimed to learn as much by asking questions as his pupils did by answering.

Which of the above is not a sentence? _____

1

1-5 If two *sentences* are joined by an 'and,' the resulting string of words is itself a _____ .

sentence

1-6 *(1) Aristotle is the father of logic, or.*
(2) Aristotle is the father of logic, or a contribution to logic.
(3) Aristotle is the father of logic, or Aristotle surely made a very great contribution to logic.
(4) Father of, Aristotle surely made a very great contribution to logic.

Which three of these strings of words are *not* sentences?
_____ _____ _____

1; 2; 4

1-7 If two sentences are joined by an 'or,' the resulting string of words is itself a _____ .

sentence

1-8 (1) *If we wish to isolate a logical form of a sentence,* then *we use single letters to represent those sentences which we analyze as elementary sentences.*
(2) *If we wish to isolate a logical form of a sentence,* then.
(3) *If elementary sentences,* then *we wish to isolate a logical form of a sentence.*
(4) *If we wish to isolate a logical form of a sentence,* then *elementary sentences.*
(5) *If we wish to isolate a logical form of a sentence,* then *we represent the sentence* and *we formalize the sentence.*

Which two of these strings of words *are* sentences? _____
_____

1
5

1-9 If two sentences are joined by an 'and,' by an 'or,' or by an 'if then,' the resulting string of words is itself a _____ .

sentence

1-10 (1) It is false that *Socrates taught by lecturing.*
(2) It is false that *if Socrates taught Plato* then *Socrates was Plato's pupil.*
(3) It is false that *since Socrates argued with precision.*

Which of the above is *not* a sentence? _____

3

1-11 If a sentence is preceded by an 'it is false that,' the resulting string of words is itself a _____ .

sentence

1-12 (1) It is false that *every string of words is a sentence.*
(2) *Some sentences have parts which are just like other sentences,* and *some sentences have no parts which are just like other sentences.*
(3) *We can represent sentences by letters,* or *we can represent certain parts of sentences by letters.*
(4) *If we analyze parts of a sentence as elementary sentences,* then *we can represent such parts by single letters.*

How many of the above are sentences? _____

four

1-13   We can make these general observations about well-formed English sentences:

1. Any string of words which is an 'and' joining two sentences is itself a sentence.

2. Any string of words which is an 'or' joining two _____ it itself a sentence.

                                                                    sentences

3. Any string of words which is an 'if then' joining two _____ is itself a sentence.

                                                                   sentences

4. Any string of words which is an 'it is false that' preceding _____ sentence is itself a sentence.

                                                                   one

Likeness of Expressions

1-14 *(1) fast*

This word may have the same meaning as each of the following words:

> *(2) quick*
> *(3) fast*

But word 1 is just like—that is, has the same shape as—which
one of the other two words? _____   3

1-15 For two words to be called like words they must have
the same shape. Which of the following are like words?

> *(1) king*   *(4) measure*
> *(2) ruler*   *(5) monarch*
> *(3) yardstick*   *(6) ruler*

_____ _____   2; 6

1-16 *(1) Socrates taught Plato.*

This sentence may have the same meaning as each of the
following sentences:

> *(2) Plato was taught by Socrates.*
> *(3) Socrates taught Plato.*

But sentence 1 is just like—that is, has the same shape as—
which one of the two sentences? _____   3

1-17 *(1) Plato taught his pupils to think carefully.*
     (2) Plato taught his students to think carefully.
     (3) Plato taught his pupils to think carefully.

For two sentences to be called like sentences they must have
the same shape. So, sentence 1 is like sentence _____ but is   3
not like sentence _____.   2

1-18   For two expressions—that is, two words or two strings of words—to be like expressions, these expressions must have the same _____.

shape

1-19   (1) *Plato taught his pupils to think carefully, and Aristotle was Plato's most famous pupil.*
(2) *Plato taught his pupils to think carefully.*
(3) *Aristotle was Plato's most famous pupil.*

Part of sentence 1 is just like sentence 2. Part of sentence 1 is just like sentence 3. Copy the part of sentence 1 which is like no part of sentence 2 or of sentence 3. _____

and

1-20   (1) *Aristotle's greatest contribution to logic was his formalizing sentences to isolate their logical forms or Aristotle's greatest contribution to logic was his systematic treatment of arguments.*
(2) *Aristotle's greatest contribution to logic was his formalizing sentences to isolate their logical forms.*
(3) *Aristotle's greatest contribution to logic was his systematic treatment of arguments.*

Copy the part of sentence 1 which is like no part of sentence 2 or of sentence 3. _____

or

1-21   (1) *If we can isolate logical forms of sentences then we can determine whether two sentences share a logical form.*
(2) *We can isolate logical forms of sentences.*
(3) *We can determine whether two sentences share a logical form.*

Copy the part of sentence 1 which is like no part of sentence 2 or of sentence 3. _____

if then

1-22   (1) *It is false that Socrates was an ugly man.*
(2) *Socrates was an ugly man.*

Copy the part of sentence 1 which is like no part of sentence 2. _____

it is false that

1-23   Notice that it is an easy matter to decide whether or not two expressions are like expressions.

If two expressions have the same shape, then they are _____ expressions.

like

1-24   *ruler*   *ruler*

       measure   *king*

If two expressions have the same meaning, are they necessarily like expressions? _____   no

1-25   Two expressions are like expressions only if they have
the same _____ .   shape

Representing Sentences Which Contain No Connecting Words

1-26   We call two expressions like expressions if and only if they have the same shape.

But why do we define 'like expressions' in this way? Such a definition is useful because, though we can not always agree whether two expressions have the same meaning, we can always agree whether two expressions have the same _____ .

shape

1-27   Symbolism in logic takes account of our inability to agree as to whether two expressions have the same meaning and exploits our ability to agree as to whether two expressions have the same _____ .

shape

1-28   Symbolism in logic exploits our ability to agree about the shape of expressions and in so doing provides a helpful device for recording content and form of language and then for considering form isolated from content.

Symbolic expressions are of two kinds—representations and formalizations.

A representation indicates both content and logical form of the represented expression, but a formalization allows us to ignore content and isolate a logical _____ of the formalized expression.

form

1-29   We represent in order to formalize: to *formalize* an expression we isolate a logical form indicated by a *representation* of that expression. So, before we can *formalize* an expression we must be able to _____ that expression.

represent

1-30 A representation is a symbolic expression each symbol of which corresponds in a known way to a part of the represented expression.

So, to represent we must know how symbols correspond to expressions—both to sentences and to connecting words. Since connecting words join sentences to form new sentences we consider first how symbols correspond to sentences which contain no _____ words.

connecting

1-31 *(1) Aristotle was one of the first logicians to treat arguments systematically.*

Sentence 1 contains no connecting words—that is, contains no 'and,' 'or,' 'if then,' or 'it is false that.' So we represent sentence 1 by using a single letter; for we are going to follow the convention of using capital letters as symbols for representing sentences which contain _____ connecting words.

no

1-32 *(1) Aristotle was born in 384 B.C.*

Following our convention, we would use a single capital letter to represent (1), since (1) is a sentence containing no 'and,' 'or,' 'if then,' or 'it is false that'—that is, a sentence containing no _____ word.

connecting

1-33 Every sentence either contains a connecting word or does not contain a connecting word. According to our convention we use a single capital letter to represent a sentence if and only if that sentence contains no _____ word.

connecting

1-34 Which one of the following can be represented by a single capital letter? _____

1

      (1) Plato was born in 427 B.C.
      (2) Plato was born in 427 B.C., and Plato died in 347 B.C.
      (3) Plato was born in 427 B.C., or Plato died in 347 B.C.
      (4) If Plato was born in 427 B.C., then Plato died in 347 B.C.
      (5) It is false that Plato died in 427 B.C.

1-35 Sentences containing no connecting words are represented by single capital letters. Moreover, we follow the further convention that sentences can be given *like* representa-

tions if and only if the sentences are *like* sentences. That
is, two sentences have representations of the same shape if
and only if the sentences have the same _____.

shape

1-36 Sentences can have like representations if and only
if the sentences are like sentences; and two sentences are
like if and only if they have the same shape. How many of the
following sentences can have like representations? _____

> (1) *Plato taught his students to think carefully.*
> (2) *Plato taught his pupils to think carefully.*
> (3) *Plato taught his pupils to think precisely.*

1-37 (1) *Plato taught his students to think carefully.*
> (2) *Plato taught his pupils to think carefully.*
> (3) *Plato taught his students to think carefully.*

Which of the above sentences could have like representations?

1; 3

1-38 (1) B   (3) E   (5) D
      (2) D   (4) F   (6) G

We use capital letters to represent sentences containing no
connecting words. Which two of the capitals would be like
representations? _____ _____

2; 5

1-39 (1) *Plato taught his students to think carefully.*
> (2) *Plato taught his students to think carefully.*

Two sentences have like representations if and only if the
sentences are like sentences. If we could use a 'B' to represent (1), then what letter would we use to represent (2)? We
would use a '_____.'

B

1-40 (1) *Plato taught his students to think carefully.*
> (2) *Plato taught his pupils to think carefully.*

If we used a 'D' to represent (1), could we use a 'D' to
represent (2)? _____

no

1-41 (1) *Plato taught his students to think carefully.*
> (2) *Plato taught his students to think carefully.*

If we use a 'G' to represent (1), could we use a 'H' to represent
(2)? _____

no

1-42   Sentences containing no connecting words are represented by single capital letters, like sentences must always have like representations, and only like sentences can have like representations.

And once we know *which* capital letters correspond to sentences of *which shape*, we can represent any sentence containing _____ connecting word.

no

1-43   A   B   C   D   E   F   G   H   I   J   K   L   M
N   O   P   Q   R   S   T   U   V   W   X   Y   Z

Any capital letter will be one of the above twenty-six shapes. Would you say that of sentences containing no connecting words, each is of one of twenty-six shapes? _____

no

1-44   There are more than twenty-six distinct shapes of sentences containing no connecting words. How then can it be arranged that we represent such sentences by capital letters and that only like sentences have like representations? This way—in a given context we, in effect, write a dictionary of representations for the elementary sentences of interest in the context. For each shape of sentence without connecting words we specify the shape of capital which represents such a sentence. Then

1. Given a sentence without connecting words we can write its representation, and
2. Given a representation we know the shape of the _____ represented.

sentence

1-45   To use only capitals to represent elementary sentences and still to require that only like sentences have like representations does make representing context-dependent. But in practice the restriction is in fact a convenience, and theoretically the kinds of symbols used to represent elementary sentences could be increased indefinitely. So given a context—that is, given the dictionary agreed on for the context—

1. When presented with an elementary sentence we can _____ that sentence, and

represent

2. When presented with a representation we know the shape of the _____ represented.

sentence

1-46   Here is a short dictionary of representations:

1. A 'B' represents 'Socrates taught Plato.'
2. A 'D' represents 'Plato taught Aristotle.'
3. A 'P' represents 'Aristotle taught Theophrastus.'
4. A 'Q' represents 'Theophrastus was a logician.'

Represent the following sentences:

> *Plato taught Aristotle.* _____   D
>
> *Aristotle taught Theophrastus.* _____   P

Write a sentence that can be represented by a 'B.'

_____   Socrates taught Plato.

Can

> *Aristotle taught Theophrastus.*

be represented by a 'Q'? _____   no

1-47   Suppose that we are in a new context and we specify the following dictionary of representations:

1. A 'B' represents 'Theophrastus composed treatises.'
2. A 'D' represents 'Aristotle gave lectures.'
3. A 'P' represents 'Plato wrote dialogues.'
4. A 'Q' represents 'Socrates taught by only word of mouth.'

Represent the following sentence:

> *Socrates taught by only word of mouth.* _____   Q

Write a sentence which can be represented by a 'D.'

_____   Aristotle gave lectures.

In this new context can

> *Theophrastus was a logician.*

be represented by a 'Q'? _____   no

1-48   Given a context and its dictionary of representations for elementary sentences

1. We can represent any elementary sentence, and
2. Given a representation we know the _____ of the   shape
sentence represented.

1-49 A representation is a symbolic expression each symbol of which corresponds in a known way to a part of the represented expression. We now know how symbols are used to represent elementary sentences—that is, how symbols are used to represent sentences that contain _____ connecting words.

no

unit **4**

Representing

Connecting Words

1-50   We know how to represent sentences containing no connecting words. But knowing only this, can we represent any of the following? _____

no

1. A sentence that is two sentences joined by an 'and,'
2. A sentence that is two sentences joined by an 'or,'
3. A sentence that is two sentences joined by an 'if then,'
4. A sentence that is one sentence preceded by an 'it is false that.'

1-51   We know how to represent elementary sentences, and once we know how to represent the connecting words

and
or
if then
it is false that

we will be able to represent sentences containing such _____ words.

connecting

1-52   Suppose we were to follow this convention:

1. An '&' represents a connecting word 'and.'
2. A '∨' represents a connecting word 'or.'
3. A '⊃' represents a connecting word 'if then.'
4. A '∼' represents a connecting word 'it is false that.'

And suppose further that a 'P' represents the elementary sentence

Convenience may direct choice of notation.

and a 'Q' represents the elementary sentence

Precedent should be respected in choice of notation.

Then the sentence

> *Convenience may direct choice of notation, and precedent should be respected in choice of notation.*

would be represented by a 'P _____ Q.'   &

1-53 Following this convention:

1. An '&' represents a connecting word 'and.'
2. A '∨' represents a connecting word 'or.'
3. A '⊃' represents a connecting word 'if then.'
4. A '∼' represents a connecting word 'it is false that.'

and supposing that a 'P' represents

> *A notation similar to that of* Principia Mathematica *may be used.*

and that a 'Q' represents

> *Lukasiewicz notation may be used.*

then the sentence

> *A notation similar to that of* Principia Mathematica *may be used, or Lukasiewicz notation may be used.*

would be represented by a 'P _____ Q.'   ∨

1-54 Following this convention:

1. An '&' represents a connecting word 'and.'
2. A '∨' represents a connecting word 'or.'
3. A '⊃' represents a connecting word 'if then.'
4. A '∼' represents a connecting word 'it is false that.'

and supposing that a 'P' represents

> *Lukasiewicz notation is chosen.*

and that a 'Q' represents

> *A notation free of punctuation is chosen.*

then the sentence

> *If Lukasiewicz notation is chosen, then a notation free of punctuation is chosen.*

would be represented by a 'P_____Q.'   ⊃

1-55 Following this convention:

1. An '&' represents a connecting word 'and.'
2. A '∨' represents a connecting word 'or.'
3. A '⊃' represents a connecting word 'if then.'
4. A '∼' represents a connecting word 'it is false that.'

and supposing that a 'P' represents

> Principia Mathematica *notation is best for present purposes.*

then the sentence

> *It is false that* Principia Mathematica *notation is best for present purposes.*

would be represented by a '_____ P.'

∼

1-56 If we were to follow this convention:

1. An '&' represents a connecting word 'and.'
2. A '∨' represents a connecting word 'or.'
3. A '⊃' represents a connecting word 'if then.'
4. A '∼' represents a connecting word 'it is false that.'

we would be using a notation similar to the notation of *Principia Mathematica*—written by Bertrand Russell and Alfred North Whitehead early in the twentieth century—and the following expressions might be some of the representations:

$$P \,\&\, Q \qquad P \vee Q \qquad P \supset Q \qquad \sim P$$

Notice that were this convention followed, the symbol representing the connecting word would be the first symbol in the representation only if the sentence represented had as its connecting word an '_____.'

it is false that

1-57 We represent in order to formalize, and we formalize in order to focus attention on logical form of expressions. Because connecting words are important for logical form, it would be convenient if the first symbol in the representation of *any* sentence containing a connecting word—an 'and,' 'or,' or 'if then' as well as an 'it is false that'—were the symbol representing this _____ word.

connecting

1-58   A representation is a symbolic expression each symbol of which corresponds in a known way to a part of the represented expression. So provided only that we make our convention explicit, we can choose to represent nonelementary sentences by putting as *first* symbol in the representation the symbol representing the _____ word.

connecting

1-59   Suppose then we were to follow this convention:

1. An '&' represents a connecting word 'and.'
2. A '∨' represents a connecting word 'or.'
3. A '⊃' represents a connecting word 'if then.'
4. A '∼' represents a connecting word 'it is false that.'
5. The first symbol in the representation of a nonelementary sentence is a symbol representing a connecting word.

And suppose further that a 'P' represents the elementary sentence

> *Lukasiewicz notation is chosen for use.*

and that a 'Q' represents the elementary sentence

> Principia Mathematica *notation still has historic interest.*

Then the nonelementary sentence

> *Lukasiewicz notation is chosen for use, and* Principia Mathematica *notation still has historic interest.*

would be represented by a '_____PQ';

&

the sentence

> *Lukasiewicz notation is chosen for use, or* Principia Mathematica *notation still has historic interest.*

would be represented by a '_____PQ';

∨

and the sentence

> *If Lukasiewicz notation is chosen for use, then* Principia Mathematica *notation still has historic interest.*

would be represented by a '_____PQ.'

⊃

1-60   Were we to follow this new convention the following might be some of the representations:

P	∨PQ
Q	⊃PQ
&PQ	∼P

where the representation of any nonelementary sentence has as its first symbol a symbol representing a connecting word. And we would read the representations as

> Pee
> Cue
> Ampersand Pee Cue
> Wedge Pee Cue
> Horseshoe Pee Cue
> Tilde Pee Cue

where

> 'Ampersand' names a '_____,'   &
> 'Wedge' names a '_____,'   ∨
> 'Horseshoe' names a '_____,' and   ⊃
> 'Tilde' names a '_____.'   ∼

1-61 Just as it is convenient to put the symbol representing the connecting word first in a representation, so is it convenient to use a notation that is easily read. Whereas '&,' '∨,' '⊃,' and '∼' historically have been named as we just saw, still these names are somewhat cumbersome; and moreover the symbols themselves are somewhat unavailable in ordinary typescript. And, too, historically there does exist a notation convention which

1. Allows us to put the symbol representing the connecting word _____, and   **first**
2. Uses easily read and easily typed symbols to represent _____ words.   **connecting**

1-62 Lukasiewicz, a Polish logician (1878–1956), used capital letters to represent connecting words in a way more or less in accord with this convention:

1. A 'K' represents an 'and,'
2. An 'A' represents an 'or,'
3. A 'C' represents an 'if then,' and
4. An 'N' represents an 'it is false that.'

Suppose that we adopt this Lukasiewicz convention and suppose further that a 'P' represents

> *Lukasiewicz notation is chosen for use.*

and that a 'Q' represents

> Principia Mathematica *notation still has historic interest.*

Then a 'KPQ' would be used to represent

> *Lukasiewicz notation is chosen for use,* _____ and
> Principia Mathematica *notation still has historic interest.*

An 'APQ' would be used to represent

> *Lukasiewicz notation is chosen for use,* _____ or
> Principia Mathematica *notation still has historic interest.*

A 'CPQ' would be used to represent

> _____ *Lukasiewicz notation is chosen for use,*   if
> _____ Principia Mathematica *notation still has*   then
> *historic interest.*

And an 'NQ' would be used to represent

> *It is false that* _____ .

Principia Mathematica
notation still has
historic interest

1-63 Connecting words are represented in Lukasiewicz notation by capital letters

> K   A   C   N

Capitals are used perhaps because they are easily readable and typable. But why these capitals?

> K   A   C   N

In German—a language in which Lukasiewicz wrote—these capitals are the first letters of appropriate German words. Though this added convenience is not reflected when the language represented is English, it seems wise to follow an established notation rather than to devise a new one. So following Lukasiewicz, we represent the connecting words

> and   if then
> or   it is false that

by the capitals

> K   A   C   ____   N

1-64 We know how to represent sentences containing no connecting words, and we know now how to represent the connecting words

> and   if then
> or   it is false that

So now we can represent not only elementary sentences but
also sentences containing the connecting words

_____   _____   and; or
_____   _____   if then; it is false that

Representing Sentences

1-65 We represent sentences in accordance with these conventions:

1. Sentences containing _____ connecting words are represented by capitals other than 'K's, 'A's, 'C's, or 'N's.

no

2. _____ words are represented as follows:

connecting

   (a) A 'K' represents an 'and',
   (b) An 'A' represents an 'or',
   (c) A 'C' represents an 'if then', and
   (d) An 'N' represents an 'it is false that'.

3. When sentences that do contain connecting words are represented, the symbol representing the connecting word precedes the symbols representing the sentences joined by the _____ word.

connecting

1-66 *(1) Socrates taught Plato.*
(2) Plato founded a school.
(3) Socrates taught Plato, and Plato founded a school.

Let's agree to represent (1) by an 'R' and (2) by a 'P.' Then since we represent 'and' by 'K,' we can represent (3) by a '_____ .'

KRP

1-67 *(1) Socrates was born in 469 B.C.*
(2) Socrates drank poison in 399 B.C.
(3) Socrates was born in 469 B.C., and Socates drank poison in 399 B.C.
(4) Socates drank poison in 399 B.C., and Socrates was born in 469 B.C.

Let's agree to represent (1) by a 'Q' and (2) by an 'R.' Then since we represent 'and' by 'K,' we can represent (3) by a '_____' and (4) by a '_____ .'

KQR; KRQ

1-68 *(1) Plato taught Aristotle well, and Aristotle founded a school.*

Suppose a 'KPQ' represents (1). Write a sentence that can be represented by a 'P.'

_____

Plato taught Aristotle well.

1-69 *(1) Aristotle taught Alexander the Great, and Alexander became a famous ruler.*

Suppose a 'KRQ' represents (1). Write a sentence that can be represented by a 'Q.'

_____

Alexander became a famous ruler.

1-70 A connecting word 'and' is represented by a '_____.'

K

1-71 *(1) Plato taught his pupils to think carefully.*
(2) Aristotle was Plato's most famous pupil.

Suppose we know that a 'P' represents (1) and a 'Q' represents (2); write a sentence that can be represented by a 'KPQ.'

_____

Plato taught his pupils to think carefully, and Aristotle was Plato's most famous pupil.

1-72 *(1) Aristotle was Plato's most brilliant pupil.*
(2) Aristotle was among Plato's best pupils.
(3) Aristotle was Plato's most brilliant pupil, or Aristotle was among Plato's best pupils.

Let's agree to represent (1) by a 'P' and (2) by a 'Q.' Then since we represent 'or' by 'A,' we can represent (3) by a '_____.'

APQ

1-73 *(1) Aristotle's greatest contribution to logic was his formalizing sentences to isolate their logical forms.*
(2) Aristotle's greatest contribution to logic was his systematic treatment of arguments.
(3) Aristotle's greatest contribution to logic was his formalizing sentences to isolate their logical forms, or Aristotle's greatest contribution to logic was his systematic treatment of arguments.
(4) Aristotle's greatest contribution to logic was his systematic treatment of arguments, or Aristotle's greatest contribution to logic was his formalizing sentences to isolate their logical forms.

Let's agree to represent (1) by a 'Q' and (2) by an 'R.' Then since we represent 'or' by 'A,' we can represent (3) by an '_____' and (4) by an '_____.'

AQR; ARQ

1-74   *(1) Socrates was very wise, or Plato describes Socrates incorrectly.*

Suppose an 'APQ' represents (1). Then write a sentence that can be represented by a 'P.'

_____

Socrates was very wise.

1-75   *(1) Aristotle admired Plato's school, or Aristotle admired Plato's work.*

Suppose an 'ARQ' represents (1). Then write a sentence that can be represented by a 'Q.'

_____

Aristotle admired Plato's work.

1-76   A connecting word 'or' is represented by an '_____.'

A

1-77   *(1) Plato founded the Academy.*
(2) Plato at least taught in the Academy.

Suppose we represent (1) by a 'P' and (2) by a 'Q.' Write a sentence that can be represented by an 'APQ.'

_____

Plato founded the Academy, or Plato at least taught in the Academy.

1-78   *(1) Aristotle had remained in Athens.*
(2) Aristotle too would have been put to death by the Athenian government.
(3) If Aristotle had remained in Athens, then Aristotle too would have been put to death by the Athenian government.

Let's agree to represent (1) by a 'P' and (2) by a 'Q.' Then since we represent 'if then' by 'C,' we can represent (3) by a '_____.'

CPQ

1-79   *(1) Aristotle taught Alexander the Great.*
(2) Aristotle deserves some credit for Alexander's achievements.
(3) If Aristotle taught Alexander the Great, then Aristotle deserves some credit for Alexander's achievements.
(4) If Aristotle taught Alexander the Great, then Aristotle taught Alexander the Great.

Let's agree to represent (1) by an 'R' and (2) by a 'P.' Then since we represent 'if then' by 'C,' we can represent (3) by a '_____' and (4) by a '_____.'

CRP; CRR

1-80 *(1) If Plato taught Aristotle, then Plato deserves praise.*

Suppose a 'CQP' represents (1). Then write a sentence that can be represented by a 'Q.'

_____

Plato taught Aristotle.

1-81 *(1) If Plato was an Athenian, then Plato was a Greek.*

Suppose a 'CRP' represents (1). Then write a sentence that can be represented by a 'P.'

_____

Plato was a Greek.

1-82 A connecting word 'if then' is represented by a '_____.'

C

1-83 *(1) Athens had put Aristotle to death.*
(2) Athens would have killed two great philosophers.

Suppose we represent (1) by a 'Q' and (2) by an 'R'; write a sentence that can be represented by a 'CQR.'

_____

If Athens had put Aristotle to death, then Athens would have killed two great philosophers.

1-84 *(1) Socrates taught by lecturing.*
(2) It is false that Socrates taught by lecturing.

Let's agree to represent (1) by an 'R.' Then since we represent 'it is false that' by 'N,' we can represent (2) by an '_____.'

NR

1-85 *(1) It is false that Aristotle taught Socrates logic.*

Suppose an 'NQ' represents (1). Then write a sentence that can be represented by a 'Q.'

_____

Aristotle taught Socrates logic.

1-86 A connecting word 'it is false that' is represented by an '_____.'

N

1-87 *(1) The Athenian government put Aristotle to death.*

Suppose that a 'P' represents (1); then write a sentence that can be represented by an 'NP.'

_____

It is false that the Athenian government put Aristotle to death.

1-88 *(1) Like expressions are expressions like in shape.*

(2) Unlike expressions are expressions unlike in shape.

(3) Some expressions which are very close in meaning are unlike expressions.

Suppose a 'P' represents (1). Then could (2) be represented by a 'P'? _____ Could (3)? _____

no; no

1-89 *(1) If sentences have like representations, then the sentences are like expressions.*

Suppose a 'CPQ' represents (1); then write a sentence that can be represented by a 'P.'

_____

Sentences have like representations.

Then write another sentence that can be represented by a 'P.'

_____

Sentences have like representations.

1-90 *(1) Only like expressions have like representations.*

Suppose a 'P' represents (1); then write another sentence that can be represented by a 'P.'

_____

Only like expressions have like representations.

1-91 In a given context only like expressions can have like representations. And further, because the same kinds of connecting words occur in every context, it is convenient *always* to let

'_____' represent 'and,'   K

'_____' represent 'or,'   A

'_____' represent 'if then,' and   C

'_____' represent 'it is false that.' N

1-92 Since we have a convention for representing connecting words, even without consulting the so-called dictionary of representations for some context, we know that

'K' represents '_____,'   and

'A' represents '_____,'   or

'C' represents '_____,' and   if then

'N' represents '_____.'   it is false that

1-93 We must make explicit our conventions for representing, because a representation is a symbolic expression which corresponds not in an arbitrary but in a _____ way to the represented expression.

known

1-94 We agree to represent sentences in accordance with these conventions:

1. Sentences containing no connecting words—that is, elementary sentences—are represented by capitals *other than* '____'s, '____'s, '____'s, or '____'s.

K; A; C; N

2. Connecting words are represented as follows:
   (*a*) A 'K' represents an '_____.'

   and

   (*b*) An 'A' represents an '_____.'

   or

   (*c*) A 'C' represents an '_____.'

   if then

   (*d*) An 'N' represents an '_____.'

   it is false that

3. When sentences that do contain connecting words are represented, the symbol representing the connecting word precedes the symbols representing the sentences joined by the _____ word.

connecting

Connectives as Representations
of Connecting Words

1-95 An expression which is two sentences properly *connected* by an 'and' is itself a sentence, no matter what two sentences the 'and' connects.

Because 'and' is used to *connect* two sentences, we call an 'and' a *connecting word*. Thus, in

> *Socrates taught Plato, and Plato founded a school.*

the 'and' is a _____ word.

connecting

1-96 Because we call an 'and' a connecting word, we call a 'K' that represents an 'and' a connective. Thus, in 'KPQ' we call the 'K' a _____ .

connective

1-97 An expression which is two sentences properly connected by an 'or' is a sentence, no matter what two sentences the 'or' connects.

Because 'or' is used to connect two sentences, we call an 'or' a connecting word. Thus, in

> *Socrates taught only informally, or Plato gave false reports.*

the 'or' is a _____ word.

connecting

1-98 Because we call an 'or' a connecting word, we call an 'A' that represents an 'or' a connective. Thus, in 'APQ' the 'A' is a _____ .

connective

1-99 An expression which is two sentences properly connected by an 'if then' is a sentence, no matter what two sentences the 'if then' connects.

Because 'if then' is used to connect two sentences, we call an 'if then' a connecting word. Thus, in

> *If Aristotle taught Alexander the Great, then Aristotle deserves some of the credit for Alexander's achievements.*

the 'if then' is a _____ word.

connecting

1-100 Because we call an 'if then' a connecting word, we call a 'C' that represents an 'if then' a connective. Thus, in 'CPQ' the 'C' is a _____ .

connective

1-101 An expression which is any sentence at all preceded by an 'it is false that' is itself a sentence.

Because an 'it is false that' when properly connected to a sentence gives another sentence, we call an 'it is false that' a connecting word. Thus, in

> *It is false that the Athenian government put Aristotle to death.*

the 'it is false that' is a _____ _____ .

connecting word

1-102 Because we call an 'it is false that' a connecting word, we call an 'N' that represents an 'it is false that' a connective. Thus, in 'NP' the 'N' is a _____ .

connective

1-103 and   if then
or   it is false that

are _____ words, but

    K   A   C   N

connecting

are _____ .

connectives

1-104 A 'K' is a connective that represents an 'and.' An 'A' is a connective that represents an 'or.' A 'C' is a connective that represents an 'if then.' An 'N' is a connective that represents an '_____ .'

it is false that

1-105 A '____' represents an 'and.' An '____' represents an 'or.' A '____' represents an 'if then.' An '____' represents an 'it is false that.'

K; A
C; N

Five Kinds of

Well-formed Sentences

1-106   *(1) Aristotle was born in 384 B.C., and Aristotle died in 322 B.C.*

Any sentence which is two sentences connected by an 'and' is called an 'and' sentence. Thus, sentence 1 is an '_____' sentence.

and

1-107   Since an 'and' sentence is a sentence which is two sentences connected by an 'and,' and since we represent an 'and' by a 'K,' we can always represent an 'and' sentence by an expression beginning with a '_____.'

K

1-108   An 'and' sentence can always be represented by an expression beginning with a '_____.'

K

1-109   The representation of an 'and' sentence will be a 'K' followed by the representations of two _____.

sentences

1-110   *(1) Socrates taught only informally, or Plato gave false reports.*

Any sentence which is two sentences connected by an 'or' is called an 'or' sentence. Thus, sentence 1 is an '_____' sentence.

or

1-111   Since an 'or' sentence is a sentence which is two sentences connected by an 'or,' and since we represent an 'or' by an 'A,' we can always represent an 'or' sentence by an expression beginning with an '_____.'

A

1-112   An 'or' sentence can always be represented by an expression beginning with an '_____.'

A

1-113 The representation of an 'or' sentence will be an 'A'
followed by the representations of two _____ .

sentences

1-114 *(1) If Aristotle was the teacher of Alexander the Great,
then Aristotle must have lived for a time in Macedonia.*

Any sentence which is two sentences connected by an 'if
then' is called an 'if then' sentence. Thus, sentence 1 is an
'_____' sentence.

if then

1-115 Since an 'if then' sentence is a sentence which is two
sentences connected by an 'if then' and since we represent
an 'if then' by a 'C,' we can always represent an 'if then' sentence by an expression beginning with a '_____ .'

C

1-116 An 'if then' sentence can always be represented by
an expression beginning with a '_____ .'

C

1-117 The representation of an 'if then' sentence will be a
'C' followed by the representations of two _____ .

sentences

1-118 *(1) It is false that Socrates taught Aristotle.*

Any sentence which is a sentence preceded by an 'it is false
that' is called an 'it is false that' sentence. Thus, sentence
1 is an '_____' sentence.

it is false that

1-119 Since an 'it is false that' sentence is a sentence preceded by an 'it is false that,' and since we represent an 'it is
false that' by an 'N,' we can always represent an 'it is false
that' sentence by an expression beginning with an '_____ .'

N

1-120 An 'it is false that' sentence can always be represented by an expression beginning with an '_____ .'

N

1-121 The representation of an 'it is false that' sentence
will be an 'N' followed by a representation of one _____ .

sentence

1-122 *(1) Socrates taught Plato.*

A sentence which contains no connecting words is called an
elementary sentence. Thus, sentence 1 is an _____
sentence.

elementary

1-123   *(1) Socrates taught Plato.*

According to our convention an elementary sentence is represented by a single capital letter. The representation of (1), then, will contain how many letters? _____   one

1-124   The representation of an 'and' sentence begins with a '_____.'   K

The representation of an 'or' sentence begins with an '_____.'   A

The representation of an 'if then' sentence begins with a '_____.'   C

The representation of an 'it is false that' sentence begins with an '_____.'   N

The representation of an elementary sentence contains only _____ letter.   one

Representing as Indicating
Content and Logical Form

1-125 The representation of a sentence indicates two things:

1. The representation indicates the *content* of the sentence represented.
2. The representation indicates a *logical form* of the sentence represented.

That is, the representation indicates both the _____ and a *logical* _____ of the sentence represented.

content
form

1-126 (1) *Socrates was learned.*
(2) *Socrates was wise.*

We say the representation of a sentence indicates the content of the sentence represented because given a representation we can write a sentence just like the sentence represented.

Thus, if a 'P' represents (1) and a 'Q' represents (2), write a sentence just like the sentence represented by a 'KPQ.'

_____

Socrates was learned, and Socrates was wise.

1-127 (1) *Socrates was learned.*
(2) *Socrates was wise.*

The representation of a sentence indicates the content of the represented sentence. Thus, if a 'P' represents (1) and a 'Q' represents (2), write a sentence just like the sentence represented by an 'APQ.'

_____

Socrates was learned, or Socrates was wise.

1-128 (1) *Socrates was learned.*
(2) *Socrates was wise.*

A representation indicates content. Thus, if a 'P' represents

(1) and a 'Q' represents (2), write a sentence just like the sentence represented by a 'CPQ'.

_____

If Socrates was learned, then Socrates was wise.

1-129 *(1) Socrates was learned.*
(2) Socrates was wise.

A representation indicates content. Thus, if a 'P' represents (1) and a 'Q' represents (2), write a sentence just like the sentence represented by an 'NP'.

_____

It is false that Socrates was learned.

1-130 *(1) Socrates was learned.*
(2) Socrates was wise.

A representation indicates content. Thus, if a 'P' represents (1) and a 'Q' represents (2), write a sentence just like the sentence represented by a 'P'.

_____

Socrates was learned.

1-131 A representation of a sentence indicates the content of the sentence represented. But the representation indicates also a logical _____ of the represented sentence.

form

1-132 We say the representation of a sentence indicates a logical form of the sentence represented because given a representation we know what kind of a sentence is represented. That is, we know whether the represented sentence is

1. An elementary sentence,
2. An 'and' sentence,
3. An '_____' sentence,
4. An '_____' sentence, or
5. An '_____' sentence.

or
if then
it is false that

1-133 The representation of a sentence indicates a logical form of the represented sentence. Thus a sentence represented by a 'P' is an _____ sentence.

elementary

1-134 The representation indicates a logical form of the represented sentence. Thus a sentence represented by a 'KPQ' is an '_____' sentence.

and

1-135   The representation indicates a logical form of the represented sentence. Thus a sentence represented by an 'APQ' is an '_____' sentence.

or

1-136   The representation indicates a logical _____ of the represented sentence. Thus a sentence represented by a 'CPQ' is an '_____' sentence.

form

if then

1-137   The representation indicates a logical _____ of the represented sentence. Thus a sentence represented by an 'NP' is an '_____' sentence.

form

it is false that

1-138   Given a representation

1. We can write a sentence just _____ the represented sentence, and

like

2. We know whether the represented sentence is

       an _____ sentence,

elementary

       an '_____' sentence,

and

       an '_____' sentence,

or

       an '_____' sentence, or

if then

       an '_____' sentence.

it is false that

1-139   The representation of a sentence indicates two things:

1. The _____ of the sentence represented, and

content

2. A logical _____ of the sentence represented.

form

unit **9**

Formalizing as Isolating
Logical Form

1-140   A representation indicates both content and a logical form of the represented sentence. But there are times when we want to ignore content and consider logical _____ in isolation.

form

1-141   A representation is an expression which *indicates* a logical form of the sentence represented. But a formalization is an expression which *isolates* a logical form of the sentence formalized. That is, to formalize a sentence is to _____ a logical form of that sentence.

isolate

1-142   Suppose a sentence is represented by some single letter, say, a 'P.' Then the sentence must be an elementary sentence, and we can formalize that sentence by writing a single *sentence variable*—once we know what a _____ variable is.

sentence

1-143   A sentence variable is any lowercase letter 'p,' 'q,' 'r,' 's,' or 't.' We formalize a sentence represented by some single letter by writing some single sentence variable. So if a sentence can be represented by a 'P,' that sentence can be formalized by a 'p,' a 'q,' an '____,' an '____,' or a '____.'

r; s; t

1-144   If a sentence can be represented by a 'P,' then that sentence can be formalized by a single sentence variable. Moreover, any sentence that can be represented by a single letter can be formalized by a single _____ _____ .

sentence variable

1-145   If a sentence can be represented by a 'P,' then that sentence can be formalized by a 'p,' a 'q,' an 'r,' an 's,' or a 't.' Moreover, any sentence that can be represented by a single letter can be formalized by a '____,' a '____,' an '____,' an '____,' or a '____.'

p; q
r; s; t

1-146 If a sentence can be represented by a 'KPQ,' then that sentence can be formalized by a 'K' followed by two unlike sentence variables. Moreover, any sentence that can be represented by a 'K' followed by two single letters can be formalized by a '_____' followed by two unlike _____ _____ .

K
sentence variables

1-147 If a sentence can be represented by a 'KPQ,' then that sentence can be formalized by any 'Kpq,' 'Krs,' 'Ktp,' and so on. Moreover, any sentence that can be represented by a 'K' followed by two single letters can be formalized by a 'Kpq,' a '_____,' a '_____,' and so on.

Krs; Ktp

1-148 If a sentence can be represented by an 'APQ,' then that sentence can be formalized by an 'A' followed by two unlike sentence variables. Moreover, any sentence that can be represented by an 'A' followed by two single letters can be formalized by an '_____' followed by two unlike _____ _____ .

A
sentence variables

1-149 If a sentence can be represented by a 'CPQ,' then that sentence can be formalized by a '_____' followed by two unlike _____ _____ . Moreover, any sentence that can be represented by a 'C' followed by two single letters can be formalized by a '_____' followed by two unlike _____ _____ .

C
sentence variables

C
sentence variables

1-150 If a sentence can be represented by an 'NP,' then that sentence can be formalized by an '_____' followed by a single _____ _____ . Moreover, any sentence that can be represented by an 'N' followed by a single letter can be formalized by an '_____' followed by a single _____ _____ .

N
sentence variable

N
sentence variable

1-151 *(1) Socrates drank hemlock.*

Suppose we can represent (1) by an 'R'. Then (1) can be formalized by any single sentence variable. Thus, a 'p' formalizes (1). Similarly, a 'q,' an 'r,' an 's,' or a 't' isolates a logical form of (1), that is, _____ (1).

formalizes

1-152 *(1) Socrates taught Plato, and Plato founded a school.*
Suppose we can represent (1) by a 'KPQ.' Then (1) can be
formalized by a 'K' followed by two unlike sentence variables.
So, a 'Kpq' formalizes (1). Similarly, (1) could be formalized
by a '_____rs' or a '_____qt.'   K; K

1-153 *(1) Kant wrote books, and Kant wrote books.*

Suppose we can represent (1) by a 'KQQ.' Then (1) can be
formalized by a 'K' followed by two *like* sentence variables.
So, a 'Kqq' formalizes (1). Similarly, (1) could be formalized
by a '_____p_____' or a '_____t_____.'   K; p; K; t

1-154 *(1) Socrates taught only informally, or Plato gave false
reports.*

Suppose we can represent (1) by an 'ASR.' Then (1) can be
formalized by an 'A' followed by two unlike sentence variables. So, an 'Asr' formalizes (1). Similarly, (1) could be formalized by an '_____rs' or an '_____qp.'   A; A

1-155 *(1) Socrates drank hemlock, or Socrates drank hemlock.*

Suppose we can represent (1) by an 'ATT.' Then (1) can be
formalized by an 'A' followed by two _____ sentence   like
variables. So, an 'App' formalizes (1). Similarly, (1) could be
formalized by an '_____q_____' or an '_____t_____.'   A; q; A; t

1-156 *(1) If Aristotle taught Alexander the Great, then
Aristotle deserves some credit for Alexander's achievements.*

Suppose we can represent (1) by a 'CQS.' Then (1) can be
formalized by a 'C' followed by two _____ sentence   unlike
variables. So, a 'Cqs' formalizes (1). Similarly, (1) could be
formalized by a '_____pq' or a '_____ps.'   C; C

1-157 *(1) If Socrates was really wise, then Socrates was really
wise.*

Suppose we can represent (1) by a 'CSS.' Then (1) can be
formalized by a 'C' followed by two _____ sentence   like
variables. So, a 'Css' formalizes (1). Similarly, (1) could be
formalized by a '_____p_____' or a '_____t_____.'   C; p; C; t

1-158 *(1) It is false that Socrates taught Aristotle.*

Suppose we can represent (1) by an 'NR.' Then (1) can be
formalized by an 'N' followed by a single _____
_____ . So, an 'Nr' formalizes (1). Similarly, (1) could be
formalized by an '_____q' or an '_____s.'

sentence variable
N; N

1-159 Recall that

and	if then
or	it is false that

are connecting words. And the letters

K   A   C   N

that represent connecting words are called _____ .

connectives

1-160 Notice, then, that formalizations are expressions
containing only connectives and sentence variables. That is,
we can isolate a logical form of a sentence by writing
an expression containing only _____ and _____
_____ .

connectives
sentence variables

1-161 In general, a formalization of a sentence will be just
like some representation of the sentence except that sentence
variables occur in the formalization in just those places where
nonconnectives occur in the representation. Thus we can
formalize a sentence if we have a _____ of that sentence.

representation

1-162 Given a sentence, we know how to represent that
sentence. Given a representation of a sentence, we now know
how to formalize that sentence. Therefore, given a sentence,
we can now isolate a logical form of that sentence—that is,
we can _____ that sentence.

formalize

unit 10

Well-formed Sentences and Well-formed Formulas (WFFs)

1-163 All the well-formed sentences we have looked at have been

1. Elementary sentences,
2. 'And' sentences,
3. 'Or' sentences,
4. 'If then' sentences, or
5. '_____' sentences.

it is false that

1-164 Notice that

1. A single sentence variable isolates a logical form of an _____ sentence;

elementary

2. A 'K' followed by two sentence variables isolates a logical form of an '_____' sentence;

and

3. An 'A' followed by two sentence variables isolates a logical form of an '_____' sentence;

or

4. A 'C' followed by two sentence variables isolates a logical form of an '_____' sentence; and

if then

5. An 'N' followed by a single sentence variable isolates a logical form of an '_____' sentence.

it is false that

1-165 The formalization of a *well-formed* sentence we call a *well-formed* formula. Thus a 'Kpq' is a _____ _____ .

well-formed formula

1-166 A well-formed formula is a formalization of a well-formed sentence. But 'well-formed formula' is difficult to write or to say. So, for short, we write 'WFF' (pronounced "Woof!") instead of '*well-formed formula*.' Thus we call a 'Kpq' a well-formed formula or, for short and from now on, a _____ .

WFF

1-167 We have noted that a well-formed sentence can be

1. An elementary sentence,
2. An 'and' sentence,
3. An 'or' sentence,
4. An 'if then' sentence, or
5. An 'it is false that' sentence.

So we can give five rules for determining whether a given expression is a WFF—that is, is a formalization of a well-formed

_____ .   sentence

1-168 The five kinds of sentences suggest five rules for recognizing WFFs.

     RULE 1. Any sentence variable is a WFF.

Any 'p,' 'q,' 'r,' 's,' or '____' is a sentence variable.   t

1-169 RULE 1. Any sentence variable is a WFF.

Copy those of the following expressions which are WFFs:

    p   q   r   s   t   p; q; r; s; t
   ____ ____ ____ ____ ____   (Any order)

1-170 RULE 1. Any sentence variable is a WFF.

Copy those of the following expressions which are WFFs:

                                              p; q
     p   i   q   o   ____ ____   (Either order)

1-171 RULE 1. Any sentence variable is a WFF.

Copy those of the following expressions which are WFFs:

                                              r; s
     r   K   s   A   ____ ____   (Either order)

1-172 RULE 1. Any sentence variable is a WFF.

Copy those of the following expressions which are WFFs:

    C   N   p   A   K   ____   p

1-173 RULE 1. Any sentence variable is a WFF.

Copy those of the following expressions which are WFFs:

    s   C   p   K   o
    A   N   q   r   t   p; q; r; s; t
   ____ ____ ____ ____ ____   (In any order)

1-174 The five kinds of sentences suggest five rules for recognizing WFFs.

 RULE 1. Any sentence variable is a WFF.
 RULE 2. Any expression which is a 'K' followed by two WFFs is a WFF.

Thus, since a 'p' is a WFF and a 'q' is a WFF, a 'Kpq' is a _____ .

WFF

1-175 RULE 1. Any sentence variable is a WFF.
 RULE 2. Any expression which is a 'K' followed by two WFFs is a WFF.

Copy those of the following expressions which are WFFs:

 Ksp   Kp   Kpr   Kqp

_____ _____ _____

Ksp; Kpr; Kqp
(In any order)

1-176 RULE 1. Any sentence variable is a WFF.
 RULE 2. Any expression which is a 'K' followed by two WFFs is a WFF.

Copy those of the following expressions which are WFFs:

 Krp   Ksqr   Kqp   Ksp

_____ _____ _____

Krp; Kqp; Ksp
(In any order)

1-177 RULE 1. Any sentence variable is a WFF.
 RULE 2. Any expression which is a 'K' followed by two WFFs is a WFF.

Copy those of the following expressions which are WFFs:

 Kpq   Krs   pqK   Kpr

_____ _____ _____

Kpq; Krs; Kpr
(In any order)

1-178 RULE 1. Any sentence variable is a WFF.
 RULE 2. Any expression which is a 'K' followed by two WFFs is a WFF.

Copy those of the following expressions which are WFFs:

 pKq   Kqp   Kpq   Kpp

_____ _____ _____

Kqp; Kpq; Kpp.
(In any order)

1-179 A 'Krs' is a WFF because it is an expression which is a '____' followed by two _____ .

K; WFFs

1-180   A 'Kpq' is a WFF because it is an expression which is a '_____' followed by two _____ .

K; WFFs

1-181   A 'Krs' is a WFF because it is a 'K' followed by two WFFs, an 'r' and an 's.' Similarly, a 'KKrsKrs' is a WFF because it is a 'K' followed by two WFFs, a '_____' and a '_____.'

Krs
Krs

1-182   A 'KKpqKrs' is a WFF because it is a 'K' followed by two WFFs, a '_____' and a '_____.'

Kpq; Krs

1-183   A 'KpKqs' is a WFF because it is a 'K' followed by two WFFs, a '_____' and a '_____.'

p; Kqs

1-184   A 'KKqsp' is a WFF because it is a 'K' followed by two WFFs, a '_____' and a '_____.'

Kqs; p

1-185   Copy those of the following expressions which are WFFs:

KpKqq   KKrsp   KKK   KKpqKsr   Kpq

_____   _____   _____   _____

KpKqq; KKrsp; KKpqKsr;
Kpq
(In any order)

1-186   Copy those of the following expressions which are WFFs:

KrKss   Kp   pqK   KKpp   Kpq

_____   _____

KrKss; Kpq
(In either order)

1-187   The five kinds of sentences suggest five rules for recognizing WFFs.

> RULE 3.   Any expression which is an 'A' followed by two WFFs is a WFF.

Thus since a 'p' is a WFF and a 'q' is a WFF, an 'Apq' is a _____ .

WFF

1-188   RULE 1.   Any sentence variable is a WFF.
RULE 3.   Any expression which is an 'A' followed by two WFFs is a WFF.

Copy those of the following expressions which are WFFs:

Arp   Asqr   Aqp   Asp

_____   _____   _____

Arp; Aqp; Asp
(In any order)

1-189 RULE 1. Any sentence variable is a WFF.

RULE 3. Any expression which is an 'A' followed by two WFFs is a WFF.

Copy those of the following expressions which are WFFs:

    Apq   Ars   pqA   Apr

_____   _____   _____

Apq; Ars; Apr
(In any order)

1-190 RULE 1. Any sentence variable is a WFF.

RULE 3. Any expression which is an 'A' followed by two WFFs is a WFF.

Copy those of the following expressions which are WFFs:

    pAq   Aqp   Apq   App

_____   _____   _____

Aqp; Apq; App
(In any order)

1-191 An 'Apq' is a WFF because it is an expression which is an 'A' followed by two _____ .

WFFs

1-192 An 'Ars' is a WFF because it is an expression which is an '____' followed by two _____ .

A; WFFs

1-193 An 'Ars' is a WFF because it is an 'A' followed by two WFFs, an 'r' and an 's.' Similarly, an 'AArsArs' is a WFF because it is an 'A' followed by two WFFs, an '_____' and an '_____ .'

Ars
Ars

1-194 An 'AApqArs' is a WFF because it is an 'A' followed by two WFFs, an '_____' and an '_____ .'

Apq; Ars

1-195 An 'ApAqs' is a WFF because it is an 'A' followed by two WFFs, a '____' and an '_____ .'

p; Aqs

1-196 An 'AAqsp' is a WFF because it is an 'A' followed by two WFFs, an '_____' and a '____ .'

Aqs; p

1-197 An 'AKqsp' is a WFF because it is an 'A' followed by two WFFs, a '_____' and a '____ .'

Kqs; p

1-198 An 'AKqsApq' is a WFF because it is an 'A' followed by two WFFs, a '_____' and an '_____ .'

Kqs; Apq

1-199 Copy those of the following which are WFFs:

ApAqq   AArsp   AAA   AApqAsr   Apq

_____   _____   _____   _____

1-200 Copy those of the following which are WFFs:

ArAss   Ap   pqA   AApp   Apq

_____   _____

1-201 The five kinds of sentences suggest five rules for recognizing WFFs.

> RULE 4. Any expression which is a 'C' followed by two WFFs is a WFF.

Thus, since a 'p' is a WFF and a 'q' is a WFF, a 'Cpq' is a _____ .

1-202 RULE 1. Any sentence variable is a WFF.
RULE 4. Any expression which is a 'C' followed by two WFFs is a WFF.

Copy those of the following expressions which are WFFs:

Crp   Csqr   Cqp   Csp

_____   _____   _____

1-203 RULE 1. Any sentence variable is a WFF.
RULE 4. Any expression which is a 'C' followed by two WFFs is a WFF.

Copy those of the following expressions which are WFFs:

Cpq   Crs   pqC   Cpr

_____   _____   _____

1-204 RULE 1. Any sentence variable is a WFF.
RULE 4. Any expression which is a 'C' followed by two WFFs is a WFF.

Copy those of the following expressions which are WFFs:

pCq   Cqp   Cpq   Cpp

_____   _____   _____

1-205 A 'Cpq' is a WFF because it is an expression which is a 'C' followed by two _____ .

1-206 A 'Crs' is a WFF because it is an expression which is a '_____' followed by two _____ .

C; WFFs

1-207 A 'Crs' is a WFF because it is a 'C' followed by two WFFs, an 'r' and an 's.' Similarly, a 'CCrsCrs' is a WFF because it is a 'C' followed by two WFFs, a '_____' and a '_____.'

Crs
Crs

1-208 A 'CCpqCrs' is a WFF because it is a 'C' followed by two WFFs, a '_____' and a '_____.'

Cpq; Crs

1-209 A 'CpCqs' is a WFF because it is a 'C' followed by two WFFs, a '_____' and a '_____.'

p; Cqs

1-210 A 'CCqsp' is a WFF because it is a 'C' followed by two WFFs, a '_____' and a '_____.'

Cqs; p

1-211 A 'CKqsp' is a WFF because it is a 'C' followed by two WFFs, a '_____' and a '_____.'

Kqs; p

1-212 A 'CAqsp' is a WFF because it is a 'C' followed by two WFFs, an '_____' and a '_____.'

Aqs; p

1-213 A 'CAsqKpp' is a WFF because it is a 'C' followed by two WFFs, an '_____' and a '_____.'

Asq; Kpp

1-214 A 'KCqpArs' is a WFF because it is a 'K' followed by two WFFs, a '_____' and an '_____.' Similarly, an 'ACqpArs' is a WFF because it is an 'A' followed by two WFFs, a '_____' and an '_____.'

Cqp; Ars

Cqp; Ars

1-215 Copy those of the following expressions which are WFFs:

CpCqq   CCrsp   CCC   CCpqCsr

_____   _____   _____

CpCqq; CCrsp; CCpqCsr
(In any order)

1-216 Copy those of the following expressions which are WFFs:

CrCss   Cp   pqC   Cpq

_____   _____

CrCss; Cpq
(In either order)

1-217   The five kinds of sentences suggest five rules for recognizing WFFs.

>   RULE 5. Any expression which is an 'N' followed by one WFF is a WFF.

Thus, since an 'r' is a WFF, an 'Nr' is a _____ .

WFF

1-218   RULE 1. Any sentence variable is a WFF.
RULE 5. Any expression which is an 'N' followed by one WFF is a WFF.

Copy those of the following expressions which are WFFs:

>   Np   N   Npr   Nq   _____   _____

Np; Nq
(In either order)

1-219   RULE 1. Any sentence variable is a WFF.
RULE 5. Any expression which is an 'N' followed by one WFF is a WFF.

Copy those of the following expressions which are WFFs:

>   Nr   rN   _____

Nr

1-220   An 'Nr' is a WFF because it is an expression which is an 'N' followed by just _____ WFF.

one

1-221   An 'Np' is a WFF because it is an expression which is an 'N' followed by a single _____ .

WFF

1-222   An 'NNp' is a WFF because it is an expression which is an 'N' followed by an 'Np,' which is a _____ .

WFF

1-223   An 'NNq' is a WFF because it is an expression which is an 'N' followed by a WFF '_____ .'

Nq

1-224   An 'NKpq' is a WFF because it is an expression which is an 'N' followed by a WFF '_____ .' Similarly an 'NApq' is a WFF because it is an expression which is an 'N' followed by a WFF '_____ .'

Kpq

Apq

1-225   An 'NCsq' is a WFF because it is an 'N' followed by a WFF '_____ .'

Csq

1-226   A 'KNpq' is a WFF because it is a 'K' followed by two WFFs, an '_____' and a '_____.'

Np; q

A 'KqNp' is a WFF because it is a 'K' followed by two WFFs, a '_____' and an '_____.'

q; Np

1-227   An 'ANpNp' is a WFF because it is an 'A' followed by two WFFs, an '_____' and an '_____.'

Np; Np

1-228   An 'NKNpNq' is a WFF because it is an 'N' followed by a '_____'; and a 'KNpNq' is a WFF because it is a 'K' followed by two WFFs, an '_____' and an '_____.'

KNpNq
Np; Nq

1-229   An 'NANrNq' is a WFF because it is an 'N' followed by an '_____'; and an 'ANrNq' is a WFF because it is an 'A' followed by two WFFs, an '_____' and an '_____.'

ANrNq
Nr; Nq

1-230   An 'NCNpKpq' is a WFF because it is an 'N' followed by a '_____'; and a 'CNpKpq' is a WFF because it is a 'C' followed by two WFFs, an '_____' and a '_____.'

CNpKpq
Np; Kpq

1-231   An 'NNKNpNr' is a WFF because it is an 'N' followed by an '_____'; and an 'NKNpNr' is a WFF because it is an 'N' followed by a '_____'; and a 'KNpNr' is a WFF because it is a 'K' followed by two WFFs, an '_____' and an '_____.'

NKNpNr
KNpNr
Np
Nr

1-232   Five rules for recognizing WFFs are the following:

RULE 1. Any _____ variable is a WFF.

sentence

RULE 2. Any expression which is 'K' followed by _____ WFFs is a WFF.

two

RULE 3. Any expression which is an 'A' followed by _____ WFFs is a WFF.

two

RULE 4. Any expression which is a 'C' followed by _____ WFFs is a WFF.

two

RULE 5. Any expression which is an 'N' followed by _____ WFF is a WFF.

one

Summary of Part 1

1-233   Symbolism in logic takes account of our inability to agree as to whether two expressions have the same meaning and exploits our ability to agree about the shape of expressions. Logic thereby provides a helpful device for recording content and logical form of language and then for considering form isolated from content.

Symbolic expressions are of two kinds—representations and formalizations.

A symbolic expression that indicates both content and logical form is a _____, whereas a symbolic expression that isolates logical form is a _____ .

representation
formalization

1-234   Two expressions which have the same shape are _____ expressions.

like

1-235   We always know whether two expressions are like expressions, because we find it easy to agree whether two expressions have the same _____ .

shape

1-236   Because a representation is a symbolic expression each symbol of which corresponds in a *known* way to a part of the represented expression, it is important that two expressions have like representations if and only if the expressions are _____ expressions.

like

1-237   That we may know how symbols correspond to represented expressions we make explicit these conventions for representation:

1. Sentences containing no connecting words—that is, elementary sentences—are represented by capitals *other than* '___'s, '___'s, '___'s, or '___'s.

K; A; C; N

2. Connecting words are represented as follows:

    a A 'K' represents an '_____,'   and

    b An 'A' represents an '_____,'   or

    c A 'C' represents an '_____,' and if then

    d An 'N' represents an '_____.'   it is false that

3. When sentences that do contain connecting words are represented, the symbol representing the connecting word precedes the symbols representing the sentences joined by the _____ word.   connecting

1-238 A representation of a sentence indicates

1. The content of the represented sentence, and
2. A logical _____ of the represented sentence.   form

1-239 Given a representation of a sentence, we can formalize that sentence. We formalize a sentence in order to isolate a _____ _____ of the sentence.   logical form

1-240 When we formalize a sentence, we disregard the _____ of the sentence in order to isolate a logical _____ of the sentence.   content
form

1-241 A WFF is a well-formed formula, and a WFF is an expression which isolates a logical form of a well-formed _____ .   sentence

1-242 A WFF is an expression

1. Which is composed of nothing but connectives and _____ variables, and   sentence
2. Which isolates a logical form of a _____ .   sentence

1-243 The five rules for recognizing WFFs correspond to the five kinds of well-formed sentences distinguished. We distinguished

    elementary sentences,
    'and' sentences,
    '_____' sentences,   or
    '_____' sentences, and   if then
    '_____' sentences.   it is false that

1-244   Five rules for recognizing WFFs are the following:

1. Any sentence variable is a WFF.
2. Any expression which is a 'K' followed by two WFFs is a WFF.
3. Any expression which is an 'A' followed by two WFFs is a WFF.
4. Any expression which is a 'C' followed by two WFFs is a WFF.
5. Any _____ which is an '_____' followed by _____ WFF is a _____ .

expression; N; one
WFF

Exercises for Part 1

1 For each of the following expressions determine whether the expression is a WFF:

a	KANpNqNANpNq	n	NKNqKpKrq
b	CCNpNqCqp	o	NKNKNprKNKNqrKNNKpqr
c	AKCpNNCrp	p	CCCpqArAstCCrpAtAsp
d	AKprKNtp	q	CCqrCApqApr
e	CCpCqrCCpqCpr	r	CCCCCpqCNrNsrtCCtpCsp
f	CCpCqrCkpqr	s	CCCpqrCCrpCsp
g	CNApqKNpNq	t	CCCpqCCrsCCspCtCrp
h	CANpNqNKpq	u	NAps
i	CANpqCpq	v	CAst
j	ApCpq	w	pAst
k	AKstNKst	x	CrAss
l	NKNNKpqr	y	CrACKrs
m	NKsNs	z	CCCpqArKstCKspArNANtKpq

2 Suppose we were using not the parenthesis-free Lukasiewicz notation which has as connectives 'K's, 'A's, 'C's, and 'N's but rather a notation more akin to *Principia's*. Then the WFF rules can be stated as follows:

(1) Any 'p,' 'q,' 'r,' 's,' or 't' is a sentence variable and is a WFF.

(2) Any expression which is an '&' between two WFFs each of which is enclosed in parentheses is a WFF.

(3) Any expression which is a '∨' between two WFFs each of which is enclosed in parentheses is a WFF.

(4) Any expression which is a '⊃' between two WFFs each of which is enclosed in parentheses is a WFF.

(5) Any expression which is a '∼' preceding one WFF enclosed in parentheses is a WFF.

We adopt the convention that an expression remains a WFF if parentheses around single sentence variables are omitted. So the following would be WFFs according to these WFF rules:

    p

    p & q

    r ∨ (p & q)

    (t ∨ (p & q)) ⊃ s

    ∼(∼ p)

For each of the following expressions determine whether the expression is a WFF:

a   ∼(p & (∼p))

b   (p & q) ⊃ (∼((∼p) ∨ q))

c   (p ⊃ q) ⊃ ((r & p)⊃q)

d $(p \& (p \supset q)) \supset (\sim p)$

e $((p \supset q) \& (r \supset s)) \supset ((p \& r) \supset (q \& s))$

f $p \supset (q \supset q)$

g $(p \supset (q \vee (p \& q))) \& q))$

h $(p \vee q) \supset (q \vee p)$

i $(p \vee ((\sim p) \& q)) \vee ((\sim p) \& (\sim q))$

j $(p \& (p \supset q)) \supset q$

k $p \vee (\sim p) \& (s \vee t)$

l $((p \supset q) \& (q \supset r)) \supset (p \supset r)$

m $((p \& q) \supset r) \supset (p \supset (q \supset r))$

n $(\sim (p \& q)) \supset ((\sim p) \vee (\sim q))$

o $(\sim (p \supset q)) \supset (p \& (\sim q))$

p $(p \supset q) \supset ((\sim q) \supset (\sim p))$

q $(\sim (p \vee (\sim (\sim q)))) \supset s$

r $t \supset (s \supset (p \supset t))$

s $((p \vee (\sim p)) \& (q \vee (\sim q))) \supset ((p \supset q) \supset ((\sim p) \supset (\sim q)))$

t $p \vee (\sim q)) \supset (\sim ((\sim p) \& q))$

u $((\sim p) \vee q) \supset (p \supset q)$

v $\sim ((\sim p) \& (\sim q))$

w $((r \vee p) \vee (r \vee q))$

x $(p \vee p) \supset p$

y $((p \& q) \& (r \& s)) \& t$

z $(p \& (p \supset q)) \supset q$

3 Using the *Principia* type of notation write a corresponding WFF for each WFF in exercise 1 above. For example, corresponding to a WFF 'NKpq' you would write a WFF '$\sim (p \& q)$.'

4 Using the Lukasiewicz notation write a corresponding WFF for each WFF in exercise 2 above. For example, corresponding to a WFF '$(p \supset q) \& ((\sim p) \vee s)$' you would write a WFF 'KCpqANps.'

5 For each of the following WFFs write an English sentence that could be formalized by such a WFF:

a CCpqCNqNp   **d** CKqpNANqNp

b KpNp   **e** CNNpp

c CKprArp

6 Reflect on the following:

a Why do we need no parentheses in Lukasiewicz notation?

b If two sentences have similar meanings, do the sentences necessarily have like representations?

c If two sentences have like representations, do the sentences necessarily have the same meaning?

d Which of the following are in English?
  (1) connectives
  (2) connecting words
  (3) WFFs
  (4) sentences
  (5) representations

e In what interesting way are WFFs, similes, maps, parables, and allegories alike?

f Representations and formalizations are each related somehow to logical form. But in terms of logical form, how does a representation differ from a formalization?

g In the usage of this book we say that there are *three* connecting words and two sentences in the following list:

  and   *The ruler is reliable.*
  and   *The ruler is reliable.*
  and

That is, words and sentences are taken as physical objects—spatial and temporal entities. Compare and contrast this usage with the usage implicit in saying "He has many words in his vocabulary" or saying "Every member of the group wrote the same sentence."

Achievement Test for Part 1

1   (1) *Van Buren was President.*
    (2) *Van Buren lived in Kinderhook.*
    (3) *If Van Buren was President, then Van Buren lived in Kinderhook.*
    Suppose (1) is represented by a 'P' and (2) is represented by a 'Q.' Then (3) is represented by a '_____.'

2   An 'it is false that' is represented by an '_____.'

3   A 'C' represents an '_____.'

4   A representation of a sentence indicates two things:
    a   The _____ of the _____ represented, and
    b   A _____ _____ of the _____ represented.

5   Suppose an 'R' represents (1) and an 'S' represents (2):
    (1) *Hawaii is a state.*
    (2) *Alaska is a state.*
    Write a sentence that can be represented by a 'KRS.' _____

6   If a sentence is represented by an 'APQ,' then we can isolate a logical form of that sentence by writing an expression beginning with an '_____' followed by two unlike _____ variables.

7   Place a check mark (√) in front of each of the following expressions which is a WFF. Place a cross (×) in front of each of the following expressions which is not a WFF.

    a ____ P   d ____ q   g ____ K   j ____ qA   m ____ Kpq
    b ____ r   e ____ Apr   h ____ s   k ____ Nq   n ____ C
    c ____ Crp   f ____ qN   i ____ N   l ____ Kss   o ____ Npr

8   Write a sentence just like the following sentence:
        Charles I capitulated.   _____

9   The representation of an 'and' sentence begins with a '_____.'

10 A 'Cpr' formalizes an '_____' sentence.

11 A WFF is an expression which is composed of nothing but _____ and _____ variables.

12 A 'Krt' formalizes an '_____' sentence.

13 The representation of an 'or' sentence begins with an '_____.'

14 The representation of an 'it is false that' sentence begins with an '_____.'

15 An 'Nq' formalizes an '_____' sentence.

16 Any sentence which can be formalized by an 'Aqp' is an '_____' sentence.

17 The representation of an 'if then' sentence begins with a '_____.'

18 Given a representation—that is, an expression which _____ a logical form of a sentence—we can formalize that sentence, that is, we can _____ a logical form of that sentence.

19 *(1) It is false that China is in Africa.*

Suppose that (1) is represented by an 'NS.' Write a sentence that can be represented by an 'S.' _____

20 *(1) Ghana is in Africa.*

Formalize sentence (1). _____

21 Put a check mark ($\sqrt{}$) in front of each of the following expressions which is a WFF. Put a cross ($\times$) in front of each of the following expressions which is not a WFF.

a	_____ AKpqr		**g**	_____ NKNKCppqq
b	_____ CCpr		**h**	_____ ACKNCApqrsNtpr
c	_____ NKNKrq		**i**	_____ AAApqr
d	_____ NKAKqrtCNpq		**j**	_____ ApArAsAps
e	_____ NNNp		**k**	_____ NKAKqrtNCNpq
f	_____ CpCCrAsCptq		**l**	_____ KAKpqKNpNqNAKpqKNpNq

22 A formalization of a sentence is a _____ , or for short, a _____ .

23 Suppose we represent

(1) Melissus meditated.

by a 'T.' How many representations unlike a 'T' could we write for the following sentence:

(2) Melissus meditated.

_____ We can choose to formalize (2) in any one of how many ways? _____

24 Here are two words

  and *and*

and here are two sentences

  Plato philosophized. *Plato philosophized.*

How many unlike sentences can you write using only the following words:

  I   *only*
  you *love*

_____ none _____ four _____ more than four

How many unlike sentences can you write using only words like the following?

  I   *only*
  you *love*

_____ none _____ less than four _____ four or more than four

25 An English sentence contains how many WFFs? _____

26 If two sentences have like representations what do you know about the sentences? _____

27 If two sentences have like formalizations what do you know about the sentences? _____

28 How many WFFs are there in English? _____

29 If a 'Q' represents

(1) Socrates survived.

write a sentence that can be represented by a 'CQQ.' _____

30 A sentence is a sequence of what? _____

31 A WFF is a sequence of what? _____

32 A formalization of a sentence contains how many capital letters that are not connectives? _____

33 A representation of a sentence contains how many lowercase letters? _____

34 For each of the following expressions in Lukasiewicz notation write a corresponding expression in *Principia* notation.

   a CKpqApq

   b NKNpNq

   c KApsNAps

   d ACpqNCNtr

35 For each of the following expressions in *Principia* notation write a corresponding expression in Lukasiewicz notation.

   a (p & q) $\vee$ ((~p) & (~q))

   b ((p $\vee$ (q & t)) & (~p)) $\supset$ (q & t)

   c (~((~p) $\supset$ q)) $\supset$ ((~p) & (~q))

   d ~(~(((~p) $\vee$ (t & q)) $\supset$ s))

Part **2**

Arguments: Their Representation, Formalization, and Validity

Anatomy of an Argument

2-1 *If we can represent sentences, then we can represent*
arguments.
We can represent sentences.
Therefore, we can represent arguments.

An argument is a sequence of sentences. The above argument is a sequence of three _____ .

sentences

2-2 *If we can represent sentences, then we can represent*
arguments.
We can represent sentences.
Therefore, we can represent arguments.

An argument is a sequence of sentences in which one sentence is said to follow from the others. In the above argument,
the third sentence is said to follow from the first two
_____ .

sentences

2-3 *If we can represent sentences, then we can represent*
arguments.
We can represent sentences.
Therefore, we can represent arguments.

The sentence that is said to follow from the other sentences
of an argument is the conclusion of that argument. In the
above argument, the third sentence is said to follow from the
first two sentences. Therefore, the third sentence is the
argument's _____ .

conclusion

2-4 *If we can represent sentences, then we can represent*
arguments.
We can represent sentences.
Therefore, we can represent arguments.

Because in the above argument the third sentence is said to
follow from the first two sentences, the third sentence is
called the argument's _____ .

conclusion

2-5   *An argument has one or more premisses.*
An argument has a conclusion.
Therefore, an argument has one or more premisses, and an argument has a conclusion.

Because in the above argument the conclusion is said to follow from the first two sentences, the first two sentences are the argument's _____ .

premisses

2-6   *If we can represent arguments, then we can formalize arguments.*
We can represent arguments.
Therefore, we can formalize arguments.

In the above argument the third sentence is said to follow from the first two sentences. So the first two sentences are the _____ of the argument and the last sentence is the argument's _____ .

premisses
conclusion

2-7   *If we can represent arguments, then we can formalize arguments.*
We can represent arguments.
Therefore, we can formalize arguments.

Copy the word that precedes the conclusion of the above argument. _____

therefore

2-8   *If we can represent arguments, then we can formalize arguments.*
We can represent arguments.
Therefore, we can formalize arguments.

In the above argument, we can tell that the third sentence is said to follow from the first two because a 'therefore' precedes the conclusion. Although other words may serve the same function, it is often the case that a 'therefore' precedes an argument's _____ .

conclusion

2-9   The conclusion of an argument is said to follow from the premisses of an argument because an argument is a sequence of sentences in which one sentence of the sequence is said to follow from the other _____ of the sequence.

sentences

Representation of an Argument

2-10 *If we can represent sentences, then we can represent arguments.*
We can represent sentences.
Therefore, we can represent arguments.

Suppose we represent the first premiss of the above argument by a 'CPQ.' We follow our convention in representing the 'if then' by a '_____.'

C

2-11 *If we can represent sentences, then we can represent arguments.*
We can represent sentences.
Therefore, we can represent arguments.

If we represent the first premiss of the above argument by a 'CPQ,' then we represent the second premiss by a '_____.'

P

2-12 *If we can represent sentences, then we can represent arguments.*
We can represent sentences.
Therefore, we can represent arguments.

If we represent the first premiss by a 'CPQ,' then we represent the conclusion by a '_____.'

Q

2-13 *If we can represent sentences, then we can represent arguments.*
We can represent sentences.
Therefore, we can represent arguments.

We know already how to represent the *premisses* and *conclusion* of the above argument. We agree to represent the *argument* by

$$\begin{array}{|l} CPQ \\ P \\ \hline Q \end{array}$$

for we adopt the convention that a 'ⱶ' represents a
'_____.'

therefore

2-14 We call a 'ⱶ' a 'therefore' indicator because a 'ⱶ'
represents a '_____.'

therefore

2-15 *If we can represent sentences, then we can represent*
arguments.
We can represent sentences.
Therefore, we can represent arguments.

When we represent the above argument by

we put above the little horizontal line of the 'therefore'
indicator the representations of the _____. Below this
little horizontal line we put the representation of the
_____.

premisses

conclusion

2-16 *If we can represent sentences, then we can represent*
arguments.
We can represent sentences.
Therefore, we can represent arguments.

When we represent the above argument by

```
 |CPQ
 |P
 |Q
```

for brevity we say simply that the representations of the
premisses are above the 'therefore' indicator ('ⱶ') and the
representation of the conclusion is below the 'therefore'
_____.

indicator

2-17 To represent an argument, we use a 'ⱶ' (a 'therefore'
indicator) and put the representations of the premisses
_____ the 'ⱶ' and the representation of the conclusion
_____ the 'ⱶ.'

above
below

Representing Arguments

2-18 *If we can represent arguments, then we can formalize arguments.*
We can represent arguments.
Therefore, we can formalize arguments.

If we represent the first premiss by a 'CSP,' we represent the argument by

$$\frac{\begin{array}{c}\rule{2cm}{0.4pt}\\\rule{2cm}{0.4pt}\end{array}}{\rule{2cm}{0.4pt}}$$

CSP
S
P

2-19 *If Aristotle's writings were studied in the Middle Ages,*
then logic was studied in the Middle Ages.
Aristotle's writings were studied in the Middle Ages.
Therefore, logic was studied in the Middle Ages.

If we represent the first premiss of the above argument by a 'CPQ,' we represent the above argument by

_____

CPQ
P
Q

2-20 *If you study logic, then you can represent arguments.*

If a 'CSP' represents the above sentence, then

CSP
S
P

represents the following argument:

_____

_____

Therefore, _____

If you study logic, then you can represent arguments.
You study logic.
You can represent arguments.

2-21   *Some arguments are valid.*
Some arguments are invalid.
Therefore, some arguments are valid, and some arguments are invalid.

Since we can represent an 'and' by a 'K,' we represent the above argument by

R
S
─────────   KRS

2-22   *The premisses often precede the conclusion.*
The conclusion is said to follow from the premisses.
Therefore, the premisses often precede the conclusion, and the conclusion is said to follow from the premisses.

If we represent the first premiss by a 'Q' and the second premiss by an 'S,' we represent the above argument by

Q
S
─────
KQS

2-23   *Arguments can be formalized, and validity depends on logical form.*

If a 'KRS' represents the above sentence, then write a sentence like the second premiss of an argument represented by

R
S
KRS
─────────────────────────   Validity depends on
                                                    logical form.

2-24   *Some arguments are valid, and some arguments are invalid.*
Therefore, some arguments are valid.

If we represent the premiss of this argument by a 'KQP,' then we represent the above argument by

                                          KQP
                                                             Q

2-25   *Some arguments are valid, and some arguments are invalid.*

   Therefore, some arguments are invalid.

If we represent the premiss of this argument by a 'KQP,' then we can represent the above argument by

_____

| KQP
|‾‾‾
| P

2-26   *Arguments can be formalized, and validity depends on logical form.*

If a 'KPR' represents the above sentence, then write a sentence like the conclusion of an argument represented by

| KPR
|‾‾‾
| R

_____

Validity depends on logical form.

2-27   We know how to represent arguments because

1. We know how to represent sentences,
2. We know how to represent a 'therefore,' and
3. We know how to indicate whether a representation is a representation of a premiss or a representation of a

_____ .

conclusion

2-28   When representing an argument, we make use of a 'therefore' indicator and put the representations of the premisses _____ the 'ⱶ' and put below the 'ⱶ' the representation of the _____ .

above

conclusion

2-29 | CPQ
   |‾‾‾
   | P
   |‾‾‾
   | Q

In the above representation the 'CPQ' represents a premiss of the argument represented and the 'P' represents a _____ of the argument represented, whereas the 'Q' represents the _____ of the argument represented.

premiss

conclusion

Formalization of an Argument

2-30   A representation of an argument, like the representation of a sentence, indicates two things:

1. A representation of an argument indicates the *content* of the argument.
2. A representation of an argument indicates a *logical* _____ of the argument.

form

2-31   *(1) If we can represent arguments, then we can formalize arguments.*

We already know, given a representation of an argument, how to write an argument just like the argument represented. For example, suppose we know a 'CPQ' represents (1). An argument just like the argument represented by

│CPQ
│P
│Q

is the following argument:

_____

_____

Therefore, _____

If we can represent arguments, then we can formalize arguments.
We can represent arguments.
We can formalize arguments.

2-32   Now we turn to isolating a logical form of an argument, given a representation of that argument. We can *isolate* a *logical form* of an argument by *formalizing* that argument. Thus, if we have a representation of an argument, we can isolate a logical form of that argument by _____ the argument.

formalizing

2-33   When we *formalize* an argument, we disregard the content of the argument in order to isolate a logical _____ of the argument.

form

2-34 Suppose we are given the following representation of an argument:

|CPQ
|P
|‾‾‾
|Q

Then

|Cpq
|p
|‾‾‾
|q

formalizes the represented argument. But the represented argument is formalized also by

|Crs
|r
|‾‾‾‾‾   s
|

2-35 Given the representation

|KQR
|‾‾‾
|Q

we can formalize the represented argument by

|Kqr
|‾‾‾
|q

We can formalize the represented argument also by

|Kps
|‾‾‾‾‾   p
|

2-36 Given the representation

|P
|Q
|‾‾‾‾
|KPQ

we can formalize the represented argument by

|p
|q
|‾‾‾‾
|Kpq

We can formalize the represented argument also by

|‾‾‾‾‾   r
|s
|‾‾‾‾
|Krs

2-37 Given the representation

$$\begin{array}{|l} CRP \\ \hline R \\ \hline P \end{array}$$

we can formalize the represented argument by

$$\begin{array}{|l} Csq \\ \hline \rule{2em}{0.4pt} \\ \hline \rule{2em}{0.4pt} \end{array}$$

s
q

2-38 Given the representation

$$\begin{array}{|l} KSP \\ \hline S \end{array}$$

we can formalize the represented argument by

$$\begin{array}{|l} Krq \\ \hline \rule{2em}{0.4pt} \end{array}$$

r

2-39 Given the representation

$$\begin{array}{|l} S \\ \hline P \\ \hline KSP \end{array}$$

we can formalize the represented argument by

$$\begin{array}{|l} \rule{2em}{0.4pt} \\ \hline \rule{2em}{0.4pt} \\ \hline Krq \end{array}$$

r
q

2-40 In the preceding frames, we have been formalizing arguments, given their _____ .

representations

2-41 To formalize an argument, given its representation, we write an expression like the representation except that sentence variables occur in the formalization in just those places where nonconnectives occur in the _____ .

representation

2-42 Recall that sentence variables are lowercase letters 'p,' '_____,' '_____,' '_____,' and '_____.'

q; r; s; t

2-43 Recall that connectives are capital letters 'K,' '____,' '____,' and '____.'

A
C; N

2-44 Since only capital letters 'K,' 'A,' 'C,' and 'N' are connectives, the two nonconnectives in a 'CRS' are an '____' and an '____.'

R
S

2-45 In an 'NKPQ' the two nonconnectives are a '____' and a '____.'

P
Q

2-46
$$\begin{array}{|l} Cpq \\ \hline p \\ \hline q \end{array}$$

is a *formalization* of an argument which is represented by

$$\begin{array}{|l} CPQ \\ \hline P \\ \hline Q \end{array}$$

because the formalization is an expression just like the representation except that in just those places where nonconnectives occur in the representation _____ _____ occur in the _____ .

sentence variables
formalization

2-47
$$\begin{array}{|l} Crs \\ \hline r \\ \hline s \end{array}$$

is a formalization of an argument which is represented by

$$\begin{array}{|l} CPQ \\ \hline P \\ \hline Q \end{array}$$

because the formalization is an expression just like the representation except that in just those places where nonconnectives occur in the representation _____ _____ occur in the _____ . Connectives occur both in the _____ and in the _____ .

sentence variables
formalization
representation;
formalization

2-48

$$
\begin{array}{|l} Cpq \\ p \\ \hline q \end{array}
$$

and

$$
\begin{array}{|l} Crs \\ r \\ \hline s \end{array}
$$

are both formalizations of an argument which is represented by

$$
\begin{array}{|l} CPQ \\ \underline{\qquad} \\ \hline \underline{\qquad} \end{array}
$$

P

Q

2-49   In writing an expression that formalizes an argument represented by

$$
\begin{array}{|l} CPQ \\ P \\ \hline Q \end{array}
$$

we can use any two unlike sentence variables we choose when we formalize the first premiss. But as soon as we formalize the argument's first premiss by, say, a 'Cpq,' we *must* use a 'p' to formalize the second premiss and a '_____' to formalize the conclusion.

q

2-50   In writing an expression that formalizes an argument represented by

$$
\begin{array}{|l} CPQ \\ P \\ \hline Q \end{array}
$$

we can use any two unlike sentence variables we choose when we formalize the first premiss. But as soon as we formalize the argument's first premiss by, say, a 'Crs,' we *must* use an 'r' to formalize the second premiss and an '_____' to formalize the conclusion.

s

2-51   Suppose we want to formalize an argument represented by

|CPQ
|P
|Q

and suppose we formalize the argument's first premiss by,
say, a 'Cpq.' Then we must use a 'p' in the formalization
wherever a 'P' occurs in the representation, and we must use
a 'q' in the formalization wherever a '_____' occurs in the   Q
representation.

2-52   Suppose we want to formalize an argument represented by

|CPQ
|P
|Q

and suppose we formalize the argument's first premiss by,
say, a 'Crs.' Then we must use an 'r' in the formalization
wherever a 'P' occurs in the representation, and we must use
an 's' in the formalization wherever a '_____' occurs in the   Q
representation.

2-53

|Cpq
|p
|q

and

|Crs
|r
|s

are both formalizations of an argument which is represented
by

|CPQ
|‾‾‾‾‾   P
|‾‾‾‾‾   Q

2-54 An argument whose representation is

```
 |CPQ
 |P
‾|Q
```

can be formalized by

```
 |Cpq
 |‾‾‾‾
‾|‾‾‾‾
```

               p
               q

or by

```
 |Crs
 |‾‾‾‾
‾|‾‾‾‾
```

               r
               s

2-55 An argument whose representation is

```
 |CPQ
 |P
‾|Q
```

can be formalized by

```
 |Cqs
 |‾‾‾‾
‾|‾‾‾‾
```

               q
               s

or by

```
 |‾‾‾‾
 |p
‾|s
```

               Cps

2-56 We now know how to formalize an argument, given a representation of the argument. In other words, given a representation of an argument, we can isolate a logical _____ of the argument represented.

               form

2-57 To formalize an argument, given a representation, we write an expression like the representation except that sentence variables occur in the _____ in just those places where nonconnectives occur in the _____. Where like nonconnectives occur in the representation like _____ _____ must occur in the formalization.

               formalization
               representation

               sentence variables

Argument Formulas (AFs)

2-58 A *well-formed formula*—or for short, a WFF—is a formalization of a _____ .

2-59 A formalization of an *argument* is an argument formula—or for short, an AF. Thus,

$$\begin{array}{|l} p \\ q \\ \hline Kpq \end{array}$$

is an AF—that is, an _____ _____

2-60 We know that

$$\begin{array}{|l} p \\ q \\ \hline Kpq \end{array}$$

formalizes an argument. Therefore,

$$\begin{array}{|l} p \\ q \\ \hline Kpq \end{array}$$

is an argument formula—or for short and from now on, an _____ .

2-61 *If John murdered Pete, then Tom is innocent.*
John murdered Pete.
Therefore, Tom is innocent.

Since

$$\begin{array}{|l} Cqs \\ q \\ \hline s \end{array}$$

formalizes the above argument, we know that

$$\begin{array}{|l} Cqs \\ q \\ \hline s \end{array}$$

is an _____

2-62 *Arnauld disputed with Malebranche.*
Maugham wrote plays.
Therefore, pineapple is expensive.

Since

> | p
> | q
> |‾r

formalizes the above argument, we know that

> | p
> | q
> |‾r

is an _____ , that is, an _____ formula.   **AF; argument**

2-63 *If history repeats itself, then liberty will always assert
itself.*
History repeats itself.
Therefore, liberty will always assert itself.

Since

> | Csq
> | s
> |‾q

formalizes the above argument, we know that

> | Csq
> | s
> |‾q

is an _____ .   **AF**

2-64 *A plum is a fruit, and a prune is a fruit.*
Walnuts grow in California.
Therefore, the sea is salty.

Since

> | Kpq
> | r
> |‾s

formalizes the above argument,

> | Kpq
> | r
> |‾s

is an _____ .   **AF**

2-65   Symbolism in logic takes account of our inability to agree as to whether two expressions have the same meaning and exploits our ability to agree about the shape of expressions. Logic thereby provides a helpful device for recording content and logical form of language and then for considering form isolated from content. Symbolic expressions are of two kinds—representations and formalizations. A symbolic expression that indicates both content and logical form is a _____, whereas a symbolic expression that isolates logical form is a _____ .

representation
formalization

2-66   A representation of an argument indicates

1. The content of the represented _____, and
2. A logical form of the represented _____ .

argument
argument

2-67   Given a representation of an argument we can formalize that _____ .

argument

2-68   We formalize an argument in order to isolate a _____ _____ of that argument.

logical form

2-69   A WFF is a well-formed formula, and a WFF is an expression which isolates a logical form of a well-formed _____ . An AF is an argument formula, and an AF is an expression which isolates a logical form not of just any sequence of sentences but of a sequence of sentences which is an _____ .

sentence

argument

2-70   A WFF is an expression
1. Which is composed of nothing but connectives and sentence variables, and
2. Which isolates a logical form of a _____ .

sentence

An AF is an expression

1. Which is composed of nothing but connectives, sentence variables, and a '_____' indicator, and
2. Which isolates a logical form of an _____ .

therefore
argument

Validity of an Argument

2-71 We know what an argument is, how to represent an argument, and how to formalize an argument. We know also that the formalization of an argument is called, for short, an _____ .

AF

2-72 But now let's turn our attention to *valid* arguments; for though some arguments are valid arguments, not all arguments are _____ arguments.

valid

2-73 Recall that an argument is a sequence of sentences in which the conclusion *is said to* follow from the premisses.

A valid argument is an argument in which the conclusion *does* follow from the _____ .

premisses

2-74 Is every valid argument an argument? _____
Is every argument a valid argument? _____

yes
no

2-75 Only those arguments are valid in which the conclusion is not only _____ to follow from the premisses but in which the conclusion actually _____ _____ _____ the premisses.

said

does follow from

2-76 Some arguments are valid; others are not valid.

How do we decide whether a given argument is a _____ argument?

valid

2-77 To decide whether an argument is valid, we must decide whether the conclusion is only said to follow from or actually does follow from the premisses. But how do we decide whether the conclusion actually _____ _____ _____ the premisses?

does follow from

2-78 Suppose we try to decide whether the following argument is a valid argument.

> If Florence Nightingale brought health to the Crimea, then Miss Nightingale was a gentle angel of mercy.
> If it is false that Nurse Nightingale spoke strongly against Army medical policies, then Florence Nightingale brought health to the Crimea.
> It is false that Miss Nightingale was a gentle angel of mercy.
> Therefore, Nurse Nightingale spoke strongly against Army medical policies.

We consider the premisses, then the conclusion, and then the relation the conclusion has to the premisses taken together. But though we can easily identify premisses and conclusion, notice that it is not so easy immediately to decide whether the conclusion actually does follow from the premisses. Is it easy, then, to decide immediately whether the argument is a valid argument? _____   no

2-79 But to decide whether an argument is valid is not *always* so difficult. Consider this argument:

> Mining is a meticulous industry.
> Pheasant is delicious.
> Therefore, personal identity is philosophically dubious.

1. Consider the premisses.
2. Consider the conclusion.
3. Consider the relation the conclusion has to the premisses taken together.

Does the conclusion actually follow from the premisses? _____ Is the argument, then, a valid argument? _____   no
          no

2-80 Consider whether this argument is valid:

> If it rained last night, then the sidewalk is wet.
> The sidewalk is wet.
> Therefore, it rained last night.

Before deciding on the argument's validity, consider that even though it didn't rain the sidewalk might be wet—say, from a gardener's hose. Does the conclusion actually follow from the premisses taken together? _____ Is the argument, then, a valid argument? _____   no
          no

2-81 We were able to decide fairly easily that an argument like

> *If it rained last night, then the sidewalk is wet.*
> *The sidewalk is wet.*
> *Therefore, it rained last night.*

is not a valid argument. But now consider this argument which is just slightly different from the preceding one:

> *If it rained last night, then the sidewalk is wet.*
> *It rained last night.*
> *Therefore, the sidewalk is wet.*

Is the second argument a valid argument—does the conclusion follow from the premisses? _____   yes

2-82 *If it rained last night, then the sidewalk is wet.*
It rained last night.
Therefore, the sidewalk is wet.

We could decide fairly easily that an argument like the one above was a valid argument. Do we know whether the conclusion is true? _____ Do we know whether the premisses   no
are true? _____   no

2-83 The validity of an argument does not depend on the truth of the premisses nor on the truth of the conclusion. For consider this argument:

> *If Connecticut is the largest state, then Connecticut is*
> *larger than Alaska.*
> *Connecticut is the largest state.*
> *Therefore, Connecticut is larger than Alaska.*

Considering the relation between premisses and conclusion we find it difficult to deny that the conclusion does follow from the premisses. But is the conclusion of this valid argument true? _____ Are both premisses true? _____   no; no

2-84 *Some Swiss are mountain climbers.*
Mice eat cheese.
Therefore, a triangle has three sides.

In this argument we would be inclined to say that both premisses are true and that the conclusion is true. But is the argument valid? _____   no

2-85 On what, then, does validity depend, if not on the truth of premisses and conclusion? The validity of an argument depends on the structure or form of the premisses in relation to the structure or form of the conclusion, since an argument is valid if and only if the conclusion follows from the premisses. Of course, if an argument is valid and, moreover, its premisses are true, then we are assured of the truth of the conclusion. Such an agument is called, technically, a sound argument. But the question of an argument's validity is not only prior to the question of an argument's soundness, but validity is important also quite independently of the question of soundness. Hence, our focus here is not on sound arguments but on _____ arguments.

valid

Logical Argument Formulas
(LAFs) and Validity

2-86 The *structure* of the argument's premisses *in relation to* the *structure* of the conclusion we call the argument's logical form. Hence, since validity depends on the structure of the premisses in relation to the structure of the conclusion, an argument's validity depends on the argument's _____ _____ .

logical form

2-87 Because validity depends on logical form, to decide on the validity of a given argument it may be helpful first to isolate the argument's logical form. And we isolate an argument's logical form by formalizing the argument—that is, by writing an argument formula, or for short, an _____ .

AF

2-88 Consider the argument

> *If Mozart was a composer, then Mozart was a musician.*
> *Mozart was a composer.*
> *Therefore, Mozart was a musician.*

If we represent this argument by

CPQ
P
‾
Q

we can formalize the argument by the AF

Cpq
‾‾‾‾‾
‾‾‾‾‾

p
q

2-89   In an argument formalized by an AF

> |Cpq
> |p
> |‾‾
> |q

we know that

1. The first premiss of the argument is an 'if then' sentence,
2. The second premiss is a sentence like the sentence following the 'if' in the first premiss, and
3. The conclusion is a sentence like the sentence following
the 'then' in the first premiss.

And so, we would decide that the argument formalized by an
AF

> |Cpq
> |p
> |‾‾
> |q

is a valid argument in virtue of our understanding of the
structure imparted by the connecting word '_____.'   **if then**

2-90   If we represent the argument

> *If you make a spectacle of yourself, then you will be seen*
> *through.*
> *You make a spectacle of yourself.*
> *Therefore, you will be seen through.*

by

                                                                  CRT

> |‾‾‾‾‾
> |R
> |‾‾
> |T

then we can formalize the argument by

> |Cpq   **p**
> |‾‾‾‾‾
> |‾‾   **q**
> |‾‾‾‾‾

2-91   *If Mozart was a composer, then Mozart was a musician.*
Mozart was a composer.
Therefore, Mozart was a musician.

> *If you make a spectacle of yourself, then you will be seen through.*
> *You make a spectacle of yourself.*
> *Therefore, you will be seen through.*

These arguments are not like arguments; hence, they have unlike representations.

But how many of the arguments can be formalized by the following AF? _____

two

```
|Cpq
|p
—
|q
```

2-92 Only like arguments have like representations, but arguments need not be like arguments to have _____ formalizations.

like

2-93 We decided about a given argument's validity by considering the argument's isolated logical form. But since validity depends on logical form and more than one argument may have the same logical form, we have also in effect decided about the validity of any argument that has the isolated form—that is, any argument that can be formalized by the AF that _____ the given argument.

formalizes

2-94 Any AF such that *any* argument that can be formalized by that AF is a valid argument we call a *logical argument formula*, or for short, a L_____ _____.

AF

2-95 We saw that an AF

```
|Cpq
|p
—
|q
```

is such that it would be difficult to deny that any argument that could be formalized by that AF is a valid argument. Hence, the AF is a _____ _____ _____, or for short, a _____.

logical argument formula
LAF (pronounced "laugh")

2-96 Given that

> Cpq
> p
> ―
> q

is a LAF, is the argument

> *If the number is a prime other than two, then the num-*
> *ber is odd.*
> *The number is a prime other than two.*
> *Therefore, the number is odd.*

a valid argument? _____   yes

2-97 *Jefferson invented the swivel chair, and Jefferson played*
the violin.
Therefore, Jefferson invented the swivel chair.

Would you call the above argument valid in virture of your
awareness that

> Cpq
> p
> ―
> q

is a LAF? _____ Is the argument valid? _____   no; yes

2-98 If we represent the argument

> *Jefferson invented the swivel chair, and Jefferson played*
> *the violin.*
> *Therefore, Jefferson invented the swivel chair.*

by a

> KSQ
> ―
> S

we can formalize the argument by the AF

> Kqs
> ―――   q

2-99   In an argument formalized by the AF

> | Kqs
> |‾‾
> | q

we know that

1. The first premiss is an '_____' sentence, and

and

2. The conclusion is a sentence just like the sentence before the 'and' in the _____.

premiss

And so we would decide that the argument formalized by an AF

> | Kqs
> |‾‾
> | q

is a valid argument in virtue of our understanding of the structure imparted by a connecting word '_____.'

and

2-100   Is every argument that can be formalized by an AF

> | Kqs
> |‾‾
> | q

a valid argument? _____

yes

Is an AF

> | Kqs
> |‾‾
> | q

a LAF? _____

yes

2-101   The AFs

> | Cpq | Kqs
> | p | ‾‾
> | ‾‾ | q
> | q

are LAFs. There are many other AFs such that any argument that can be formalized by the AF is a valid argument—that is, there are many other LAFs. But at this point, rather than exploring without system the wide variety of LAFs in order to catalogue them for use in deciding validity of arguments, we present in the next chapter a more systematic and economical treatment of LAFs and propose a new definition of valid argument in terms of this systematic treatment.

Arguments and Arguments

2-102 Compare these two sentences:

An argument is a sequence of sentences in which the conclusion is said to follow from the premisses.

Arnauld and Malebranche had a bitter argument about the nature of ideas, and the argument lasted for many years.

Does the second sentence make sense? But would we say of a sequence of sentences that it was bitter? The word 'argument' seems to have in the second sentence a meaning different from the meaning in the first. But is there any relation between the two?

Perhaps the most familiar use of the word 'argument' is to refer to a dispute or a quarrel. And what is at the base of a quarrel? A difference of opinion as to some question. One opponent holds a certain point of view; the other disputant not only fails to share that opinion but actively opposes it by putting forth a conflicting view.

Each tries to persuade the other to adopt the alien position. Attempts at persuasion consist in offering "reasons" for one's own or against an opponent's point of view. Such an attempt to establish an opinion for another by prefacing the statement with supporting remarks is in fact the proposing of an argument, in our technical sense of the word 'argument.' If the supporting remarks are themselves true and the opinion really follows from these remarks, then the argument is both valid and sound; and a conclusion has been established. But of course, an established conclusion is not always an accepted one. Nor is an accepted conclusion always an established one. Thus it is that in a dispute, especially in a bitter one, the "argument" we offer is rarely valid, and more rarely still, sound. In dispute, an "argument" tends to be a mere "putting before"—that is, a mere premissing of an as yet unacceptable opinion with views hopefully more palatable to the opponent and views, moreover, calculated to incline him to accept the disputed opinion. In this rhetorical use of argument, convincingness rather than validity or soundness is the prime concern.

To guard against another's rhetorical use of argument, attention to an argument's validity and soundness is advantageous; in a truth-seeking context, indispensable. Determining soundness requires not only establishing validity of an argument but also truth of the argument's premisses. Establishing truth or falsity is outside the province of logic; calling attention to the need for such establishing is well within logic's scope; establishing validity is one of the tasks most distinctive of logic.

And so we concentrate here on argument not as a dispute but as a sequence of sentences in which a conclusion is said to follow from premisses, and we concentrate not on convincingness or soundness but on _____ .   validity

Summary of Part 2

2-103   An argument is a sequence of _____ in which
the conclusion is _____ _____ _____ _____
the premises.

sentences
said to follow from

2-104   When representing an argument we use a 'therefore'
indicator and put the representation of the premises
_____ the 'ⱶ' and put below the 'ⱶ' the conclusion's
_____ .

above
representation

2-105   The representation of an argument indicates two
things—the content of the argument and a logical form of the
argument. But to isolate a logical form of the argument, we
_____ the argument.

formalize

2-106   An AF is the formalization of an _____. The
premises of the argument are formalized by the _____
above the 'ⱶ' of the AF. The WFF below the 'ⱶ' of the AF formalizes the argument's _____ .

argument
WFFs

conclusion

2-107   Can unlike arguments have like representations?
_____ Can unlike arguments have like formalizations?
_____

no
yes

2-108   An argument is a sequence of sentences in which
the conclusion is *said* to follow from the premises. But a *valid*
argument is an argument in which the conclusion is not
merely said to follow from but actually _____ _____
_____ the premises.

does follow from

2-109   The validity of an argument depends not on the truth
of premises and conclusion but on the _____ between
premises and conclusion.

relation

2-110   Because validity depends on the structure of the
premises in relation to the structure of the conclusion, we
say that validity depends on the argument's _____
_____ .

logical form

2-111 We say that validity depends on logical form because validity depends on the argument's structure, and the argument's structure depends on placement and choice of _____ words and on likeness of _____ within premisses and conclusion.

connecting; shape

2-112 Since validity depends on logical form, we isolate logical form to help us decide on the argument's validity.

Any argument formula which is such that every argument formalizable by that AF is a valid argument is a _____ _____ _____, or for short, a _____.

logical argument formula; LAF

Exercises for Part 2

1   For each of the following AFs write two unlike arguments each of which could be formalized by that AF:

a | Cpq
    | CNqNp

b | Krs
    | t
    | Apq

c | Cpq
    | Crs
    | ANqNs
    | ANrNp

d | CKqpt
    | Nt
    | ANqNp

e | Cpq
    | Crp
    | Crq

2   Could a valid argument have a false conclusion? Under what conditions?

3   Could an invalid argument have a true conclusion?

4   In what contexts is it most important to have a sound argument—that is, a valid argument with true premisses?

5   In what contexts is the soundness of an argument unimportant, provided the argument is valid?

6   To claim an argument is valid because it has the form isolated by the AF

    | Cpq
    | q
    | p

is to commit the so-called "fallacy of affirming the consequent." Present an argument that can be formalized by this AF and show why the conclusion does not necessarily follow from the premises. Then compare the above AF with the *LAF*

    | Cpq
    | p
    | q

and suggest why a person might be inclined to commit the above fallacy.

7   A scientist might argue as follows:

If my theory is correct, then the observations made agree with the theory's predictions.

The observations made agree with the theory's predictions.

Therefore, my theory is correct.

To claim such an argument valid is to commit the "fallacy of affirming the consequent." What is the attitude of most experimental scientists toward such arguments? To what extent is this attitude plausible?

8 a
$$\begin{array}{|l}\text{Cpq}\\ \text{Nq}\\ \hline \text{Np}\end{array}$$
b
$$\begin{array}{|l}\text{Cpq}\\ \text{Np}\\ \hline \text{Nq}\end{array}$$

One of the above AFs we would be inclined to call a LAF; but to claim an argument is valid because it has the form isolated by the other of the above AFs is, traditionally speaking, to commit the "fallacy of denying the antecedent." Determine which of the AFs is not a LAF by producing an argument that can be formalized by that AF but whose conclusion does not follow from the premises. Why is the "fallacy of denying the antecedent" well named? Why might a person be inclined to commit the fallacy?

9 For each of the following AFs, use the *Principia* type of notation and write an AF that could formalize any argument that could be formalized by the AF in Lukasiewicz notation. For example, corresponding to an AF
$$\begin{array}{|l}\text{CNAprKrq}\\ \text{NApr}\\ \hline \text{Krq}\end{array}$$
you would write
$$\begin{array}{|l}(\sim(p \lor r)) \supset (r \,\&\, q)\\ \sim(p \lor r)\\ \hline r \,\&\, q\end{array}$$

a
$$\begin{array}{|l}\text{CANptKrs}\\ \text{NKrs}\\ \hline \text{CCqpKpNt}\end{array}$$
b
$$\begin{array}{|l}\text{CtAsp}\\ \text{CNqKpr}\\ \text{AtNq}\\ \hline \text{AAspKpr}\end{array}$$
c
$$\begin{array}{|l}\text{CpCqCst}\\ \text{Cpq}\\ \hline \text{ANpCst}\end{array}$$
d
$$\begin{array}{|l}\text{ANpNq}\\ \text{CArsq}\\ \text{CKstp}\\ \hline \text{ANArsNKst}\end{array}$$
e
$$\begin{array}{|l}\text{KCpqCqp}\\ \text{Np}\\ \hline \text{Nq}\end{array}$$

10 For each of the following AFs, use the Lukasiewicz notation and write an AF that could formalize any argument that could be formalized by the AF in the *Principia* notation.

a
$$\begin{array}{|l}(\sim(p \,\&\, q)) \supset (r \lor s)\\ (\sim r) \,\&\, (\sim s)\\ \hline t \supset (\sim(\sim p))\end{array}$$
b
$$\begin{array}{|l}(s \lor q) \,\&\, (s \lor r)\\ r \lor (\sim t)\\ t \supset q\\ \hline t \lor s\end{array}$$

c
$$\begin{array}{|l}((q \lor t) \,\&\, (\sim p)) \supset s\\ \hline (q \lor t) \supset ((\sim p) \supset s)\end{array}$$
d
$$\begin{array}{|l}(p \supset q) \,\&\, (q \supset p)\\ \hline (p \,\&\, q) \lor ((\sim p) \,\&\, (\sim q))\end{array}$$
e
$$\begin{array}{|l}\sim((s \,\&\, t) \lor (q \lor p))\\ \hline (\sim(s \,\&\, t)) \,\&\, (\sim(q \lor p))\end{array}$$

11 An argument is a sequence of sentences in which one sentence is said to follow from the others. What is a sequence? Given a sequence, how can you tell whether or not the sequence is an argument?

Achievement Test for Part 2

1   An argument is a sequence of sentences in which the conclusion is _____ from the premisses.

2   In representing an argument, we use a 'Ⱶ' as a '_____' indicator. We put above the 'Ⱶ' the representations of the _____ and below the 'Ⱶ' the representation of the _____ .

3   We are going to represent the following argument:

>   *Wilson was a Democrat, and Harding was a Republican.*
>   *Therefore, Harding was a Republican.*

Suppose we represent the premiss of this argument by a 'KSR.' Write a representation of the argument. _____

4   (a)   *If Hoover won the election, then Smith lost the election.*

If a 'CPQ' represents (a), write a sentence which could be the conclusion of an argument represented by

    | CPQ
    | P
    ‾‾‾
    | Q

_____

5   If we can represent an argument by

    | CRS
    | R
    ‾‾‾
    | S

we can formalize that argument by either of the following:

    | Crs | Cpq
    |‾‾‾‾‾‾‾ |‾‾‾‾‾‾‾
    Ⱶ‾‾‾‾‾‾   Ⱶ‾‾‾‾‾‾

6   Validity depends on logical _____, and a formalization of an argument isolates a logical _____ of that argument.

7   A formalization of an argument is an _____ formula, or for short, an _____ .

8   *If New York is the poorest state in the Union, then Texas is the smallest state in the Union.*
    New York is the poorest state in the Union.
    Therefore, Texas is the smallest state in the Union.

Is the above argument valid? _____

Is the conclusion of the above argument true? _____

9   An argument is a sequence of what? _____

10   What distinguishes a valid argument from an invalid one? _____

11   A valid argument contains how many WFFs? _____

12 If two arguments have like representations, what do you know about the arguments? _____

13 If two arguments have like formalizations, what do you know about the arguments? _____

14 The conclusion of an argument is which sentence in the argument? _____

15 If an argument is formalized by an AF

$$\begin{array}{|l} Cpq \\ p \\ \hline q \end{array}$$

what is the conclusion of that argument? _____

16 What is formalized by the WFFs above the 'therefore' indicator of a formalization of an argument? _____

17 What is formalized by the WFF below the 'therefore' indicator of a formalization of an argument? _____

18 An AF contains how many sentences? _____

19 The representation of a valid argument contains how many sentence variables?

20 In the formalization of a valid argument, there are how many WFFs below the 'therefore' indicator? _____

21 A sound argument is a valid argument with true premisses. Are there any valid arguments that are unsound? _____

22 Just as an argument is a sequence of sentences, so a representation of an argument is a sequence of _____ of sentences; and an AF is a sequence of formalizations of _____ .

23 Are there any two unlike arguments that can be formalized by the same AF?

24 For each of the following AFs in Lukasiewicz notation write a corresponding AF in *Principia* notation:

a
$$\begin{array}{|l} Cpq \\ Cqr \\ Cpt \\ \hline Art \end{array}$$

b
$$\begin{array}{|l} CpCqt \\ \hline CKpqt \end{array}$$

c
$$\begin{array}{|l} CAKtpqr \\ \hline CNrKANpNtNq \end{array}$$

25 For each of the following AFs in *Principia* notation write a corresponding AF in Lukasiewicz notation.

a
$$\begin{array}{|l} r \supset (t \,\&\, p) \\ \hline (\sim t) \supset (\sim r) \end{array}$$

b
$$\begin{array}{|l} p \lor q \\ \sim p \\ \hline \sim q \end{array}$$

c
$$\begin{array}{|l} p \supset (q \supset (\sim t)) \\ q \,\&\, t \\ \hline \sim p \end{array}$$

Part **3**

Validity Systematically
Defined: Specification
of Logical System F

Validity Redefined through

System F

3-1   Rhetorical use of arguments aside, invalid arguments are usually regarded as bad arguments. But how do we decide if a given argument is valid or not? We may simply inspect the argument and "see" that it is valid, that is, "see" that from the _____ the _____ does follow.

premisses; conclusion

3-2   For some arguments deciding validity by inspection is fairly easy. But consider the argument

> If it is false that if Caesar wooed Cleopatra then Antony withdrew his suit, then respect for Caesar was less strong in Antony's breast than was his love for Cleopatra.
> Therefore, if it is false that respect for Caesar was less strong in Antony's breast than was his love for Cleopatra, then if it is false that Antony withdrew his suit then it is false that Caesar wooed Cleopatra.

Is first-glance inspection sufficient to decide validity here? _____

no

3-3   Since validity depends on logical form, isolating logical form sometimes facilitates a decision about an argument's validity. The argument

> If it is false that if Caesar wooed Cleopatra then Antony withdrew his suit, then respect for Caesar was less strong in Antony's breast than was his love for Cleopatra.
> Therefore, if it is false that respect for Caesar was less strong in Antony's breast than was his love for Cleopatra, then if it is false that Antony withdrew his suit then it is false that Caesar wooed Cleopatra.

can be formalized by the AF

> CNCpqr
> ———
> CNrCNqNp

But in this instance even considering the argument's form in isolation may not allow us to make a quick decision on the argument's validity. Moreover, once decision is somehow made, is it certain that another can be brought to "see" the argument's validity or lack of it? _____

no

3-4 If valid argument is defined as an argument whose conclusion actually does follow from the premisses, there is no way to decide validity but to "see" that the conclusion does follow. But we have noted that trying to decide validity by just looking to "see" seems an inadequate guide when an argument is complicated or when we want not just to see for ourselves but to show someone else that an argument is valid.

In an attempt to provide a more adequate guide for deciding and showing validity, we propose another definition of valid argument. The new definition exploits validity's dependence on logical form but is not a mere cataloguing of AFs such that every argument that can be formalized by the AF is a valid argument—that is, not a mere cataloguing of _____.

LAFs

3-5 In Part 3 valid argument is redefined in terms of system F,[1] which can be regarded as a systematic treatment of LAFs.
1. The choice of a small and finite number (nine) of kinds of LAFs is basic to system F.
2. Each kind of LAF chosen is such that it is difficult to deny that in any argument that can be formalized by the LAF the conclusion does follow from the premisses.
3. The redefinition of valid argument in terms of system F will amount to choosing nine kinds of LAFs and then maintaining that an argument is valid if it is possible to proceed from the premisses to the conclusion of the argument by a series of arguments of these nine logical _____ forms only.

argument

[1] System F can be viewed as the reformulation in the present work of F. B. Fitch's subordinate-proof formulation of sentential calculus, provided his rule of restricted negation introduction is replaced by unrestricted negation introduction—that is, though system F is a classical sentential calculus, and in that respect unlike Fitch's intuitionistic calculus, both calculi are natural-deduction formulations. Compare *Symbolic Logic*, New York, 1952, especially chaps. 1 and 2.

3-6   The proposed redefinition is this:

> A valid argument is an argument that can be formalized
> by an AF that corresponds to a proof in system F.

Before we can make use of the redefinition as a guide for
deciding validity of arguments, we must know

1. What is the logical system F, that is, what is the proposed
systematic treatment of logical argument formulas, and
2. What is meant by saying that an AF corresponds to a proof
in _____ _____ .   system F

Symbols in System F

3-7 System F is a system of logic. Let's see how we describe
a _____ of logic.   system

3-8 We describe a system of logic by specifying

1. The symbols in the system,
2. The WFFs in the system,
3. The LAFs in the system, and
4. The proofs in the system.

Thus, since system F is a system of logic, we describe system
F by specifying

1. The _____ in system F,   symbols
2. The _____ in system F,   WFFs
3. The _____ in system F, and   LAFs
4. The _____ in system F.   proofs

3-9 We describe system F by specifying

1. The *symbols* in system F,
2. The WFFs in system F,
3. The LAFs in system F, and
4. The proofs in system F.

We specify first the _____ in system F.   symbols

3-10 The only symbols in system F are

1. Sentence variables,
2. Connectives, and
3. 'Therefore' indicators.

Thus every symbol in system F is either

1. A _____ _____, or   sentence variable
2. A _____, or   connective
3. A 'Ⱶ'.

3-11 The only sentence variables in system F are any 'p,' 'q,' 'r,' 's,' or 't.' Thus, since any sentence variable in system F is a symbol in system F, any '_____,' '_____,' '_____,' '_____,' or '_____' is a symbol in system F.

p; q; r
s; t

3-12 The only connectives in system F are any 'K,' 'A,' 'C,' or 'N.'

Thus, since any connective in system F is a symbol in system F, any '_____,' '_____,' '_____,' or '_____' is a symbol in system F.

K; A; C; N

3-13 Since every symbol in system F is a sentence variable, a connective, or a 'therefore' indicator, every symbol in system F is

1. A 'p,' a '_____,' an '_____,' an '_____,' or a '_____'; or
2. A 'K,' an '_____,' a '_____,' or an '_____'; or
3. A '_____.'

q; r; s; t
A; C; N
⊢

3-14 Copy those of the following which are symbols in system F:

    K   i   q   s
    m   o   M ⊢

_____   _____   _____   _____

K; q; s; ⊢

3-15 No matter what candidate is presented it seems most unlikely there could be any disagreement as to whether or not that candidate is a symbol in system F. So, technically speaking, we have *effectively* specified the _____ in system F.

symbols

WFFs in System F

3-16 We describe system F by specifying

1. The symbols in system F,
2. The *WFFs* is system F,
3. The LAFs in system F, and
4. The proofs in system F.

We have just specified the symbols in system F; next we
specify the _____ in system F.

WFFs

3-17 We specify the WFFs in system F as follows:

1. Any sentence variable in system F is a WFF in system F.
2. Any expression which is a 'K' followed by two WFFs in system F is a WFF in system F.
3. Any expression which is an 'A' followed by two WFFs in
system F is a WFF in system F.
4. Any expression which is a 'C' followed by _____
WFFs in system F is a WFF in system F.

two

5. Any expression which is an 'N' followed by _____
WFF in system F is a WFF in system F.

one

3-18 An expression is a WFF in system F if and only if the
expression is seen to be a WFF according to the five
_____ rules just stated.

WFF

3-19 Copy those of the following expressions which are
WFFs in system F:

q	i	NC
Nq	Apq	AcKp
Krs	Cqp	NCNqNp

_____ _____ _____

_____ _____ _____

q; Nq; Krs
Apq; Cqp; NCNqNp

3-20 Notice that given any expression we can decide whether or not that expression is a WFF in system F. Because we can make this decision, no matter what expression we are given, we have effectively specified the _____ in system F.

WFFs

LAFs in System F

A   K-in LAFs

3-21   We describe system F by specifying

1. The symbols in system F,
2. The WFFs in system F,
3. The *LAFs* in system F, and
4. The proofs in system F.

We have already specified the symbols in system F and the
WFFs in system F; next we specify the _____ in system F.   LAFs

3-22   System F has nine kinds of LAFs. It has

K-in LAFs	K-out LAFs
A-in LAFs	A-out LAFs
C-in LAFs	C-out LAFs
N-_____ LAFs	N-_____ LAFs

        repetition LAFs

in; out

3-23   There are four kinds of connectives in system F—'K's,
'A's, 'C's, and 'N's. Notice that corresponding to each kind of
connective in system F there are two kinds of LAFs in system
F—in-LAFs and _____-LAFs. We will notice too that the   out
structure of these in-LAFs and out-LAFs is not unrelated to
our convention that

1. A connective 'K' represents a connecting word '_____,'   and
2. A connective 'A' represents a connecting word '_____,'   or
3. A connective 'C' represents a connecting word '_____,'   if then
and
4. A connective 'N' represents a connecting word '_____.'   it is false that

3-24 Instead of saying that we have K-in LAFs and K-out LAFs, we say, for short, that we have Ki and Ko LAFs. Similarly:

> Ai LAFs are A-in LAFs.
> Ci LAFs are C-in LAFs.
> Ni LAFs are _____ LAFs.   N-in
>
> Ao LAFs are A-out LAFs.
> Co LAFs are C-out LAFs.
> _____ LAFs are _____ LAFs.   No; N-out

3-25 Let us look first at a Ki LAF:

        1│ p
        2│ q
        3│ Kpq   1, 2, Ki

This LAF has as its first item a WFF 'p,' as its second item a WFF 'q,' and as its last item a WFF '_____.'   Kpq

3-26 Here is another Ki LAF:

        1│ r
        2│ s
        3│ Krs   1, 2, Ki

This LAF has as its first item a WFF '_____,' as its second item   r
a WFF '_____,' and as its last item a WFF '_____.'   s; Krs

3-27   1│ Apq
             2│ r
             3│ KApqr   1, 2, Ki

In the above Ki LAF, the first item is a WFF '_____,' the   Apq
second item is a WFF '_____,' and the last item is a WFF   r
'_____Apqr.'   K

3-28   1│ q
             2│ Crp
             3│ KqCrp   1, 2, Ki

In this Ki LAF, the first item is a WFF '_____,' the second item   q
is a WFF '_____,' and the last item is a WFF '_____qCrp.'   Crp; K

3-29 Consider the following Ki LAF:

```
1 | Nr
2 | Kpq
3 | KNrKpq     1, 2, _____
```
                                                              Ki

In this Ki LAF the first item is a WFF 'Nr,' the second item is
a WFF 'Kpq,' and the last item is a WFF '_____NrKpq.'   K

3-30 Every Ki LAF is a sequence of items: the last item is
a WFF which is a 'K' followed by two WFFs, the first of which
is just like the first item of the LAF, and the second of which
is just like the second item of the LAF. Thus every Ki LAF has
as its last item a WFF beginning with a '_____.'   K

3-31
```
1 | p
2 | q
3 | Kpq      1, 2, Ki
```

The above sequence of items is a Ki LAF because the last item
is a WFF which is a 'K' followed by two WFFs, the first of which
is just like the first item of the sequence, and the second of
which is just like the _____ item of the sequence.   second

3-32
```
1 | Nr
2 | Kpq
3 | KNrKpq     1, 2, Ki
```

The above sequence of items is a Ki LAF because its last item
is a WFF which is a '_____' followed by two WFFs, the first of   K
which is just like the _____ item of the sequence and the   first
second of which is just like the _____ item of the   second
sequence.

3-33
```
1 | p
2 | q
3 | Kpq      _____, _____, _____
```
                                                              1; 2; Ki

The above sequence of items is a Ki LAF because its last item
is a WFF which is a '_____' followed by two WFFs, the first of   K
which is just like item _____ of the sequence, and the second   1
of which is just like item _____ of the sequence.   2

3-34   1 | p
     2 | q
     3 | Kpq   1, 2, Ki

Since we can think of the 'Kpq' as the *last* item of a Ki LAF whose first item is item 1 and whose second item is item 2, a '1, 2, Ki' is a good reason for the last item of the above sequence. So, we write a '1, 2, Ki' to the right of the _____ item of the sequence.

                                            last

3-35   1 | r
     2 | s
     3 | Krs   _____, _____, _____   1; 2; Ki

3-36   1 | _____
     2 | p
     3 | Krp   1, 2, Ki   r

3-37   1 | _____
     2 | CsNp
     3 | KAtsCsNp   1, 2, Ki   Ats

3-38   1 | t
     2 | _____
     3 | Ktq   1, 2, Ki   q

3-39   1 | NApq
     2 | _____
     3 | KNApqKNtr   1, 2, Ki   **KNtr**

3-40   1 | _____
     2 | _____
     3 | Ksp   1, 2, Ki   s
                                              p

3-41   1 | _____
     2 | _____
     3 | KKpqKst   1, 2, Ki   **Kpq**
                                              Kst

3-42   1 | p   1 | t
     2 | t   2 | p
     3 | _____   1, 2, Ki   3 | _____   1, 2, Ki   **Kpt; Ktp**

3-43

1	CNtNq			1	Aqs		
2	Aqs			2	CNtNq		
3	____	1, 2, Ki		3	____	1, 2, Ki	

KCNtNqAqs; KAqsCNtNq

3-44 Can a Ki LAF have as its last item a WFF beginning with an 'A'? _____

no

3-45 Can a Ki LAF have as its last item a WFF beginning with a 'C'? _____

no

3-46 Can a Ki LAF have as its last item a WFF beginning with an 'N'? _____

no

3-47 Can a Ki LAF have as its last item a WFF that does not begin with a connective? _____

no

3-48 Every Ki LAF has as its last item a WFF beginning with a connective, and that connective is a '____.'

K

3-49 A Ki LAF has how many items? _____

three

3-50 Write a Ki LAF whose last item is a 'Krt.' _____

r
t
Krt[1]

3-51 *Boole was a nineteenth-century logician.*
Boole was an Irish mathematician.
Therefore, Boole was a nineteenth-century logician, and
Boole was an Irish mathematician.

The above argument can be formalized by the Ki LAF

p
q
Kpq

Moreover, the conclusion of the argument actually does follow from the premises—that is, the argument is a _____ argument.

valid

---

[1] Neither the numbers nor the indications of good reasons are, strictly speaking, part of the LAF. But since the numbers are a helpful bookkeeping device, it is well when writing a LAF to number the items.

3-52 Let's see why every argument that can be formalized by a Ki LAF is a _____ argument.

valid

3-53 *Boole was a nineteenth-century logician.*
Boole was an Irish mathematician.
Therefore, Boole was a nineteenth-century logician, and
Boole was an Irish mathematician.

The conclusion of the above argument is a sentence which is two sentences connected by an '_____'; the first sentence is like the _____ premiss, and the second sentence is like the _____ premiss. It seems difficult to deny that the conclusion *does* follow from the premisses, that is, that the argument is a _____ argument.

and
first
second

valid

3-54 Every argument which can be formalized by a Ki LAF has a conclusion which is two sentences joined by an '_____'; the first sentence is like the _____ premiss, and the second sentence is like the _____ premiss. Thus it seems plausible to agree that every argument which can be formalized by a Ki LAF is an argument which would be recognized as a _____ argument.

and; first
second

valid

B K-out LAFs

3-55 System F has four kinds of connectives—'K's, 'A's, 'C's, and 'N's. Corresponding to each kind of connective in system F there are two kinds of LAFs—in-LAFs and _____-LAFs. The structure of these LAFs is not unrelated to our convention that

out

1. A connective '_____' represents a connecting word 'and,'
2. A connective '_____' represents a connecting word 'or,'
3. A connective '_____' represents a connecting word 'if then,' and
4. A connective '_____' represents a connecting word 'it is false that.'

K
A
C

N

3-56 We have been looking at Ki LAFs, that is, at K-in LAFs. Now let's look at some K-out LAFs, that is, at some K _____ LAFs.

o

3-57   Here is a Ko LAF:

```
1 | Kpq
2 | p      1, Ko
```

This LAF has as its first item a WFF '_____pq' and as its last   K
item a WFF '_____.'   p

3-58   Here is another Ko LAF:

```
1 | Kpq
2 | q      1, Ko
```

This LAF has as its first item a WFF '_____pq' and as its last   K
item a WFF '_____.'   q

3-59   1 | Krs
            2 | r   1, Ko

This sequence of items is a Ko LAF because its item 1 is a
WFF which is a 'K' followed by two WFFs, the first of which is
just like item _____ of the LAF.   2

3-60   1 | Krs
            2 | s   1, Ko

This sequence of items is a Ko LAF because its item 1 is a WFF
which is a 'K' followed by two WFFs, the second of which is
just like item _____ of the LAF.   2

3-61   Every Ko LAF is a sequence of items: the first item is
a 'K' followed by two WFFs, one of which is just like the last
item of the LAF. Thus every Ko LAF has as its first item a WFF
beginning with a '_____.'   K

3-62   1 | Krp
            2 | r   1, Ko

The above sequence of items is a Ko LAF because its item 1
is a 'K' followed by two WFFs, the first of which is just like item
_____ of the sequence.   2

3-63 1 | KNrp
      2 | p   1, Ko

The above sequence of items is a Ko LAF because its item
1 is a '_____' followed by two WFFs, the second of which is   K
just like item _____ of the sequence.   2

3-64 1 | Kpq
      2 | p   1, Ko

Since we can think of the 'p' as the *last* item of a Ko LAF whose
first item is item 1, a '1, Ko' is a good reason for the last item
of the above sequence. So, we write a '1, Ko' to the right of
the _____ item of the sequence.   last

3-65 1 | Kpq
      2 | q   1, Ko

Since we can think of the 'q' as the *last* item of a Ko LAF whose
first item is item 1, a '1, Ko' is a good reason for the last item
of the above sequence. So, we write to the right of the last
item of the sequence a '_____.'   1, Ko

3-66 1 | Krs
      2 | r   _____ , _____   1; Ko

3-67 1 | Krs
      2 | s   _____ , _____   1; Ko

3-68 1 | KAqt_____   Np
      2 | Np   1, Ko

3-69 1 | K_____Apq   Ars
      2 | Ars   1, Ko

3-70 Can a Ko LAF have as its first item a WFF beginning
with an 'A'? _____   no

3-71 Can a Ko LAF have as its first item a WFF beginning
with a 'C'? _____   no

3-72 Can a Ko LAF have as its first item a WFF beginning
with an 'N'? _____   no

3-73   Can a Ko LAF have as its first item a WFF that does not begin with a connective? _____

no

3-74   Every Ko LAF has as its first item a WFF beginning with a connective, and that connective is a '_____.'

K

3-75   A Ko LAF has how many items? _____

two

3-76   Write a Ko LAF whose first item is a 'Krt.'

$$\begin{array}{c|c} 1 & Krt \\ \hline 2 & r \end{array} \quad \text{or} \quad \begin{array}{c|c} 1 & Krt \\ \hline 2 & t \end{array}$$

3-77   Write two Ko LAFs each with a 'KNps' as a first item but with unlike last items.

$$\begin{array}{c|c} 1 & KNps \\ \hline 2 & Np \end{array} \quad \begin{array}{c|c} 1 & KNps \\ \hline 2 & s \end{array}$$

3-78   *Peano was a modern logician, and Peano was an Italian mathematician.*
Therefore, Peano was a modern logician.

Peano was a modern logician, and Peano was an Italian mathematician.
Therefore, Peano was an Italian mathematician.

The first of the above arguments can be formalized by the Ko LAF

$$\begin{array}{|l} Kpq \\ \hline \end{array}$$

p

and the second argument can be formalized by the Ko LAF

$$\begin{array}{|l} Kpq \\ \hline \end{array}$$

q

Moreover, in both arguments the conclusion actually does follow from the premiss—that is, both arguments are _____ arguments.

valid

3-79   Let's see why every argument that can be formalized by a Ko LAF is a _____ argument.

valid

3-80   *Peano was a modern logician, and Peano was an Italian mathematician.*
Therefore, Peano was a modern logician.

Peano was a modern logician, and Peano was an Italian mathematician.
Therefore, Peano was an Italian mathematician.

In each of the above arguments the premiss is two sentences connected by an '_____,' and the _____ of the argument is a sentence like one of those sentences. It seems difficult to deny that in each argument the conclusion *does* follow from the premiss, that is, that the argument is a _____ argument.

and; conclusion

valid

3-81   Every argument which can be formalized by a Ko LAF is an argument whose premiss is a sentence which is two sentences connected by an '_____' and whose _____ is a sentence just like one of those two sentences. Thus it seems plausible to agree that every argument which can be formalized by a Ko LAF is an argument which would be recognized as a _____ argument.

and; conclusion

valid

3-82   1 | p
2 | q
3 |‾‾‾‾‾pq   1, 2, K____

1 |____pq
2 | p   1, K____

K; i

K
o

C   A-in LAFs

3-83   System F has four kinds of connectives—'K's, 'A's, 'C's, and 'N's. Corresponding to each kind of connective in system F there are two kinds of LAFs— _____ -LAFs and _____-LAFs.

in
out

The structure of these LAFs is not unrelated to our convention that

1. A connective 'K' represents a connecting word '_____,'
2. A connective 'A' represents a connecting word '_____,'
3. A connective 'C' represents a connecting word '_____,' and
4. A connective 'N' represents a connecting word '_____.'

and
or
if then

it is false that

3-84   We are now able to identify K-in LAFs and K-out LAFs. Now let's look at some A-in LAFs, that is, at some A＿＿＿ LAFs.

i

3-85   Here is an Ai LAF:

```
1 | p
2 | Apq      1, Ai
```

This LAF has as its first item a WFF '＿＿＿' and as its last item a WFF '＿＿＿ ＿＿＿q.'

p
A; p

3-86   Here is another Ai LAF:

```
1 | p
2 | Aqp      1, Ai
```

This LAF has as its first item a WFF '＿＿＿' and as its last item a WFF '＿＿＿q＿＿＿.'

p
A; p

3-87
```
1 | p
2 | Apq      1, Ai
```

This sequence of items is an Ai LAF because its last item is a WFF which is an 'A' followed by two WFFs, the first of which is just like item ＿＿＿ of the sequence.

1

3-88
```
1 | p
2 | Aqp      1, Ai
```

This sequence of items is an Ai LAF because its last item is an 'A' followed by two WFFs, the second of which is just like item ＿＿＿ of the sequence.

1

3-89   Every Ai LAF is a sequence of items: the last item is an 'A' followed by two WFFs, one of which is just like the first item of the LAF.

Thus, every Ai LAF has as its last item a WFF beginning with an '＿＿＿.'

A

3-90
```
1 | r
2 | Ars      1, Ai
```

The above sequence of items is an Ai LAF because its last item is an 'A' followed by two WFFs, one of which is just like item ＿＿＿ of the sequence.

1

3-91 1 | Nq
     2 | ApNq   1, Ai

The above sequence of items is an Ai LAF because its last item
is an '_____' followed by two WFFs, one of which is just like   **A**
item _____ of the sequence.   **1**

3-92 1 | p
     2 | Apq   1, Ai

Since we can think of the 'Apq' as the *last* item of an Ai LAF
whose first item is item 1, a '1, Ai' is a good reason for the
last item of the sequence. So, we write a '1, Ai' to the right
of the _____ item of the sequence.   **last**

3-93 1 | q
     2 | Apq   1, Ai

Since we can think of the 'Apq' as the *last* item of an Ai LAF
whose first item is item 1, a '1, Ai' is a good reason for the last
item of the sequence. So we write to the right of the last item
of the sequence a '_____.'   **1, Ai**

3-94 1 | s
     2 | Asp   _____ , _____   **1; Ai**

3-95 1 | p
     2 | Asp   _____ , _____   **1; Ai**

3-96 1 | Crs
     2 | _____pCrs   1, Ai   **A**

3-97 1 | Cps
     2 | At _____   1, Ai   **Cps**

3-98 Can an Ai LAF have as its last item a WFF beginning
with a 'K'? _____   **no**

3-99 Can an Ai LAF have as its last item a WFF beginning
with a 'C'? _____   **no**

3-100 Can an Ai LAF have as its last item a WFF beginning
with an 'N'? _____   **no**

3-101 Can an Ai LAF have as its last item a WFF that does not begin with a connective? _____

no

3-102 Every Ai LAF has as its last item a WFF beginning with a connective, and that connective is an '_____.'

A

3-103 An Ai LAF has how many items? _____

two

3-104 Write an Ai LAF whose last item is an 'Art.'

$$1 \mid r \qquad \text{or} \qquad 1 \mid t$$
$$2 \mid Art \qquad\qquad 2 \mid Art$$

3-105 Write two Ai LAFs each with an 'ANps' as a last item but with unlike first items.

$$1 \mid Np \qquad\qquad 1 \mid s$$
$$2 \mid ANps \qquad 2 \mid ANps$$

3-106 *Boole was the father of mathematical logic.*
Therefore, Boole was the father of mathematical logic, or Boole made at least a very great contribution to mathematical logic.

Boole made at least a very great contribution to mathematical logic.
Therefore, Boole was the father of mathematical logic, or Boole made at least a very great contribution to mathematical logic.

The first of the above arguments can be formalized by the Ai LAF

$$\begin{array}{|c} \hline \\ \hline Apq \end{array}$$

p

and the second argument can be formalized by the Ai LAF

$$\begin{array}{|c} \hline \\ \hline Apq \end{array}$$

q

Moreover, in both arguments the conclusion actually does follow from the premiss—that is, both arguments are _____ arguments.

valid

3-107 Let's see why every argument formalized by an Ai LAF is a _____ argument.

valid

3-108   *Boole was the father of mathematical logic.*
Therefore, Boole was the father of mathematical logic, or Boole made at least a very great contribution to mathematical logic.

Boole made at least a very great contribution to mathematical logic.
Therefore, Boole was the father of mathematical logic, or Boole made at least a very great contribution to mathematical logic.

In each of the above arguments the conclusion is two sentences connected by an '_____,' and the _____ of the argument is a sentence just like one of those sentences. It seems difficult to deny that in each argument the conclusion *does* follow from the premiss, that is, that the argument is a _____ argument.

3-109   Any argument which can be formalized by an Ai LAF has a conclusion which is two sentences connected by an '_____' and a _____ just like one of these sentences. Thus it seems plausible to agree that every argument which can be formalized by an Ai LAF is an argument which would be recognized as a _____ argument.

D   A-out LAFs

3-110   System F has four kinds of connectives—'K's, 'A's, 'C's, and 'N's. Corresponding to each kind of connective in system F there are two kinds of LAFs—_____-LAFs and _____-LAFs.

The structure of these LAFs is not unrelated to our convention that

1. A connective 'K' represents a connecting word '_____,'
2. A connective 'A' represents a connecting word '_____,'
3. A connective 'C' represents a connecting word '_____,' and
4. A connective 'N' represents a connecting word '_____.'

3-111   We are now able to identify Ki LAFs, Ko LAFs, and Ai LAFs. Now let's look at some A-out LAFs, that is, at some A____ LAFs.

3-112   Here is an Ao LAF:

```
1 |AKqpKrq
2 |2.1 |Kqp
  |2.2 |q          2.1, Ko
3 |3.1 |Krq
  |3.2 |q          3.1, Ko
4 |q               1, 2, 3, Ao
```

This Ao LAF has as its first item a WFF beginning with an
'____.'   A

3-113
```
1 |AKqpKrq
2 |2.1 |Kqp
  |2.2 |q          2.1, Ko
3 |3.1 |Krq
  |3.2 |q          3.1, Ko
4 |q               1, 2, 3, Ao
```

This Ao LAF has a *WFF* as its first item. But item 2 of this Ao
LAF is a sequence of items. Similarly, item 3 of this Ao LAF is
a _____ of items.   sequence

3-114
```
1 |AKqpKrq
2 |2.1 |Kqp
  |2.2 |q          2.1, Ko
3 |3.1 |Krq
  |3.2 |q          3.1, Ko
4 |q               1, 2, 3, Ao
```

Item 2 of this Ao LAF is a sequence of items; so is item 3. An
item which is a sequence of items is called, for short, a tail
item. Thus item 2 is a _____ item.   tail

3-115
```
1 |AKqpKrq
2 |2.1 |Kqp
  |2.2 |q          2.1, Ko
3 |3.1 |Krq
  |3.2 |q          3.1, Ko
4 |q               1, 2, 3, Ao
```

Item 3 of this Ao LAF is a sequence of items. Thus, item 3 is
a _____ item.   tail

3-116 1 | AKqpKrq
2 | 2.1 | Kqp
    | 2.2 | q   2.1, Ko
3 | 3.1 | Krq
    | 3.2 | q   3.1, Ko
4 | q   1, 2, 3, Ao

Item 1 of this Ao LAF is a WFF which is an 'A' followed by two WFFs. The first of these WFFs is a '_____.' Notice that   **Kqp**
the only item above the 'ⱂ' for item 2 is also a '_____.'   **Kqp**

3-117 1 | AKqpKrq
2 | 2.1 | Kqp
    | 2.2 | q   2.1, Ko
3 | 3.1 | Krq
    | 3.2 | q   3.1, Ko
4 | q   1, 2, 3, Ao

Item 1 of this LAF is a WFF which is an 'A' followed by two WFFs. The second of these WFFs is a '_____.' Notice   **Krq**
that the only item above the 'ⱂ' for item 2 is also a '_____.'   **Krq**

3-118 1 | AKqpKrq
2 | 2.1 | Kqp
    | 2.2 | q   2.1, Ko
3 | 3.1 | Krq
    | 3.2 | q   3.1, Ko
4 | q   1, 2, 3, Ao

Item 4 of this Ao LAF is a WFF '_____.' Notice also: **q**

    The last item of item 2 is a WFF '_____';   **q**
    The last item of item 3 is a WFF '_____.'   **q**

3-119 1 | AKqpKrq
2 | 2.1 | Kqp
    | 2.2 | q   2.1, Ko
3 | 3.1 | Krq
    | 3.2 | q   3.1, Ko
4 | q   1, 2, 3, Ao

Every Ao LAF has four items:

    Item 1 is a WFF item;
    Item 2 is a tail item;

    Item 3 is a _____ item;   **tail**
    Item 4 is a _____ item.   **WFF**

3-120 1 | AKqpKrq
    2 | 2.1 | Kqp
       | 2.2 | q   2.1, Ko
    3 | 3.1 | Krq
       | 3.2 | q   3.1, Ko
    4 | q   1, 2, 3, Ao

Every Ao LAF has four items:

> Item 1 is an 'A' followed by two WFFs;
> Item 2 has as its only item above the 'Ⱶ' for item 2
> a WFF just like the first WFF following the 'A' in item
> 1, and every item of item 2 can be given a good
> reason;
> Item 3 has as its only item above the 'Ⱶ' for item 3 a
> WFF just like the _____ WFF following the 'A' in   **second**
> item 1, and every item of item 3 can be given a good
> reason;
> Item 4 is a WFF just like the last item of item _____   **2**
> and item _____ .   **3**

3-121 Every Ao LAF has four items:

> Item 1 is a WFF item;
> Item 2 is a tail item, each item of which can be given
> a _____ reason;   **good**
> Item 3 is a _____ item, each _____ of   **tail; item**
> which can be given a good _____ ;   **reason**
> Item 4 is a WFF item.

3-122 1 | AKqpKrq
    2 | 2.1 | Kqp
       | 2.2 | q   2.1, Ko
    3 | 3.1 | Krq
       | 3.2 | q   3.1, Ko
    4 | q   1, 2, 3, Ao

Every Ao LAF has four items:

> Item 1 is a WFF item beginning with an '_____';   **A**
> Item 2 is a _____ item whose only item above   **tail**
> the 'Ⱶ' for item 2 is a WFF like the _____ WFF   **first**
> following the 'A' in item 1 and whose last item is a
> WFF like item 4; and further, tail item 2 must be so

constructed that each item of tail item 2 can be given

a _____ reason;

Item 3 is a _____ item whose only item above

the 'ⱶ' for item 3 is a WFF like the _____ WFF

following the 'A' in item 1 and whose last item is a

WFF like item 4; and further, tail item 3 must be so

constructed that each _____ of tail item 3 can

be given a _____ _____ ;

Item 4 is a WFF item like the _____ item of tail

item _____ and tail item _____ .

3-123
```
1 | AKqpKrq
2 | 2.1 | Kqp
  | 2.2 | q        2.1, Ko
3 | 3.1 | Krq
  | 3.2 | q        3.1, Ko
4 | q              1, 2, 3, Ao
```

Since we can think of the 'q' which is item 4 as the *last* item
of an Ao LAF whose first item is item 1, whose second item
is the tail item 2, and whose third item is the tail item _____,
a '1, 2, 3, Ao' is a good reason for the last item of the above
sequence of four items. So, we write a '1, 2, 3, Ao' to the right
of the _____ item.

3-124
```
1 | AKqpKrq
2 | 2.1 | Kqp
  | 2.2 | q        2.1, Ko
3 | 3.1 | Krq
  | 3.2 | q        3.1, Ko
4 | q              ____, ____, ____, ____
```

3-125
```
1 | AKtsKpt
2 | 2.1 | Kts
  | 2.2 | t        2.1, Ko
  | 2.3 | Atq      2.2, Ai
3 | 3.1 | _____
  | 3.2 | t        3.1, Ko
  | 3.3 | Atq      3.2, Ai
4 | Atq           1, 2, 3, Ao
```

3-126 1 | AKsrs
    2 | 2.1 |————————   **Ksr**
         | 2.2 | s   2.1, Ko
         | 2.3 | Asp   2.2, Ai
    3 | 3.1 |————————   **s**
         | 3.2 | Asp   3.1, Ai
    4 | Asp   1, 2, 3, Ao

3-127 1 | AKNprKtNp
    2 | 2.1 | KNpr
         | 2.2 | Np   2.1, Ko
    3 | 3.1 | KtNp
         | 3.2 | Np   3.1, Ko
    4 |————————   1, 2, 3, Ao   **Np**

3-128 1 | AtKst
    2 | 2.1 | t
         | 2.2 | Ktt   2.1, 2.1, Ki
    3 | 3.1 | Kst
         | 3.2 | t   3.1, Ko
         | 3.3 | Ktt   3.2, 3.2, Ki
    4 |————————   1, 2, 3, Ao   **Ktt**

3-129 1 |————NqKNqr   **A**
    2 | 2.1 | Nq
         | 2.2 | AtNq   2.1, Ai
    3 | 3.1 | KNqr
         | 3.2 | Nq   3.1, Ko
         | 3.3 | AtNq   3.2, Ai
    4 | AtNq   1, 2, 3, Ao

3-130 1 | A———————— ————————   **Kpq; KAstp**
    2 | 2.1 | Kpq
         | 2.2 | p   2.1, Ko
    3 | 3.1 | KAstp
          | 3.2 | p   3.1, Ko
    4 |————   1, 2, 3, Ao   **p**

3-131

```
1 |_____                              ANsKNrNs
2 | 2.1 | Ns
  | 2.2 | AtNs        2.1, Ai
3 | 3.1 | KNrNs
  | 3.2 | Ns          3.1, Ko
  | 3.3 | AtNs        3.2, Ai
4 | AtNs              1, 2, 3, Ao
```

3-132 Can an Ao LAF have as its first item a WFF beginning with a 'K'? _____

no

3-133 Can an Ao LAF have as its first item a WFF beginning with a 'C'? _____

no

3-134 Can an Ao LAF have as its first item a WFF beginning with an 'N'? _____

no

3-135 Can an Ao LAF have as its first item a WFF that does not begin with a connective? _____

no

3-136 Every Ao LAF has as its first item a WFF beginning with a connective, and that connective is an '____.'

A

3-137 An Ao LAF has how many WFF items? _____
An Ao LAF has how many tail items? _____ An Ao LAF has how many items? _____

two
two
four

3-138 Write an Ao LAF whose first item is an 'AKrts' and whose last item is an 'Asr.'

```
*1 | AKrts
 2 | 2.1 | Krt
   | 2.2 | r
   | 2.3 | Asr
 3 | 3.1 | s
   | 3.2 | Asr
 4 | Asr¹
```

¹ A star (*) preceding a response indicates that the response given is not the only correct response.

3-139   *Frege wrote and Frege taught, or Frege lectured and*
Frege wrote.
Frege wrote and Frege taught.
Therefore, Frege wrote.
Frege lectured and Frege wrote.
Therefore, Frege wrote.
Therefore, Frege wrote.

The above argument can be formalized by the Ao LAF

| AKpqKrp
|| Kpq
|| ⊢̲̲̲̲̲   p
|| Krp
|| ⊢̲̲̲̲̲   p
| ⊢̲̲̲̲̲   p

Moreover, the argument is a valid argument—that is, the conclusion actually does follow from the premiss. For whether
Frege both wrote and taught or else both lectured and wrote,
in either case Frege _____ .   **wrote**

3-140   Let's see why every argument that can be formalized
by an Ao LAF is a _____ argument.   **valid**

3-141   *Frege wrote and Frege taught, or Frege lectured and*
Frege wrote.
Frege wrote and Frege taught.
Therefore, Frege wrote.
Frege lectured and Frege wrote.
Therefore, Frege wrote.
Therefore, Frege wrote.

Since the first premiss of the above argument is two sentences connected by an '_____' and the conclusion is   **or**
a sentence which actually does follow from each of those two
sentences, we recognize that the above argument is a
_____ argument.   **valid**

3-142   Every argument which can be formalized by an Ao
LAF is an argument whose first premiss is two sentences connected by an '_____' and whose conclusion is a sentence   **or**
which actually does _____ _____ each of those two   **follow from**
sentences.

Thus it seems plausible to agree that every argument which
can be formalized by an Ao LAF is an argument which would
be recognized as a _____ argument.   **valid**

3-143

```
1 | p
2 |——pq              1, ——              A; Ai

1 |——KqpKrq                             A
2 | 2.1 | Kqp
  | 2.2 | q           2.1, Ko
3 | 3.1 | Krq
  | 3.2 | q           3.1, Ko
4 | q                 1, 2, 3, A——       o
```

3-144

```
1 | p
2 | q
3 | Kpq               ——, ——, ——        1; 2; Ki

1 | Kpq
2 | p                 ——, ——             1; Ko

1 | p
2 | Apq               ——, ——             1; Ai

1 | AKpqKqq
2 | 2.1 | Kpq
  | 2.2 | q           2.1, Ko
3 | 3.1 | Kqq
  |     | q           3.1, Ko
4 | q                 ——, ——, ——, ——     1; 2; 3; Ao
```

E C-in LAFs

3-145 System F has four kinds of connectives—'K's, 'A's, 'C's, and 'N's.

Corresponding to each kind of connective in system F there are two kinds of LAFs—_____-LAFs and _____ -LAFs.   in; out

The structure of these LAFs is not unrelated to our convention that

1. A connective '____' represents a connecting word 'and,'   K
2. A connective '____' represents a connecting word 'or,'   A
3. A connective '____' represents a connecting word 'if then,' and   C
4. A connective '____' represents a connecting word 'it is false that.'   N

3-146 We have already looked at Ki LAFs, Ko LAFs, Ai LAFs, and Ao LAFs. Now let's look at some C-in LAFs, that is, at some C _____ LAFs.

i

3-147 Here is a Ci LAF:

```
1 |1.1 |p
  |1.2 |Apq        1.1, Ai
2 |CpApq           1, Ci
```

This Ci LAF has as its last item a WFF beginning with a '_____.'

c

3-148
```
1 |1.1 |p
  |1.2 |Apq        1.1, Ai
2 |CpApq           1, Ci
```

This Ci LAF has a WFF item as its last item. But the first item of this Ci LAF is a sequence of items, that is, item 1 is a _____ item.

tail

3-149
```
1 |1.1 |p
  |1.2 |Apq        1.1, Ai
2 |CpApq           1, Ci
```

This Ci LAF has as its last item a WFF which is a 'C' followed by two WFFs. The first of these WFFs is a '_____.' Notice that the only item above the '⊦' for item 1 is also a WFF '____ '.

p
p

3-150
```
1 |1.1 |p
  |1.2 |Apq        1.1, Ai
2 |CpApq           1, Ci
```

This Ci LAF has as its last item a WFF which is a 'C' followed by two WFFs. The second of these WFFs is an '_____.' Notice that the *last* item of item 1 is also a WFF '_____.'

Apq
Apq

3-151
```
1 |1.1 |p
  |1.2 |Apq        1.1, Ai
2 |CpApq           1, Ci
```

Every Ci LAF has two items:

Item 1 is a _____ item;

tail

Item 2 is a _____ item.

WFF

3-152 1 │1.1 │p
         │1.2 │Apq   1.1, Ai
         2 │CpApq   1, Ci

Every Ci LAF has two items:

> Item 2 is a 'C' followed by two WFFs;
> Item 1 has as its only item above the 'Ⱶ' for item 1 a
> WFF just like the first WFF following the 'C' in item 2
> and has as its last item a WFF just like the _____   second
> WFF following the 'C' in item 2; and every item of
> item 1 can be given a _____ reason.   good

3-153 Every Ci LAF has two items:

> Item 2 is a _____ item;   WFF
> Item 1 is a _____ item each item of which can   tail
> be given a _____ _____ .   good reason

3-154 1 │1.1 │p
         │1.2 │Apq   1.1, Ai
         2 │CpApq   1, Ci

Every Ci LAF has two items:

> Item 1 is a _____ item whose only item above   tail
> the 'Ⱶ' for item 1 is a WFF like the _____ WFF   first
> following the 'C' in item 2 and whose last item is a
> WFF like the _____ WFF following the 'C' in   second
> item 2; and further, tail item 1 must be so con-
> structed that each _____ of tail item 1 can be   item
> given a good _____ ;   reason
> Item 2 is a _____ item beginning with a 'C'   WFF
> which is followed by two WFFs, the first of which is
> like the only item above the 'Ⱶ' for item 1 and the
> second of which is like the _____ item of item   last
> ____ .   1

3-155 1 │1.1 │p
         │1.2 │Apq   1.1, Ai
         2 │CpApq   1, Ci

Since we can think of the 'CpApq' as the last item of a Ci LAF
whose first item is the tail item 1, a '1, Ci' is a good reason for
the last item of the above sequence. So, we write to the right
of the last item of the sequence a '_____ .'   1, Ci

3-156 1 | 1.1 | q
         | 1.2 | Arq   1.1, Ai
        2 | CqArq   _____ , _____   1; Ci

3-157 1 | 1.1 | _____   Krq
         | 1.2 | q   1.1, Ko
         | 1.3 | Aqt   1.2, Ai
        2 | CKrqAqt   1, Ci

3-158 1 | 1.1 | Kst
         | 1.2 | s   1.1, Ko
         | 1.3 | _____   1.2, 1.2, Ki   Kss
        2 | CKstKss   1, Ci

3-159 1 | 1.1 | _____   KNpr
         | 1.2 | Np   1.1, Ko
         | 1.3 | _____   1.2, Ai   AsNp
        2 | CKNprAsNp   1, Ci

3-160 1 | 1.1 | Nt
         | 1.2 | AsNt   1.1, Ai
        2 | _____ NtAsNt   1, Ci   C

3-161 1 | 1.1 | KNtq
         | 1.2 | q   1.1, Ko
         | 1.3 | Asq   1.2, Ai
        2 | _____   1, Ci   CKNtqAsq

3-162 1 | 1.1 | KNqKqt
         | 1.2 | Nq   1.1, Ko
         | 1.3 | Kqt   1.1, Ko
         | 1.4 | q   1.3, Ko
         | 1.5 | KqNq   1.4, 1.2, Ki
        2 | _____   1, Ci   CKNqKqtKqNq

3-163 Can a Ci LAF have as its last item a WFF beginning with a 'K'? _____   no

3-164 Can a Ci LAF have as its last item a WFF beginning with an 'A'? _____   no

3-165 Can a Ci LAF have as its last item a WFF beginning with an 'N'? _____   no

3-166 Can a Ci LAF have as its last item a WFF that does not begin with a connective? _____

no

3-167 Every Ci LAF has as its last item a WFF beginning with a connective, and that connective is a '_____.'

C

3-168 A Ci LAF has how many WFF items? _____ A Ci LAF has how many tail items? _____ A Ci LAF has how many items? _____

one
one
two

3-169 Write a Ci LAF whose second item is a 'CKrqAsr.'

```
*1 | 1.1 | Krq
   | 1.2 | r̄
   | 1.3 | Asr
 2 | CKrqAsr
```

3-170   *Frege wrote and Frege lectured.*
  Therefore, Frege wrote.
  Therefore, if Frege wrote and Frege lectured, then Frege wrote.

The above argument can be formalized by the Ci LAF

```
 ||————————
 |E————————
 |CKpqp
```

Kpq
p

Moreover, the argument is a valid argument. For suppose that Frege both wrote and lectured; then surely Frege wrote. So, *if* Frege wrote and lectured, *then* Frege _____ .

wrote

3-171 Let's see why every argument that can be formalized by a Ci LAF is a _____ argument.

valid

3-172   *Frege wrote and Frege lectured.*
  Therefore, Frege wrote.
  Therefore, if Frege wrote and Frege lectured, then Frege wrote.

Since the conclusion of the above argument is two sentences connected by an '_____' such that the second sentence actually does follow from the first sentence, we recognize that the above argument is a _____ argument.

if then

valid

3-173 Every argument which can be formalized by a Ci LAF has a conclusion which is two sentences connected by an '_____' such that the second sentence actually does _____ _____ the first sentence.

if then
follow from

Thus it seems plausible to agree that every argument which can be formalized by a Ci LAF would be recognized as a _____ argument.

valid

F C-out LAFs

3-174 System F has four kinds of connectives—'K's, 'A's, 'C's, and 'N's. Corresponding to each kind of connective in system F there are two kinds of LAFs— _____ -LAFs and _____ -LAFs. The structure of these LAFs is not un-related to our convention that

in
out

1. a connective 'K' represents a connecting word '_____,'
2. a connective 'A' represents a connecting word '_____,'
3. a connective 'C' represents a connecting word '_____,' and
4. a connective 'N' represents a connecting word '_____.'

and
or
if then

it is false that

3-175 We have looked at

Ki LAFs	Ko LAFs
Ai LAFs	Ao LAFs
Ci LAFs	

Now let's look at some C-out LAFs, that is, at some C_____ LAFs.

o

3-176 Here is a Co LAF:

```
1 | Cpq
2 | p
3 | q        1, 2, Co
```

Item 1 of the above LAF is a WFF item '_____.' Item 2 of the above LAF is a WFF item '_____.' Item 3 of the above LAF is a WFF item '_____.'

Cpq
p
q

3-177 Here is a Co LAF:

```
1 | Cpq
2 | p
3 | q        1, 2, Co
```

Item 1 of this Co LAF is a WFF beginning with a '_____.'   c

3-178
```
1 | Cpq
2 | p
3 | q        1, 2, Co
```

Item 1 of this Co LAF is a 'C' followed by two WFFs. The first
of these WFFs is a WFF '_____.' Notice that item 2 is also a   p
WFF '_____.'   p

3-179
```
1 | Cpq
2 | p
3 | q        1, 2, Co
```

Item 1 of this Co LAF is a 'C' followed by two WFFs. The second
of these WFFs is a WFF '_____.' Notice that item 3 is also a   q
WFF '_____.'   q

3-180
```
1 | Cpq
2 | p
3 | q        1, 2, Co
```

Every Co LAF has three items:

> Item 1 is a WFF which is a 'C' followed by two WFFs;
> Item 2 is a WFF which is just like the _____ WFF   first
> following the 'C' in item 1;
> Item 3 is a WFF which is just like the _____ WFF   second
> following the 'C' in item 1.

3-181
```
1 | Cpq
2 | p
3 | q        1, 2, Co
```

Since we can think of the 'q' as the *last* item of a Co LAF whose
first item is item 1 and whose second item is item 2, a good
reason for the last item of the above sequence is a '_____.'   1, 2, Co

3-182
```
1 | Cpq
2 | p
3 | q        _____ , _____ , _____
```
1; 2; Co

3-183 1 | Cst
       2 | s
       3 |‾‾‾‾   1, 2, Co   t

3-184 1 | CKqtr
       2 |‾‾‾‾‾‾‾   Kqt
       3 | r   1, 2, Co

3-185 1 | CNtAKpsq
       2 |‾‾‾‾‾‾‾   Nt
       3 |‾‾‾‾‾‾‾   1, 2, Co   AKpsq

3-186 1 |‾‾‾‾‾‾‾   CNKqts
       2 | NKqt
       3 | s   1, 2, Co

3-187 Can a Co LAF have as its first item a WFF beginning
with a 'K,' an 'A,' or an 'N'? _____   no

3-188 Can a Co LAF have as its first item a WFF that does
not begin with a connective? _____   no

3-189 A Co LAF has how many WFF items? _____ A Co   three
LAF has how many tail items? _____ A Co LAF has how   none
many items? _____   three

3-190 Write a Co LAF whose first item is a 'CKpNpKqNq.'   1 | CKpNpKqNq
                                        2 | KpNp
                                        3 | KqNq

3-191 *If Russell read Frege, then* Principia Mathematica *was
influenced by Frege.*
        Russell read Frege.
        Therefore, Principia Mathematica *was influenced by
Frege.*

The above argument can be formalized by the Co LAF

    |‾‾‾‾‾‾‾   Cpq
    | p
    | q

Moreover, the conclusion of the argument actually does follow from the premisses. For if we grant both that Frege was read by Russell and that if Frege was read by Russell then *Principia Mathematica* was influenced by Frege, it follows that *Principia Mathematica* was influenced by _____ .

Frege

3-192 Let's see why every argument that can be formalized by a Co LAF is a _____ argument.

valid

3-193 *If Russell read Frege, then* Principia Mathematica *was influenced by Frege.*
Russell read Frege.
Therefore, Principia Mathematica *was influenced by Frege.*

The first premiss of the above argument is two sentences connected by an '_____,' the second premiss is a sentence just like the first of these two sentences, and the _____ of the argument is a sentence just like the second of these two sentences. It seems difficult to deny that the conclusion *does* follow from the premisses, that is, that the argument is a _____ argument.

if then

conclusion

valid

3-194 Every argument which can be formalized by a Co LAF is an argument whose first premiss is two sentences connected by an '_____'; the second premiss is a sentence just like the first of these two sentences, and the _____ of the argument is a sentence just like the second of these two sentences. Thus it seems plausible to agree that every argument which can be formalized by a Co LAF is an argument which would be recognized as a _____ argument.

if then
conclusion

valid

3-195

1	1.1	Kpq
	1.2	p	1.1, Ko
2	____Kpqp	1, C____

C; i

1	____pq
2	p
3	q	1, 2, C____

C

o

3-196

```
1 | p
2 | q
3 | Kpq          ____, ____, ____        1; 2; Ki

1 | Kpq
2 | p            ____, ____              1; Ko

1 | p
2 | Apq          ____, ____              1; Ai

1 | AKpqKrp
2 | 2.1 | Kpq
  | 2.2 | p      2.1, Ko
3 | 3.1 | Krp
  | 3.2 | p      3.1, Ko
4 | p            ____, ____, ____, ____   1; 2; 3; Ao

1 | 1.1 | Kpq
  | 1.2 | p      1.1, Ko
2 | CKpqp        ____, ____              1; Ci

1 | Cpq
2 | p
3 | q            ____, ____, ____        1; 2; Co
```

G N-in LAFs

3-197 System F has four kinds of connectives—'K's, 'A's, 'C's, and 'N's. Corresponding to each kind of connective in system F there are two kinds of LAFs—_____-LAFs and _____-LAFs. The structure of these LAFs is not un-related to our convention that

    in

    out

1. A connective '____' represents a connecting word 'and,'   **K**
2. A connective '____' represents a connecting word 'or,'   **A**
3. A connective '____' represents a connecting word 'if then,'   **C**
4. A connective '____' represents a connecting word 'it is false that.'   **N**

3-198 We have already looked at

    Ki LAFs   Ko LAFs
    Ai LAFs   Ao LAFs
    Ci LAFs   Co LAFs

Now let's look at some N-in LAFs, that is, at some N _____
LAFs.

i

3-199   Here is an Ni LAF:

```
1 │1.1 │KqKpNp
  │1.2 │KpNp          1.1, Ko
2 │NKqKpNp            1, Ni
```

This Ni LAF has as its last item a WFF beginning with
an '_____.'

N

3-200
```
1 │1.1 │KqKpNp
  │1.2 │KpNp          1.1, Ko
2 │NKqKpNp            1, Ni
```

This Ni LAF has two items:

> The last item is a WFF beginning with an '_____';   N
> The first item is a sequence of items, that is, a
> _____ item.   tail

3-201
```
1 │1.1 │KqKpNp
  │1.2 │KpNp          1.1, Ko
2 │NKqKpNp            1, Ni
```

The *last* item of this Ni LAF is a WFF which is an 'N' followed
by a '_____.' Notice that the only item above the 'Ⱶ' for   **KqKpNp**
item 1 is also a '_____.'   **KqKpNp**

3-202
```
1 │1.1 │KqKpNp
  │1.2 │KpNp          1.1, Ko
2 │NKqKpNp            1, Ni
```

Item 1 of this Ni LAF is a tail item. The last item of this tail
item is a 'K' followed by two WFFs—a '_____' and an   **p**
'_____.'   **Np**

3-203   A 'KpNp' is a contradictory WFF. A contradictory
WFF is a WFF which is a 'K' followed by two WFFs, the second
of which is an 'N' followed by a WFF just like the first WFF
following the 'K.' Another contradictory WFF is a 'KqN_____.'   **q**

3-204   A 'KqNq' is a contradictory WFF because a 'KqNq' is
a '_____' followed by two WFFs, the second of which is an
'N_____' and the first of which is a '_____.'

K

q; q

3-205   A contradictory WFF is a 'K' followed by two WFFs,
the second of which is an 'N' followed by a WFF like the first
WFF following the 'K .' Copy those of the following which are
contradictory WFFs:

KNtt   KtNt

_____

KtNt

3-206   Copy those of the following which are contradictory
WFFs:

KrNr   KpNp
KNrr   KCpqCpq
KNqq   KCpqNCpq
KNNqq   KqNp
NKpNp   KNqNNq

_____ _____ _____ _____

KrNr; KpNp; KCpqNCpq;
KNqNNq

3-207   *(1) Man triumphs, and it is false that man triumphs.*

(1) can be formalized by a 'KpNp.' Thus, (1) can be formalized by a _____ WFF.

contradictory

3-208   *(1) Man triumphs, and it is false that man triumphs.*

We call a sentence a contradiction if the sentence can be
formalized by a contradictory WFF. Thus, since (1) can be
formalized by a 'KpNp,' which is a _____ WFF, (1) is a
_____ .

contradictory
contradiction

3-209   *(1) Virtue prospers, or it is false that virtue prospers.*
(2) Virtue prospers, and it is false that crime pays.
(3) Virtue prospers, and it is false that virtue prospers.
(4) KqNq
(5) AqNq
(6) KqNp

Which of the above are contradictory WFFs? _____ Which of
the above are contradictions? _____

4

3

3-210   1 | 1.1 | KqKpNp
              | 1.2 | KpNp   1.1, Ko
              2 | NKqKpNp   1, Ni

Item 1 of this Ni LAF is a tail item. Notice that the *last* item of
item 1 is a '_____,' that is, the last item of item 1 is a
_____ WFF.

KpNp

contradictory

3-211   1 | 1.1 | KqKpNp
              | 1.2 | KpNp   1.1, Ko
              2 | NKqKpNp   1, Ni

Every Ni LAF has two items:

    Item 1 is a _____ item;

    Item 2 is a _____ item.

tail

WFF

3-212   1 | 1.1 | KqKpNp
              | 1.2 | KpNp   1.1, Ko
              2 | NKqKpNp   1, Ni

Every Ni LAF has two items:

    Item 2 is an 'N' followed by one WFF;

    Item 1:

        has as its only item above the '⊢' for item 1 a WFF

        just like the WFF following the 'N' in item _____,

        has as its *last* item a _____ WFF, and

        is so constructed that every item of item 1 can be

        given a _____ reason.

2

contradictory

good

3-213   Every Ni LAF has two items:

    Item 1 is a _____ item, each item of which can

    be given a _____ _____;

    Item 2 is a _____ item.

tail

good reason

WFF

3-214 1 | 1.1 | KqKpNp
       | 1.2 | KpNp   1.1, Ko
     2 | NKqKpNp   1, Ni

Every Ni LAF has two items:

    Item 1 is a _____ item whose only item above   **tail**
    the 'ⱶ' for item 1 is a WFF like the WFF following the
    'N' in item 2 and whose last item is a _____   **contradictory**
    WFF; and further, tail item 1 must be so constructed
    that each _____ of tail item 1 can be given a   **item**
    good _____;   **reason**
    Item 2 is an 'N' followed by a WFF like the only item
    above the 'ⱶ' for item ____ .   **1**

3-215 1 | 1.1 | KqKpNp
       | 1.2 | KpNp   1.1, Ko
     2 | NKqKpNp   1, Ni

Since we can think of the 'NKqKpNp' as the *last* item of an Ni
LAF which has as its first item the tail item 1, a good reason
for the last item of the above sequence is a '_____.'   **1, Ni**

3-216 1 | 1.1 | KqKpNp
       | 1.2 | KpNp   1.1, Ko
     2 | NKqKpNp   ____ , ____   **1; Ni**

3-217 1 | 1.1 | _____   **KKtNpNt**
       | 1.2 | KtNp   1.1, Ko
       | 1.3 | Nt   1.1, Ko
       | 1.4 | t   1.2, Ko
       | 1.5 | KtNt   1.4, 1.3, Ki
     2 | NKKtNpNt   1, Ni

3-218 1 | 1.1 | KKtNpNt
       | 1.2 | KtNp   1.1, Ko
       | 1.3 | Nt   1.1, Ko
       | 1.4 | t   1.2, Ko
       | 1.5 | KtNt   1.4, 1.3, Ki
     2 | N_____   1, Ni   **KKtNpNt**

3-219

1	1.1	KrKsNr		
	1.2	r	1.1, Ko	
	1.3	KsNr	1.1, Ko	
	1.4	Nr	1.3, Ko	
	1.5	Kr_____	1.2, 1.4, Ki	**Nr**
2		NKrKsNr	1, Ni	

3-220

1	1.1	KKNtNss		
	1.2	KNtNs	1.1, Ko	
	1.3	s	1.1, Ko	
	1.4	Ns	1.2, Ko	
	1.5	K_____Ns	1.3, 1.4, Ki	**s**
2		NKKNtNss	1, Ni	

3-221

1	1.1	KKpNqCNqNp		
	1.2	KpNq	1.1, Ko	
	1.3	CNqNp	1.1, Ko	
	1.4	Nq	1.2, Ko	
	1.5	Np	1.3, 1.4, Co	
	1.6	p	1.2, Ko	
	1.7	KpNp	1.6, 1.5, Ki	
2		_____KKpNqCNqNp	1, Ni	**N**

3-222

1	1.1	KCpNpp		
	1.2	CpNp	1.1, Ko	
	1.3	p	1.1, Ko	
	1.4	Np	1.2, 1.3, Co	
	1.5	KpNp	1.3, 1.4, Ki	
2		_____	1, Ni	**NKCpNpp**

3-223 Can an Ni LAF have as its last item a WFF that begins with a 'K,' an 'A,' or a 'C'? _____   **no**

3-224 Can an Ni LAF have as its last item a WFF that does not begin with a connective? _____   **no**

3-225 The last item of every Ni LAF begins with a connective, and that connective is an '_____ .'   **N**

3-226 An Ni LAF has how many WFF items? _____ An Ni LAF has how many tail items? _____ An Ni LAF has how many items? _____

one
one
two

3-227   Every Ni LAF has two items—item 1 is a _____
item, and item 2 is a _____ item. Further,

> Item 2 is an 'N' followed by one WFF;
> Item 1:
>> has as its only item above the 'Ⱶ' for item 1 a WFF
>> just like the WFF following the 'N' in item _____,
>> has as its last item a _____ WFF, and
>> is so constructed that every item of item 1 can be
>> given a _____ reason.

tail
WFF

2
contradictory

good

3-228   Write an Ni LAF whose last item is an 'NKqKtNq.'

*1	1.1	KqKtNq
	1.2	q̄
	1.3	KtNq
	1.4	Nq
	1.5	KqNq
2		NKqKtNq

3-229   *Venn pioneered, and it is false that Venn pioneered.*
Therefore, Venn pioneered, and it is false that Venn
pioneered.
Therefore, it is false that Venn pioneered and it is false
that Venn pioneered.

The above argument can be formalized by the Ni LAF

```
 ||KpNp
 |KpNp
 |―――― KpNp
```

N

Moreover, the argument is a valid argument. For if we grant
that Venn both did and did not pioneer, something absurd
follows—namely, that he both did and did not pioneer. So, it
follows then that it must be false that Venn both did and did
_____ pioneer.

not

3-230   Let's see why every argument which can be formalized by an Ni LAF is a _____ argument.

valid

3-231   Every argument which can be formalized by an
Ni LAF is an argument whose conclusion is a sentence which
is an '_____' followed by a sentence from which an
absurdity—a contradiction—can be shown to follow. Thus it

it is false that

seems plausible to agree that every argument which can be formalized by an Ni LAF is an argument which would be recognized as a _____ argument.

valid

H   N-out LAFs

3-232   System F has four kinds of connectives—'K's, 'A's, 'C's, and 'N's.

Corresponding to each kind of connective in system F there are two kinds of LAΓs—_____-LAΓs and _____-LAΓs.

in; out

The structure of these LAFs is not unrelated to our convention that

1. A connective 'K' represents a connecting word '_____,'   and
2. A connective 'A' represents a connecting word '_____,'   or
3. A connective 'C' represents a connecting word '_____,'   if then and
4. A connective 'N' represents a connecting word '_____.'   it is false that

3-233   We have already looked at

Ki LAFs	Ko LAFs
Ai LAFs	Ao LAFs
Ci LAFs	Co LAFs
Ni LAFs	

Now let's look at some N-out LAFs, that is, at some N _____ LAFs.

o

3-234   Here is an No LAF:

```
1 |1.1 |NCKpqp
  |1.2 |1.2.1 |Kpq
  |    |1.2.2 |p        1.2.1, Ko
  |1.3 |CKpqp           1.2, Ci
  |1.4 |KCKpqpNCKpqp    1.3, 1.1, Ki
2 |CKpqp               1, No
```

An No LAF has _____ items. Item 1 is a _____ item, and item 2 is a _____ item.

two; tail
WFF

3-235   Here is an No LAF:

```
1 |1.1 |NCKpqp
  |1.2 |1.2.1 |Kpq
  |    |1.2.2 |p              1.2.1, Ko
  |1.3 |CKpqp                 1.2, Ci
  |1.4 |KCKpqpNCKpqp          1.3, 1.1, Ki
2 |CKpqp                      1, No
```

The first item of an No LAF is a tail item, and the only item
above the 'ⱶ' for tail item 1 is a WFF beginning with an '_____.'   N

3-236
```
1 |1.1 |NCKpqp
  |1.2 |1.2.1 |Kpq
  |    |1.2.2 |p              1.2.1, Ko
  |1.3 |CKpqp                 1.2, Ci
  |1.4 |KCKpqpNCKpqp          1.3, 1.1, Ki
2 |CKpqp                      1, No
```

Item 1 of an No LAF is a tail item, and item 2 is a WFF item.
The only item above the 'ⱶ' for tail item 1 of the above No LAF
is an 'N' followed by a '_____'; item 2 of the LAF is also a   CKpqp
WFF '_____.'   CKpqp

3-237
```
1 |1.1 |NCKpqp
  |1.2 |1.2.1 |Kpq
  |    |1.2.2 |p              1.2.1, Ko
  |1.3 |CKpqp                 1.2, Ci
  |1.4 |KCKpqpNCKpqp          1.3, 1.1, Ki
2 |CKpqp                      1, No
```

Item 1 of this No LAF is a tail item. The only item above the
'ⱶ' for tail item 1 is a WFF beginning with an '_____.' The last   N
item of the tail item is a 'K_____ N_____.' That is,   CKpqp; CKpqp
the last item of the tail item is a _____ WFF.   contradictory

3-238
```
1 |1.1 |NCKpqp
  |1.2 |1.2.1 |Kpq
  |    |1.2.2 |p              1.2.1, Ko
  |1.3 |CKpqp                 1.2, Ci
  |1.4 |KCKpqpNCKpqp          1.3, 1.1, Ki
2 |CKpqp                      1, No
```

Every No LAF has two items:

     Item 1 is a _____ item, and   tail
     Item 2 is a _____ item.   WFF

3-239

```
1 | 1.1 | NCKpqp
  | 1.2 | 1.2.1 | Kpq
  |     | 1.2.2 | p           1.2.1, Ko
  | 1.3 | CKpqp             1.2, Ci
  | 1.4 | KCKpqpNCKpqp      1.3, 1.1, Ki
2 | CKpqp                   1, No
```

Every No LAF has two items:

Item 1:

has as its only item above the 'Ⱶ' for item 1 a WFF
which is an '_____' followed by one WFF,   N

has as its last item a _____ WFF, and   contradictory

is so constructed that every item of item 1 can be

given a _____ reason;   good

Item 2 is a WFF just like the WFF following the 'N' in

the only item above the 'Ⱶ' for item _____ .   1

3-240   Every No LAF has two items:

Item 1 is a _____ item, each item of which can   tail

be given a _____ _____ ;   good reason

Item 2 is a _____ item.   WFF

3-241

```
1 | 1.1 | NCKpqp
  | 1.2 | 1.2.1 | Kpq
  |     | 1.2.2 | p           1.2.1, Ko
  | 1.3 | CKpqp             1.2, Ci
  | 1.4 | KCKpqpNCKpqp      1.3, 1.1, Ki
2 | CKpqp                   1, No
```

Every No LAF has two items:

Item 1 is a _____ item whose only item above   tail

the 'Ⱶ' for item 1 is a WFF which is an '_____' followed   N

by one WFF and whose last item is a _____ WFF;   contradictory

and further, tail item 1 must be so constructed that

each _____ of tail item 1 can be given a good   item

_____ ;   reason

Item 2 is a _____ item just like the WFF follow- WFF

ing the '_____' in the only item above the 'Ⱶ' for item   N

_____ .   1

3-242

1	1.1	NCKpqp	
	1.2	1.2.1	Kpq
		1.2.2	p	1.2.1, Ko
	1.3	CKpqp	1.2, Ci
	1.4	KCKpqpNCKpqp	1.3, 1.1, Ki
2	CKpqp		1, No

Since we can think of the 'CKpqp' as the *last* item of an No LAF whose first item is the tail item 1, a good reason for the last item of the above sequence is a '_____.   1, No

3-243

1	1.1	NCKpqp	
	1.2	1.2.1	Kpq
		1.2.2	p	1.2.1, Ko
	1.3	CKpqp	1.2, Ci
	1.4	KCKpqpNCKpqp	1.3, 1.1, Ki
2	CKpqp		_____ , _____ 1; No

3-244   CpKpp

1	1.1	NCpKpp	
	1.2	1.2.1	p
		1.2.2	Kpp	1.2.1, 1.2.1, Ki
	1.3	CpKpp	1.2, Ci
	1.4	KCpKppNCpKpp	1.3, 1.1, Ki
2	_____		1, No CpKpp

3-245   CpKpp

1	1.1	N_____	
	1.2	1.2.1	p
		1.2.2	Kpp	1.2.1, 1.2.1, Ki
	1.3	CpKpp	1.2, Ci
	1.4	KCpKppNCpKpp	1.3, 1.1, Ki
2	CpKpp		1, No

3-246

1	1.1	NCKsNrNr	
	1.2	1.2.1	KsNr
		1.2.2	Nr	1.2.1, Ko
	1.3	CKsNrNr	1.2, Ci
	1.4	K_____NCKsNrNr	1.3, 1.1, Ki CKsNrNr
2	CKsNrNr		1, No

3-247

1	1.1	NCpApq	
	1.2	1.2.1	p
		1.2.2	Apq	1.2.1, Ai
	1.3	CpApq	1.2, Ci
	1.4	KCpApq_____	1.3, 1.1, Ki NCpApq
2	CpApq		1, No

3-248

```
1 | 1.1 |____CKqNpAtNp                              N
  | 1.2 | 1.2.1 | KqNp
  |     | 1.2.2 | Np                1.2.1, Ko
  |     | 1.2.3 | AtNp              1.2.2, Ai
  | 1.3 | CKqNpAtNp                 1.2, Ci
  | 1.4 | KCKqNpAtNpNCKqNpAtNp      1.3, 1.1, Ki
2 | CKqNpAtNp                       1, No
```

3-249

```
1 | 1.1 |_____                                 NCKtst
  | 1.2 | 1.2.1 | Kts
  |     | 1.2.2 | t              1.2.1, Ko
  | 1.3 | CKtst                  1.2, Ci
  | 1.4 | KCKtstNCKtst           1.3, 1.1, Ki
2 | CKtst                        1, No
```

3-250 Can the only item above the 'Ⱶ' for the tail item of an
No LAF begin with a 'K,' an 'A,' or a 'C'?   no

3-251 Can the only item above the 'Ⱶ' for the tail item of an
No LAF be a WFF that does not begin with a connective?

_____   no

3-252 The only item above the 'Ⱶ' for the tail item of an No
LAF begins with a connective, and that connective is an
'____.'   N

3-253 An No LAF has how many WFF items? _____   one
An No LAF has how many tail items? _____ An No LAF   one
has how many items? _____   two

3-254 Every No LAF has two items: item 1 is a _____   tail
item, and item 2 is a _____ item. Further,   WFF

    Item 1:
        has as its only item above the 'Ⱶ' for item 1 a WFF
        beginning with an '____,'   N
        has as its last item a _____ WFF, and   contradictory
        is so constructed that every item of item 1 can be
        given a _____ reason;   good
    Item 2 is a WFF just like the WFF following the '____'   N
    in the only item above the 'Ⱶ' for tail item ____.   1

3-255 Write an Ni LAF whose last item is a 'CKsqs.'

```
*1 1.1 | NCKsqs
    1.2 | 1.2.1 | Ksq
        | 1.2.2 | s
    1.3 | CKsqs
    1.4 | KCKsqsNCKsqs
  2 | CKsqs
```

3-256 Let's see why every argument which can be formalized by an No LAF is a _____ argument.

valid

3-257 Every argument which can be formalized by an No LAF has a conclusion such that an absurdity—a contradiction—can be shown to follow from a sentence which is an 'it is _____ that' preceding a sentence like the _____ of the argument. Thus it seems plausible to agree that every argument which can be formalized by an No LAF is an argument which would be recognized as a _____ one.

false; conclusion

valid

3-258

```
1 | 1.1 | KqKpNp
  | 1.2 | KpNp              1.1, Ko
2 |_____KqKpNp             1, N_____        N; i

1 | 1.1 |_____CKpqp                          N
  | 1.2 | 1.2.1 | Kpq
  |     | 1.2.2 | p         1.2.1, Ko
  | 1.3 | CKpqp            1.2, Ci
  | 1.4 | KCKpqpNCKpqp     1.3, 1.1, Ki
2 | CKpqp                  1, N_____        o
```

I Repetition LAFs

3-259 We have looked at

Ki LAFs   Ci LAFs
Ai LAFs   Ni LAFs

Name four more kinds of LAFs we have looked at:

_____LAFs   _____LAFs   Ko; Ao
_____LAFs   _____LAFs   Co; No

3-260 Let's look now at the ninth kind of LAFs in system F. Repetition LAFs are the last kind of LAFs. But for short, these LAFs are called rep LAFs. Let's look at some rep LAFs—that is, at some _____ LAFs.

repetition

3-261 Here is a rep LAF:

```
1 | p
2 | p    1, rep
```

A rep LAF has two items. Item 1 is a _____ item, and item 2 is a _____ item. Moreover, item 1 is just like item ____ .

WFF
WFF
2

3-262 Here is another rep LAF:

```
1 | KpArs
2 |_____    1, rep
```

KpArs

3-263
```
1 | r
2 | r    1, rep
```

Since we can think of the 'r' as the *last* item of a rep LAF whose first item is item 1, a good reason for the last item of the sequence is a '_____ .'

1, rep

3-264 Write a rep LAF whose *first* item is a 'Cpq.'

```
1 | Cpq
2 | Cpq
```

3-265 Write a rep LAF whose *last* item is a 'Cpq.'

```
1 | Cpq
2 | Cpq
```

3-266 Can the first item of a rep LAF begin with a 'K'? _____ With an 'A'? _____ With a 'C'? _____ With an 'N'? _____ With a sentence variable? _____

yes; yes; yes
yes; yes

3-267 Can the last item of a rep LAF begin with a 'K'? _____ With an 'A'? _____ With a 'C'? _____ With an 'N'? _____ With a sentence variable? _____

yes; yes; yes
yes; yes

3-268 A rep LAF has how many WFF items? _____ A rep LAF has how many tail items? _____ A rep LAF has how many items? _____

two
none
two

3-269   Every rep LAF has two items. Both items are
_____ items, and item 1 is just like item _____.

3-270   Let's see why every argument which can be formalized by a rep LAF is a _____ argument.

3-271   *System F has nine kinds of LAFs.*
Therefore, system F has nine kinds of LAFs.

Since the premiss of this argument is a sentence which is
exactly like the _____ of the argument, it seems difficult
to deny that the conclusion *does* follow from the premiss, that
is, that the argument is a _____ argument.

3-272   Any argument which can be formalized by a rep LAF
is an argument whose premiss is a sentence just like the
_____ of the argument. Thus it seems plausible to
agree that every argument which can be formalized by a rep
LAF is an argument which would be recognized as a
_____ argument.

3-273   What are the nine kinds of LAFs in system F?

_____LAFs	_____LAFs
_____LAFs	_____LAFs
_____LAFs	_____LAFs
_____LAFs	_____LAFs
_____LAFs	

Review of Symbols, WFFs,
and LAFs in System F

3-274   We began our description of system F by specifying

1. The symbols in system F, and
2. The WFFs in system F.

We have just finished specifying

3. The _____ in system F.   LAFs

3-275   The symbols in system F are of three kinds—sentence variables, connectives, and 'therefore' indicators. The
sentence variables in system F are any 'p,' '_____,' '_____,'   q; r
'_____,' or '_____.'   s; t

The connectives in system F are any 'K,' _____,' _____,'   A; C
or '_____.'   N

A 'ŀ' is a '_____' indicator in system F.   therefore

3-276   The WFFs in system F are completely specified by
these five rules:

1. Any _____ variable in system F is a WFF in system F.   sentence
2. Any 'K' followed by _____ WFFs in system F is a WFF   two
in system F.
3. Any 'A' followed by two WFFs in system F is a WFF in
system _____ .   F
4. Any 'C' followed by two _____ in system F is a WFF in   WFFs
system F.
5. Any '_____' followed by _____ WFF in system F is a   N; one
WFF in system F.

3-277   System F has four kinds of connectives—'K's, 'A's,
'C's, and 'N's. Corresponding to each kind of connective in
system F there are two kinds of LAFs—in-LAFs and _____   out
-LAFs. The structure of these LAFs is not unrelated to our
convention that

1. A connective 'K' represents a connecting word '_____,'   and
2. A connective 'A' represents a connecting word '_____,'   or
3. A connective 'C' represents a connecting word '_____,'   if then
and
4. A connective 'N' represents a connecting word '_____.'   it is false that

3-278 System F has only nine kinds of LAFs:

Ki	LAFs	Ko	LAFs		
____	LAFs	____	LAFs	Ai	Ao
____	LAFs	____	LAFs	Ci	Co
____	LAFs	____	LAFs	Ni	No
	_____ LAFs			rep	

3-279 System F has rep LAFs, in-LAFs, and _____   out
-LAFs.

3-280 The last item of every in-LAF begins with a connective, for

The *last* item of a Ki LAF begins with a connective
'_____,'   K

The *last* item of an Ai LAF begins with a connective
'_____,'   A

The *last* item of a Ci LAF begins with a connective
'_____,' and   C

The *last* item of an Ni LAF begins with a connective
'_____.'   N

3-281 The last item of every out-LAF need not begin with a connective, but the last item of every in-LAF must begin with a _____ .   connective

3-282 The *first* item of a Ko LAF begins with a connective
'_____.'   K

The first item of an Ao LAF begins with a connective '_____.'   A

The first item of a Ci LAF begins with a connective '_____.'   C

The only item above the 'ⱶ' for the tail item of an No
LAF begins with a connective '_____.'   N

3-283 Name three kinds of LAFs that have exactly two items, both of which are WFF items.

_____ _____ _____

3-284 Name three kinds of LAFs that have exactly two items, one of which is a tail item, the other a WFF item.

_____ _____ _____

3-285 Name two kinds of LAFs that have exactly three items.

_____ _____

3-286 Name the one kind of LAF that has exactly four items.

_____

3-287 Name the three kinds of LAFs that have just one tail item.

_____ _____ _____

3-288 Name the two kinds of LAFs that have one tail item, the last item of which is a contradictory WFF.

_____ _____

3-289 Name the one kind of LAF that has exactly two tail items.

_____

3-290 We have effectively specified the LAFs in system F, because given any sequence of items we can decide whether or not that sequence is a LAF in system F. For a sequence of items is a LAF in system F if and only if the sequence is a LAF of one of these nine kinds:

_____ _____   _____ _____

_____ _____   _____ _____

_____ _____   _____ _____

_____ _____   _____ _____

_____ _____

And we can always decide whether or not a sequence of items is a LAF of a given kind.

3-291 Identify the following LAFs:

```
1 | p
2 | q
3 | Kpq              _____, _____, _____        1; 2; Ki
```

```
1 | p
2 | Apq              _____, _____              1; Ai
```

```
1 | 1.1 | Kpq
  | 1.2 | p          1.1, Ko
2 | CKpqp            _____, _____              1; Ci
```

```
1 | 1.1 | KqKpNp
  | 1.2 | KpNp       1.1, Ko
2 | NKqKpNp          _____, _____              1; Ni
```

3-292 Identify the following LAFs:

```
1 | Kpq
2 | p                _____, _____              1; Ko
```

```
1 | AKqpKrq
2 | 2.1 | Kqp
  | 2.2 | q          2.1, Ko
3 | 3.1 | Krq
  | 3.2 | q          3.1, Ko
4 | q                _____, _____, _____, _____    1; 2; 3; Ao
```

```
1 | Cpq
2 | p
3 | q                _____, _____, _____       1; 2; Co
```

```
1 | 1.1 | NCKpqp
  | 1.2 | 1.2.1 | Kpq
  |     | 1.2.2 | p       1.2.1, Ko
  | 1.3 | CKpqp           1.2, Ci
  | 1.4 | KCKpqpNCKpqp    1.3, 1.1, Ki
2 | CKpqp                 _____, _____         1; No
```

3-293 Complete the following LAFs:

```
1 | p
2 | q
3 |____pq        1, 2, Ki                              K

1 | p
2 |____pq        1, Ai                                 A

1 | 1.1 | Kpq
  | 1.2 | p      1.1, Ko
2 |____Kpqp      1, Ci                                 C

1 | 1.1 | KqKpNp
  | 1.2 | KpNp   1.1, Ko
2 |____KqKpNp    1, Ni                                 N
```

3-294 Complete the following LAFs:

```
1 |____pq                                             K
2 | p            1, Ko

1 |____KqpKrq                                         A
2 | 2.1 | Kqp
  | 2.2 | q      2.1, Ko
3 | 3.1 | Krq
  | 3.2 | q      3.1, Ko
4 | q            1, 2, 3, Ao

1 |____pq                                             C
2 | p
3 | q            1, 2, Co

1 | 1.1 |____CKpqp                                    N
  | 1.2 | 1.2.1 | Kpq
  |     | 1.2.2 | p      1.2.1, Ko
  | 1.3 | CKpqp          1.2, Ci
  | 1.4 | KCKpqpNCKpqp   1.3, 1.1, Ki
2 | CKpqp                1, No
```

Proofs in System F

A Items

3-295 We describe system F by specifying

1. The symbols in system F,
2. The WFFs in system F,
3. The LAFs in system F, and
4. The *proofs* in system F.

We have already specified the symbols in system F, the WFFs in system F, the LAFs in system F; next we specify the _____ in system F.

proofs

3-296 A proof is a sequence of items, each of which has a good reason.

We have seen that items are of two kinds:

1. WFF items, and
2. _____ items.

tail

3-297 Items are of two kinds. A WFF item is simply a WFF. Thus, a 'Cpq' is a _____ item.

WFF

3-298 Items are of two kinds. A WFF item is simply a WFF, but a tail item is a _____ of items.

sequence

3-299 In the Ci LAF

```
1 | 1.1 | Kpq
  | 1.2 | p        1.1, Ko
2 | CKpqp          1, Ci
```

Item 1 is a _____ item, and item 2 is a _____ item.

tail; WFF

3-300 A proof is a sequence of items each of which has a good reason. But how do we know what is a good reason for an item of a sequence? Since every item of a sequence must be either a WFF item or a tail item, we will know what is a good reason for any kind of item once we know

What is a good reason for a _____ item, and   WFF

What is a good reason for a _____ item.   tail

B   Good Reasons for WFF Items

3-301 Since every item of a sequence must be either a WFF item or a tail item, we will know what is a good reason for any kind of item once we know what is a good reason for a WFF item and what is a good reason for a tail item. We will consider what is a good reason for a tail item once we know what is a good reason for a _____ item.   WFF

3-302 WFF items of a sequence are either

1. *Above* the 'therefore' indicator ('⊢') for the sequence, or
2. _____ the 'therefore' indicator ('⊢') for the sequence.   below

3-303 Since every WFF item of a sequence must be either above the '⊢' for the sequence or else below the '⊢' for the sequence, we will know what is a good reason for any WFF item of a sequence once we know

What is a good reason for a WFF item _____ the   above
'⊢' for the sequence, and

What is a good reason for a WFF item _____ the   below
'⊢' for the sequence.

3-304 A hypothesis—or, for short, a hyp—is something we assume in order to discover what follows from it. From now on, instead of writing 'hypothesis,' let's write, for short,

'_____.'   hyp

3-305   A 'hyp' is a good reason for a WFF item of the sequence if and only if the WFF is *above* the 'ⱶ' for the sequence.

```
1 | Cpq    hyp
2 | Kpr    hyp
3 | p      2, Ko
4 | q      1, 3, Co
```

Since item 1 and item 2 are both WFF items which are _____ the 'ⱶ' for the sequence, a good reason for item 1 and for item 2 is a '_____ .'

above

hyp

3-306   If a WFF item is above the 'ⱶ' for the sequence, what can be given as a good reason for that WFF item? A '_____ .'

hyp

3-307   Where must a WFF item of a sequence be placed with respect to the 'ⱶ' for that sequence if the WFF is to have a 'hyp' as a good reason? The WFF item must be placed _____ the 'ⱶ' for the _____ .

above; sequence

3-308   A hypothesis is something we assume in order to discover what follows from it. We may assume whatever we please *provided that* we make clear that what we assume has status only as premiss or hypothesis.   We make clear that a sentence has status only as hypothesis by putting the formalization of the sentence not below but _____ the 'there-fore' indicator for the sequence and by giving as a good reason for the WFF which formalizes the sentence a '_____ .'

above

hyp

3-309   We know what is a good reason for a WFF item of a sequence when the item is above the 'ⱶ' for the sequence. So, we will know what is a good reason for any WFF item of a sequence once we know what is a good reason for a WFF item of a sequence when the WFF item is _____ the 'ⱶ' for the sequence.

below

3-310   We think of the WFF items *above* the 'ⱶ' for a sequence as the formalizations of hypotheses. We can think of the WFF items *below* the 'ⱶ' for a sequence as formalizations of sentences that follow in some sense from these hypotheses.   In terms of system F, we say we must think of a WFF item below the 'ⱶ' for the sequence as the last item of a LAF. For we saw the LAFs in system F to be such that any argument

that can be formalized by a LAF in system F is a valid argument—that is, an argument in which the conclusion actually
does _____ _____ the premisses.

follow from

3-311 If a WFF item of a sequence is below the 'ᚺ' for the
sequence, we must be able to think of the WFF as the last
item of a LAF. And so, a good reason for a WFF item below the
'ᚺ' will indicate the kind of LAF of which this WFF item is being
thought of as the _____ item.

last

3-312 A WFF item below the 'ᚺ' for the sequence must be
thought of as the last item of a LAF. A good reason for such a
WFF item indicates two things:

1. *The kind of LAF* of which this WFF item is being thought of
as the _____ item, and

last

2. *Which preceding items* are being thought of as preceding
items of this _____ .

LAF

3-313

```
1 | Kpr      hyp
2 | Cpq      hyp
3 | p        1, Ko
4 | q        2, 3, Co
```

Item 3 is a WFF item _____ the 'ᚺ' for the sequence.

below

Item 3 is a '_____.' Item 1 is a '_____ pr.' Item 1 and item 3

p; K

are items of the same sequence, and item 1 _____

precedes

item 3. So, a '1, Ko' is a good reason for item 3, since item 3
can be thought of as the last item of a _____ LAF whose

Ko

first item is item _____ .

1

3-314

```
1 | Kpr      hyp
2 | Cpq      hyp
3 | p        1, Ko
4 | q        2, 3, Co
```

Item 4 is a WFF item _____ the 'ᚺ' for the sequence.

below

Item 4 is a '_____.' Item 2 is a '_____pq.' Item 3 is a '_____.'

q; C; p

Item 2, item 3, and item 4 are items of the same sequence,
and both item 2 and item 3 _____ item 4. So, a '2, 3, Co'

precede

is a good reason for item 4, since item 4 can be thought of as
the last item of a _____ LAF whose first item is item

Co

_____ and whose second item is item _____ .

2; 3

3-315 Every WFF item of a sequence is either _____ the 'ꞁ' for the sequence or _____ the 'ꞁ' for the sequence. A 'hyp' is a good reason for a WFF item of a sequence if and only if that WFF item is _____ the 'ꞁ' for the sequence. An indication of

1. The kind of LAF of which a WFF item is being thought of as the last item, and
2. Which preceding items are being thought of as preceding items of this LAF

is a good reason for a WFF item of a sequence if and only if that WFF item is _____ the 'ꞁ' for the sequence.

above
below

above

below

3-316

1	KpKqr	hyp
2	p	1, Ko
3	Kqr	1, Ko
4	r	3, Ko
5	Kpr	2, 4, Ki

Item 1 is a WFF item _____ the 'ꞁ' for the sequence. So, a 'hyp' is a good reason for item _____ .

above
1

3-317

1	KpKqr	hyp
2	p	1, Ko
3	Kqr	1, Ko
4	r	3, Ko
5	Kpr	2, 4, Ki

Item 2 is a WFF item _____ the 'ꞁ' for the sequence. Item 2 is a '_____.' Item 1 is a '_____pKqr.' Item 1 and item 2 are items of the same sequence, and item 1 _____ item 2. So, a '1, Ko' is a good reason for item 2, since item 2 can be thought of as the last item of a _____ LAF whose first item is item _____ .

below
p; K
precedes

Ko
1

3-318

1	KpKqr	hyp
2	p	1, Ko
3	Kqr	1, Ko
4	r	3, Ko
5	Kpr	2, 4, Ki

Item 3 is a WFF item _____ the 'ꞁ' for the sequence. Item 3 is a '_____.' Item 1 is a '_____pKqr.' Item 1 and item 3 are items of the same sequence, and item 1 _____ item 3. So, a '1, Ko' is a good reason for item 3, since item 3 can be thought of as the last item of a _____ LAF whose first item is item _____ .

below
Kqr; K
precedes

Ko
1

3-319

1	KpKqr	hyp
2	p	1, Ko
3	Kqr	1, Ko
4	r	3, Ko
5	Kpr	2, 4, Ki

Item 4 is a WFF item _____ the 'Ⱶ' for the sequence.   below
Item 4 is an '_____.' Item 3 is a '_____qr.' Item 3 and item 4   r; K
are items of the same sequence, and item 3 _____   precedes
item 4. So, a '_____Ko' is a good reason for item 4, since   3
item 4 can be thought of as the last item of a _____ LAF   Ko
whose first item is item _____ .   3

3-320

1	KpKqr	hyp
2	p	1, Ko
3	Kqr	1, Ko
4	r	3, Ko
5	Kpr	2, 4, Ki

Item 5 is a WFF item _____ the 'Ⱶ' for the sequence.   below
Item 5 is a '_____.' Item 2 is a '____.' Item 4 is an '____.'   Kpr; p; r
Item 2, item 4, and item 5 are items of the same sequence,
and both item 2 and item 4 precede item _____ . So, since   5
item 5 can be thought of as the last item of a Ki LAF whose
first item is item _____ and whose second item is item _____ ,   2; 4
a good reason for item 5 is a '_____ .'   2, 4, Ki

3-321   Every WFF item of a sequence is either above or else
below the 'Ⱶ' for that sequence. If the WFF item is above the
'Ⱶ' for the sequence, then a good reason for that item is a
'_____.' If the WFF item is below the 'Ⱶ' for the se-   hyp
quence, then that item must be thought of as the _____   last
item of a _____ , and a good reason for that item is an   LAF
indication of

1. The kind of _____ , and   LAF
2. Which preceding items are being thought of as preceding
   _____ of the LAF.   items

3-322   A sequence of items each of which has a good reason
is a _____ .   proof

C Some Proofs in System F

3-323 A proof is a sequence of _____ each of which has a good reason.

items

3-324 Items are of two kinds—WFF items and tail items. A WFF item is simply a _____ .

WFF

3-325 A proof is a sequence of items each of which has a good _____ .

reason

3-326 Every WFF item of a proof is either

1. Above the 'Ⱶ' for the proof and has as a good reason a '_____ ,' or

hyp

2. Below the 'Ⱶ' for the proof and can be thought of as the _____ item of a _____ .

last; LAF

3-327

1	KKpqr	_____	hyp
2	s	_____	hyp
3	Kpq	1, Ko	
4	q	3, Ko	
5	Kqs	4, 2, Ki	

The above is a sequence of how many WFF items? _____

5

3-328 Complete the following:

1	CKpqr	hyp	
2	p	hyp	
3	q	hyp	
4	Kpq	2, 3, _____	Ki
5	r	1, 4, _____	Co

Does each item in the above sequence have a good reason?

_____

yes[1]

---

[1] Because every item is a WFF which is either above the 'Ⱶ' for the sequence and has a 'hyp' as a good reason or else is below the 'Ⱶ' for the sequence and can be thought of as the last item of a LAF.

3-329

1	Cpq	hyp	
2	p	hyp	
3	q	1, 2, Co	
4	Kpq	_____ , _____ , _____	2; 3; Ki

The above sequence is a sequence of items, and each item has a good reason. Is the above sequence a proof? _____   yes

3-330

1	CArpq	hyp	
2	r	_____	hyp
3	Arp	2, Ai	
4	q	1, 3, _____	Co
5	Krq	_____ , _____ , _____	2; 4; Ki

The above sequence is a proof because it is a sequence of _____ , and each item has a good _____ .   items; reason

3-331

1	CpKrq	hyp	
2	p	hyp	
3	s	_____	hyp
4	Krq	_____ , _____ , Co	1; 2
5	r	_____ , Ko	4
6	Krs	_____ , _____ , Ki	5; 3
7	KKrsp	_____ , _____ , Ki	6; 2

Is the above sequence a proof? _____   yes

3-332

1	Cpq	hyp	
2	p	hyp	
3	q	1, 2, Co	
4	_____	2, 3, Ki	Kpq

Is the above sequence a proof? _____   yes

3-333

1	CKpqr	hyp	
2	p	hyp	
3	q	hyp	
4	_____	2, 3, Ki	Kpq
5	_____	1, 4, Co	r

Is the above sequence a proof? _____   yes

3-334

1	CArpq	hyp	
2	r	hyp	
3	Arp	2, Ai	
4	_____	1, 3, Co	q
5	_____	2, 4, Ki	Krq

Is the above sequence a proof? _____   yes

3-335

1	KKpqr	hyp	
2	s	hyp	
3	Kpq	_____ , _____	1; Ko
4	q	_____ , _____	3; Ko
5	_____	4, 2, Ki	Kqs

Is the above sequence a proof? _____   yes

3-336

1	CpKrq	hyp	
2	p	hyp	
3	s	hyp	
4	_____	1, 2, Co	Krq
5	r	_____ , Ko	4
6	_____	5, 3, Ki	Krs
7	_____	6, 2, Ki	KKrsp

This sequence is a proof because it is a sequence of _____ ,   items
and each _____ has a good reason.   item

3-337   A sequence of items each of which has a good reason
is a _____ .   proof

D   Good Reasons for Tail Items

3-338   A proof is a sequence of items each of which has a
good reason. Every item is either a WFF item or a tail item. We
know already what is a good reason for a WFF item. We consider now what is a good reason for a _____ item.   tail

3-339   A WFF item is simply a WFF, but a tail item is itself a
sequence of WFF items or a sequence of WFF items and tail
items. That is, a tail item is a sequence of _____ .   items

3-340

```
1 | Cpq              hyp
2 | 2.1 | r          hyp
  | 2.2 | Cpq        1, rep
  | 2.3 | 2.3.1 | p  hyp
  |     | 2.3.2 | q  2.2, 2.3.1, Co
  | 2.4 | Cpq        2.3, Ci
3 | CrCpq            2, Ci
```

The WFF items of the above proof are item _____ and item _____. The tail item of the above proof is item _____. The proof has how many items? _____ The WFF items of item 2 are item _____, item _____, and item _____. Item 2.3 of item 2 is a _____ item. Item 2 has how many items? _____

3-341 A tail item is itself a _____ of items.

3-342 A tail item has a good reason if each of its items has a good _____.

3-343 A tail item is a _____ of items. The items of a tail item are either WFF items or tail items. A tail item has a good reason if each of its _____ has a good reason.

3-344

```
1 | CCppr            hyp
2 | 2.1 | p          hyp
  | 2.2 | p          2.1, rep
3 | Cpp              2, Ci
4 | r                1, 3, Co
```

Item 1 is a WFF item of the sequence and is not below but is _____ the 'Ⱶ' for the sequence. So, a 'hyp' is a good reason for item _____.

3-345

```
1 | CCppr            hyp
2 | 2.1 | p          hyp
  | 2.2 | p          2.1, rep
3 | Cpp              2, Ci
4 | r                1, 3, Co
```

Item 2 is a tail item of the sequence. So, item 2 has a good reason if each _____ of item 2 has a good reason.

3-346

1	CCppr	hyp
2	2.1 p	hyp
	2.2 p	2.1, rep
3	Cpp	2, Ci
4	r	1, 3, Co

Item 2.1 is a WFF item of item 2 and is _____ the 'ⱶ' for

tail item 2. So, a 'hyp' is a good reason for item _____.

Item 2.2 is a WFF item of item 2 and is _____ the 'ⱶ' for

tail item 2. Item 2.2 is a '_____.' Item 2.1 is a '_____.' Item

2.1 and item 2.2 are items of the same sequence, the tail

item _____, and item 2.1 does not follow but does _____

item 2.2. So, a '2.1, rep' is a good reason for item 2.2, since

item 2.2 can be thought of as the last item of a _____

LAF whose first item is item _____. Since every item of

tail item 2 has a good reason, item _____ has a good reason.

above

2.1

below

p; p

2; precede

rep

2.1

2

3-347

1	CCppr	hyp
2	2.1 p	hyp
	2.2 p	2.1, rep
3	Cpp	2, Ci
4	r	1, 3, Co

Item 3 is a WFF item of the sequence and is _____ the

'ⱶ' for the sequence. Item 3 is a '_____.' Item 2 is a tail

item which has as its only item above the 'ⱶ' for item 2 a

'_____' and has as its last item a '_____.' Item 2 and item 3

are items of the same sequence, and item 2 does not follow

but does _____ item 3. So, a '2, Ci' is a good reason for

item 3, since item 3 can be thought of as the last item of a

_____ LAF whose first item is item _____.

below

Cpp

p; p

precede

Ci; 2

3-348

1	CCppr	hyp
2	2.1 p	hyp
	2.2 p	2.1, rep
3	Cpp	2, Ci
4	r	1, 3, Co

Item 4 is a WFF item of the sequence and is _____ the

'ⱶ' for the sequence.

Item 4 is an '_____.' Item 1 is a '_____Cppr.' Item 3 is

a '_____.' Item 1, item 3, and item 4 are items of the

same sequence, and both item 1 and item 3 precede item

_____. So, since item 4 can be thought of as the last item of

a Co LAF whose first item is item _____ and whose second

item is item _____, a good reason for item 4 is a '_____.'

below

r; C

Cpp

4

1

3; 1, 3, Co

3-349

```
1 | CCppr      hyp
2 | 2.1 | p     hyp
  |   2.2 | p    2.1, rep
3 | Cpp        2, Ci
4 | r          1, 3, Co
```

The above sequence is a proof because it is a sequence of items, and each _____ has a good _____ .

3-350

```
1 | AKpqKqr      hyp
2 | s            hyp
3 | 3.1 | Kpq    hyp
  |   3.2 | q     3.1, Ko
4 | 4.1 | Kqr    hyp
  |   4.2 | q     4.1, Ko
5 | q            1, 3, 4, Ao
6 | Kqs          5, 2, Ki
```

Item 1 is a WFF item of the sequence and is _____ the '⊢' for the sequence. So, a good reason for item 1 is a '_____.' Since item 2 is also a WFF item of the sequence and is above the '⊢' for the sequence, a 'hyp' is a good reason also for item _____ .

3-351

```
1 | AKpqKqr      hyp
2 | s            hyp
3 | 3.1 | Kpq    hyp
  |   3.2 | q     3.1, Ko
4 | 4.1 | Kqr    hyp
  |   4.2 | q     4.1, Ko
5 | q            1, 3, 4, Ao
6 | Kqs          5, 2, Ki
```

Item 3 is a tail item of the sequence. So, item 3 has a good reason if each _____ of item 3 has a good reason.

3-352

```
1 | AKpqKqr      hyp
2 | s            hyp
3 | 3.1 | Kpq    hyp
  | 3.2 | q      3.1, Ko
4 | 4.1 | Kqr    hyp
  | 4.2 | q      4.1, Ko
5 | q            1, 3, 4, Ao
6 | Kqs          5, 2, Ki
```

Item 3.1 is a WFF item of item 3 and is _____ the 'Ⱶ' for
item 3. So, a 'hyp' is a good reason for item _____ .
Item 3.2 is a WFF item of item 3 and is _____ the 'Ⱶ' for
item 3. Item 3.2 is a '_____.' Item 3.1 is a '_____pq.' Item 3.1
and item 3.2 are items of the same sequence, and item 3.1
_____ item 3.2. So, a '3.1, Ko' is a good reason for item
3.2, since item 3.2 can be thought of as the last item of a
_____ LAF whose first item is item _____ .

above
3.1
below
q; K

precedes

Ko; 3.1

3-353

```
1 | AKpqKqr      hyp
2 | s            hyp
3 | 3.1 | Kpq    hyp
  | 3.2 | q      3.1, Ko
4 | 4.1 | Kqr    hyp
  | 4.2 | q      4.1, Ko
5 | q            1, 3, 4, Ao
6 | Kqs          5, 2, Ki
```

Item 4 is a tail item of the sequence. So, item 4 has a good
reason if each item of item _____ has a good reason.

4

3-354

```
1 | AKpqKqr      hyp
2 | s            hyp
3 | 3.1 | Kpq    hyp
  | 3.2 | q      3.1, Ko
4 | 4.1 | Kqr    hyp
  | 4.2 | q      4.1, Ko
5 | q            1, 3, 4, Ao
6 | Kqs          5, 2, Ki
```

Item 4.1 is a WFF item of item 4 and is _____ the 'Ⱶ' for
item 4. So, a 'hyp' is a good reason for item _____ . Item
4.2 is a WFF item of item 4 and is _____ the 'Ⱶ' for item
4. Item 4.2 is a '_____.' Item 4.1 is a '_____qr.' Item 4.1 and
item 4.2 are items of the same sequence, and item 4.1
_____ item 4.2. So, a '4.1, Ko' is a good reason for item

above
4.1
below
q; K

precedes

4.2, since item 4.2 can be thought of as the last item of
a _____ LAF whose first item is item _____ . Since
every item of tail item 4 has a good reason, item _____ has
a good reason.

Ko; 4.1
4

3-355

1	AKpqKqr	hyp
2	s	hyp
3	3.1 | Kpq	hyp
	3.2 | q	3.1, Ko
4	4.1 | Kqr	hyp
	4.2 | q	4.1, Ko
5	q	1, 3, 4, Ao
6	Kqs	5, 2, Ki

Item 5 is a WFF item of the sequence and is _____ the
'Ⱶ' for the sequence. Item 5 is a '_____.' Item 1 is an
'_____KpqKqr.' Item 3 is a tail item whose only item above
the 'Ⱶ' for item 3 is a '_____' and whose last item is a
'_____.' Item 4 is a tail item whose only item above the 'Ⱶ' for
item 4 is a '_____' and whose last item is a '_____.' Item
1, item 3, item 4, and item 5 are items of the same sequence;
and items 1, 3, and 4 each _____ item 5. So, a '1, 3, 4,
Ao' is a good reason for item 5, since item 5 can be thought
of as the last item of an _____ LAF whose first item is
item _____, whose second item is item _____, and whose
third item is item _____ .

below
q
A
Kpq
q
Kqr; q

precedes

Ao
1; 3
4

3-356

1	AKpqKqr	hyp
2	s	hyp
3	3.1 | Kpq	hyp
	3.2 | q	3.1, Ko
4	4.1 | Kqr	hyp
	4.2 | q	4.1, Ko
5	q	1, 3, 4, Ao
6	Kqs	5, 2, Ki

Item 6 is a WFF item of the sequence and is _____ the
'Ⱶ' for the sequence. Item 6 is a '_____.' Item 5 is
a '_____.' Item 2 is a '_____.' Item 2, item 5, and item 6 are
all items of the same sequence; and both item 2 and item 5
_____ item 6. So, since item 6 can be thought of as the
last item of a Ki LAF whose first item is item _____ and whose
second item is item _____, a good reason for item 6 is a
'_____.'

below
Kqs
q; s

precede
5
2
5, 2, Ki

3-357

1	AKpqKqr	hyp
2	s	hyp
3	3.1 Kpq	hyp
	3.2 q	3.1, Ko
4	4.1 Kqr	hyp
	4.2 q	4.1, Ko
5	q	1, 3, 4, Ao
6	Kqs	5, 2, Ki

The above sequence is a sequence of _____. Each item has a good _____. So, the above sequence is a _____.

items

reason

proof

3-358 A proof is a sequence of items each of which has a good reason. Items are of two kinds:

1. _____ items, and
2. _____ items.

WFF

tail

3-359 A WFF item of a sequence has a good reason if

1. The item is above the 'ⱶ' for the _____ and so has a 'hyp as a good reason, or

2. The item is below the 'ⱶ' for the _____ and can be thought of as the last item of a LAF whose preceding items are preceding items of the same _____ (or preceding items in that sequence of which the *sequence* is an item).

A tail item is a sequence of items and has a good reason if each item of the _____ has a good reason.

sequence

sequence

sequence

sequence

E Some More Proofs in System F

3-360 Items are of two kinds:

1. _____ items, and
2. _____ items.

A tail item is itself a sequence of _____.

WFF

tail

items

3-361 1 | Cpq
    2 | 2.1 | r
       2.2 | Cpq
       2.3 | 2.3.1 | p
             2.3.2 | q
             2.3.3 | Atq
       2.4 | CpAtq
    3 | CrCpAtq

The above sequence has how many items? _____   three

3-362 1 | Cpq
    2 | 2.1 | r
       2.2 | Cpq
       2.3 | 2.3.1 | p
             2.3.2 | q
             2.3.3 | Atq
       2.4 | CpAtq
    3 | CrCpAtq

The above sequence has three items. The WFF items of the
sequence are item _____ and item _____. Item 2 of the   1; 3
sequence is a _____ item.   tail

3-363 1 | Cpq
    2 | 2.1 | r
       2.2 | Cpq
       2.3 | 2.3.1 | p
             2.3.2 | q
             2.3.3 | Atq
       2.4 | CpAtq
    3 | CrCpAtq

Item 2 is a tail item. Item 2 has how many items? _____   four

3-364 1 | Cpq
    2 | 2.1 | r
       2.2 | Cpq
       2.3 | 2.3.1 | p
             2.3.2 | q
             2.3.3 | Atq
       2.4 | CpAtq
    3 | CrCpAtq

Item 2 is a tail item and has four items. Item 2 has how many
WFF items? _____   three

3-365

```
1 | Cpq
2 | 2.1 | r
  | 2.2 | Cpq
  | 2.3 | 2.3.1 | p
  |     | 2.3.2 | q
  |     | 2.3.3 | Atq
  | 2.4 | CpAtq
3 | CrCpAtq
```

Item 2 is a tail item. Item 2 has three WFF items, but item 2.3
of item 2 is a _____ item.

tail

3-366 Items are of two kinds—WFF items and tail items.
A tail item is itself a sequence of items. Thus, a tail item may
have as items both WFF items and _____ items.

tail

3-367

```
1 | CpCqr
2 | 2.1 | Cpq
  | 2.2 | CpCqr
  | 2.3 | 2.3.1 | p
  |     | 2.3.2 | Cqr
  |     | 2.3.3 | q
  |     | 2.3.4 | r
  | 2.4 | Cpr
3 | CCpqCpr
```

The above sequence has how many WFF items? _____

The above sequence has how many tail items? _____

The above sequence has how many items? _____

two
one
three

3-368

```
1 | CpCqr
2 | 2.1 | Cpq
  | 2.2 | CpCqr
  | 2.3 | 2.3.1 | p
  |     | 2.3.2 | Cqr
  |     | 2.3.3 | q
  |     | 2.3.4 | r
  | 2.4 | Cpr
3 | CCpqCpr
```

Item 2 is a tail item. Item 2 has how many WFF items?
_____ Item 2 has how many tail items? _____ Item
2 has how many items? _____

three; one
four

3-369   1 | CpCqr
    2 | 2.1 | Cpq
        | 2.2 | CpCqr
        | 2.3 | 2.3.1 | p
        | | 2.3.2 | Cqr
        | | 2.3.3 | q
        | | 2.3.4 | r
        | 2.4 | Cpr
    3 | CCpqCpr

Item 2.3 is a tail item of item 2. Item 2.3 has how many WFF
items? _____ Item 2.3 has how many tail items?   four
_____ Item 2.3 has how many items? _____   none; four

3-370   1 | Cpq
    2 | 2.1 | r
        | 2.2 | Cpq
        | 2.3 | 2.3.1 | p
        | | 2.3.2 | q
        | | 2.3.3 | Atq
        | 2.4 | CpAtq
    3 | CrCpAtq

Which items are items of the sequence of which item 1 is an
item? Item _____ and item _____. Which items are items of   2; 3
the sequence of which item 2.1 is an item? Item _____,   2.2
item _____, and item _____.   2.3; 2.4

3-371   1 | Cpq
    2 | 2.1 | r
        | 2.2 | Cpq
        | 2.3 | 2.3.1 | p
        | | 2.3.2 | q
        | | 2.3.3 | Atq
        | 2.4 | CpAtq
    3 | CrCpAtq

Which items are items of the sequence of which item 3 is an
item and also precede item 3? Item _____ and item _____.   1; 2
Which items are items of the sequence of which item 2.4 is
an item and also precede item 2.4? Item _____, item   2.1
_____, and item _____. Which items are items of   2.2; 2.3
the sequence of which item 2.3.3 is an item and also precede
item 2.3.3? Item _____ and item _____.   2.3.1; 2.3.2

3-372 1 | Cpr
2 | Cqr
3 | Apq
4 | 4.1 | p
⎸ 4.2 | r
5 | 5.1 | q
⎸ 5.2 | r
6 | r

Which items are items of the sequence of which item 4.1 is an item? Item _____

4.2

3-373 1 | Cpr
2 | Cqr
3 | Apq
4 | 4.1 | p
⎸ 4.2 | r
5 | 5.1 | q
⎸ 5.2 | r
6 | r

The sequence of which item 5.2 is an item has how many items? _____

two

3-374 1 | Cpr
2 | Cqr
3 | Apq
4 | 4.1 | p
⎸ 4.2 | r
5 | 5.1 | q
⎸ 5.2 | r
6 | r

Which items are items of the sequence of which item 5 is an item and also precede item 5? Item _____, item _____, item _____, and item _____. Which items are items of the sequence of which item 5.2 is an item and also precede item 5.2? Item _____. Which items are items of the sequence of which item 4.2 is an item and also precede item 4.2? Item _____. How many items are items of the sequence of which item 4.1 is an item and also precede item 4.1? _____

1; 2
3; 4

5.1

4.1

3-375

```
1 │ Cpr
2 │ Cqr
3 │ Apq
4 │ 4.1 │ p
  │ 4.2 │ r
5 │ 5.1 │ q
  │ 5.2 │ r
6 │ r
```

Item 5.1 is an item of item 5. Which items are preceding items
of item 5? _____ Which items are preceding items of the
sequence of which item 5 is an item? Item _____, item _____,
item _____, and item _____.

1; 2

3; 4

3-376 Items are of two kinds—WFF items and tail items.
And a proof is a sequence of items each of which has a good
_____.

reason

3-377 Items are of two kinds—WFF items and tail items.

A WFF item of a sequence has a good reason if

1. The item is above the 'ŀ' for the _____ and so has a
'hyp' as a good reason, or

sequence

2. The item is below the 'ŀ' for the _____ and can be
thought of as the last item of a LAF whose preceding items are

sequence

     (a) preceding items of the same _____, or

sequence

     (b) preceding items in the sequence of which the
     sequence is an _____.

item

A tail item has a good reason if each _____ of the tail
item has a good reason.

item

3-378

1	Cpr	hyp
2	Cqr	hyp
3	Apq	hyp
4	4.1 p	hyp
	4.2 r	1, 4.1, Co
5	5.1 q	hyp
	5.2 r	2, 5.1, Co
6	r	3, 4, 5, Ao

The above sequence is a proof because it is a sequence of items each of which has a good reason. Why is a '2, 5.1, Co' a good reason for item 5.2? Item 5.2 is a WFF item of item 5 and is _____ the 'ⱶ' for item 5. Item 2 is a '_____qr.' Item 5.1 is a '_____.' Both item 2 and item 5.1 precede item 5.2. Further, item 5.1 is an item of the same sequence as item _____, and item 2 is an item of the same _____ as item 5. So, a '2, 5.1, Co' is a good reason for item 5.2 since item 5.2 can be thought of as the last item of a _____ LAF whose first item is item _____ and whose second item is item _____ .

below; C

q

5.2

sequence

Co; 2

5.1

3-379

1	Cpr	hyp
2	Cqr	hyp
3	Apq	hyp
4	4.1 p	hyp
	4.2 r	1, 4.1, Co
5	5.1 q	hyp
	5.2 r	2, 5.1, Co
6	r	3, 4, 5, Ao

A '4.2, rep' is *not* a good reason for item 5.2. Why?

1. Item 4.2 is *not* an item of item 5, and
2. Item 4.2 is *not* an item of the sequence of which item 5 is an _____ .

item

So, item 5.2 *cannot* be thought of as the last item of a rep LAF since item 4.2 is neither

1. A preceding item of the same sequence as item 5.2, nor
2. A preceding item of the sequence of which item _____ is an item.

5

3-380

1	p	_____
2	Apq	_____ , _____

hyp

1; Ai

3-381

1	q		hyp
2	2.1	p	_____	hyp
	2.2	Apq	2.1, _____	Ai
3	CpApq	2, Ci	
4	KqCpCpq	1, 3, Ki	

3-382

1	Krq	_____	hyp
2	r	_____ , _____	1; Ko

3-383

1	p	hyp	
2	2.1	Krq	_____	hyp
	2.2	r	_____ , _____	2.1; Ko
3	CKrqr	2, Ci	
4	KpCKrqr	1, 3, Ki	

3-384

1	s	_____	hyp
2	t	_____	hyp
3	Kst	1, 2, Ki	
4	4.1	r	_____	hyp
	4.2	Arp	_____ , _____	4.1; Ai
5	CrArp	4, Ci	
6	KKstCrArp	3, 5, Ki	

3-385

1	AqKqp	hyp	
2	2.1	q	_____	hyp
	2.2	q	_____ , rep	2.1
3	3.1	Kqp	_____	hyp
	3.2	q	_____ , Ko	3.1
4	q	1, 2, 3, Ao	

3-386

1	t	hyp	
2	ArKqs	hyp	
3	3.1	r	hyp	
	3.2	Arq	_____ , _____	3.1; Ai
4	4.1	Kqs	_____	hyp
	4.2	q	_____ , _____	4.1; Ko
	4.3	Arq	_____ , _____	4.2; Ai
5	Arq	2, 3, 4, Ao	
6	KtArq	1, 5, Ki	

3-387

```
1 | Csp          _____        hyp
2 | AsKqp        _____        hyp
3 | 3.1 | s
  |  3.2 | p
4 | 4.1 | Kqp
  |  4.2 | p
5 | p
```

3-388

```
1 | Csp          hyp
2 | AsKqp        hyp
3 | 3.1 | s
  |  3.2 | p
4 | 4.1 | Kqp
  |  4.2 | p
5 | p
```

A 'hyp' is a good reason for item 1 and for item 2 because item 1 and item 2 are both WFF items of the sequence and are _____ the '⊢' for the sequence.   above

3-389

```
1 | Csp          hyp
2 | AsKqp        hyp
3 | 3.1 | s      _____        hyp
  |  3.2 | p
4 | 4.1 | Kqp
  |  4.2 | p
5 | p
```

3-390

```
1 | Csp          hyp
2 | AsKqp        hyp
3 | 3.1 | s      hyp
  |  3.2 | p
4 | 4.1 | Kqp
  |  4.2 | p
5 | p
```

A 'hyp' is a good reason for item 3.1 of item 3 because item 3.1 is a WFF item of item _____ and is above the '⊢' for item _____ .   3
          3

3-391

```
1 | Csp            hyp
2 | AsKqp          hyp
3 | 3.1 | s        hyp
  |   3.2 | p      _____, _____, _____    1; 3.1; Co
4 | 4.1 | Kqp
  |   4.2 | p
5 | p
```

3-392

```
1 | Csp            hyp
2 | AsKqp          hyp
3 | 3.1 | s        hyp
  |   3.2 | p      1, 3.1, Co
4 | 4.1 | Kqp
  |   4.2 | p
5 | p
```

A '1, 3.1, Co' is a good reason for item 3.2 of item 3 because
item 3.2 is a WFF item of item 3 and is below the 'ⱶ' for item
_____ and can be thought of as the last item of a Co   3
_____ whose first item is item _____ and whose second   LAF; 1
item is item _____ .   3.1

3-393

```
1 | Csp            hyp
2 | AsKqp          hyp
3 | 3.1 | s        hyp
  |   3.2 | p      1, 3.1, Co
4 | 4.1 | Kqp      _____                       hyp
  |   4.2 | p
5 | p
```

3-394

```
1 | Csp            hyp
2 | AsKqp          hyp
3 | 3.1 | s        hyp
  |   3.2 | p      1, 3.1, Co
4 | 4.1 | Kqp      hyp
  |   4.2 | p
5 | p
```

A 'hyp' is a good reason for item 4.1 of item 4 because item
4.1 is a WFF item of item _____ and is above the 'ⱶ' for item   4
_____ .   4

3-395

1	Csp	hyp
2	AsKqp	hyp
3	3.1 s	hyp
	3.2 p	1, 3.1, Co
4	4.1 Kqp	hyp
	4.2 p	_____ , _____
5	p	

4.1; Ko

3-396

1	Csp	hyp
2	AsKqp	hyp
3	3.1 s	hyp
	3.2 p	1, 3.1, Co
4	4.1 Kqp	hyp
	4.2 p	4.1, Ko
5	p	

A '4.1, Ko' is a good reason for item 4.2 because item 4.2 is
a WFF item of item 4 and is below the 'ᚼ' for item _____ and
can be thought of as the last item of a Ko _____ whose
first item is item _____ .

4
LAF
4.1

3-397

1	Csp	hyp
2	AsKqp	hyp
3	3.1 s	hyp
	3.2 p	1, 3.1, Co
4	4.1 Kqp	hyp
	4.2 p	4.1, Ko
5	p	_____ , _____ , _____ , _____

2; 3; 4; Ao

3-398

1	Csp	hyp
2	AsKqp	hyp
3	3.1 s	hyp
	3.2 p	1, 3.1, Co
4	4.1 Kqp	hyp
	4.2 p	4.1, Ko
5	p	2, 3, 4, Ao

A '2, 3, 4, Ao' is a good reason for item 5 because item 5 is
a _____ item of the sequence and is below the '_____'
for the sequence and can be thought of as the last item of an
Ao _____ whose first item is item _____, whose second
item is item _____, and whose third item is item _____ .

WFF; ᚼ

LAF; 2
3; 4

3-399 Items are of two kinds—WFF items and tail items. A WFF item of a sequence has a good reason if

1. The item is above the 'Ͱ' for the _____ and so has a 'hyp' as a good reason, or

sequence

2. The item is below the 'Ͱ' for the _____ and can be thought of as the last item of a LAF whose preceding items are

sequence

  (*a*) preceding items of the same _____, or

sequence

  (*b*) preceding items in the sequence of which the *sequence* is an _____.

item

A tail item has a good reason if each _____ of the tail item has a good reason.

item

3-400 Items are of two kinds—WFF items and tail items. And a sequence of items each of which has a good reason is a _____ .

proof

3-401 Given any sequence of items we can now decide whether that sequence is a proof in system F. For if every item has a good reason the sequence is a proof, and every item is either a WFF item or a tail item. A WFF item of a sequence has a good reason if and only if

1. The WFF item is above the 'Ͱ' for the sequence and has as a reason a '_____,' or

hyp

2. The WFF item is below the 'Ͱ' for the sequence and can be thought of as the last item of one of these nine kinds of LAFs

_____ LAFs	_____ LAFs	Ki	Ko
_____ LAFs	_____ LAFs	Ai	Ao
_____ LAFs	_____ LAFs	Ci	Co
_____ LAFs	_____ LAFs	Ni	No
_____ LAFs		rep	

where the preceding items of the LAF are

  (*a*) preceding items of the same sequence, or

  (*b*) preceding items in the sequence of which the sequence is an item.

A tail item has a good reason if and only if each of its _____ has a good reason, and the items of the tail item will be either WFF items, about whose reasons we can decide, or else _____ items, which have good reasons if and

items

tail

only if each of *their* _____ has a good reason, and so on. And eventually we can always decide whether or not a tail item has a good reason, since eventually we will come to a tail item none of whose items are tail items but all of whose items are _____ items, about whose reasons we can decide.

items

WFF

3-402   Because given any sequence of items we can always decide whether or not each of the items has a good reason, we have effectively specified the _____ in system F, for a proof is a sequence of _____ each of which has a good _____ .

proofs
items
reason

Summary of Part 3

3-403   We have now adequately described system F, for we have specified

1. The _____ in system F,
2. The _____ in system F,
3. The _____ in system F, and
4. The _____ in system F.

3-404   But why are we interested in system F? Because we are proposing a redefinition of valid argument in terms of the systematic treatment of LAFs provided by the logical system F. But why offer another definition of valid argument? A redefinition is offered for the following reason. If we realize that a valid argument is one whose conclusion not only is said to follow but actually does follow from the premises, we have a basic understanding of validity. Still, this characterization of valid argument may well be a less than adequate guide in deciding validity, both when an argument is complicated and when an argument's validity is to be established for another person.

The proposed redefinition is this:

A valid argument is an argument that can be formalized by an _____ that corresponds to a _____ in system F.

3-405   This redefinition of valid argument in terms of system F proposes that an argument is valid if and only if it can be formalized by a LAF of system F or if there is some proof in system F whose only hypotheses are formalizations of the argument's _____ and whose last item is a _____ of the argument's conclusion.

3-406   The redefinition in terms of system F amounts to maintaining the difficulty of denying that an argument could be formalized by a LAF of the system and yet be such that the conclusion does not follow from the premises, and maintaining further that an argument's conclusion follows from its premises if and only if the argument's form is a LAF or else it is possible to proceed from the argument's premises to its conclusion by using only arguments whose forms are _____ .

3-407   We know that an AF is an argument formula and we know how to formalize an argument, given its representation. So we can use system F in deciding an argument's validity once we know how an AF _____ to a proof in system F.   corresponds

Exercises for Part 3

1   For each of the following specifications, write a LAF of system F—provided the specifications are consistent with LAFs as specified in system F.

   a   A Ki LAF whose last item is a 'KCNtpNq'

   b   A Ki LAF whose first item is a 'q'

   c   A Ki LAF whose last item is a 'q'

   d   A Ki LAF whose second item is a 'q'

   e   A Ko LAF whose last item is a 'Krt'

   f   A Ko LAF whose first item is a 'q'

   g   A Ko LAF whose last item is a 'q'

   h   A Ko LAF with exactly three items

   i   A Ki LAF with exactly two items

   j   A Ko LAF whose first item is of length two—that is, contains exactly two symbols

   k   An Ai LAF whose last item is an 'Apq'

   l   An Ai LAF whose first item is an 'r'

   m   Two unlike Ai LAFs whose last item is an 'ApKrs'

   n   An Ao LAF whose last item is a 'Ctr'

   o   An Ao LAF such that the last item of the second item is a 'Ctr'

  p   An Ao LAF whose first item is an 'AKrsArr' (An '' preceding an exercise indicates that the exercise is of special difficulty.)

   q   An Ao LAF such that the last item of the third item is a 'Ctr'

   r   An Ao LAF such that the first item of the second item is a 'p'

   s   An Ao LAF such that the first item of the third item is a 't'

   t   An Ao LAF that has exactly five items

   u   A Ci LAF whose last item is a 'Kpq'

   v   A Ci LAF whose last item is a 'Cpp'

   w   A Ci LAF such that the first item of the first item is a 'AKpqKrq'

   x   A Ci LAF whose last item is a 'CKpqApr'

   y   A Ci LAF whose first item is a 'p'

   z   A Co LAF whose second item is a 'Cpq'

  aa   A Co LAF whose first item is a 'Cpq'

  bb   A Co LAF whose last item is a 'Cpq'

  cc   A Co LAF whose first item is a 'KpCqt'

  dd   An Ni LAF whose last item is an 'NKApqNApq'

  *ee   An Ni LAF such that the first item of the first item is an 'NCpp'

  ff   An Ni LAF such that the last item of the first item has exactly one connective

  gg   An Ni LAF whose last item is an 'NKCpqKpNq'

  hh   An Ni LAF whose last item is an 'NKKpqNApq'

ii An No LAF whose first item is an 'Np'

jj An No LAF whose last item is an 'NKpNp'

kk An No LAF whose last item is a 'CKpqApq'

ll An No LAF such that the last item of the first item contains exactly one 'N'

mm An No LAF such that the last item of the first item contains no connectives.

nn A rep LAF whose first item contains exactly half as many symbols as does the last item

oo A rep LAF whose last item begins with a connective

pp A rep LAF whose last item does not begin with a connective

qq A rep LAF whose first item begins with a connective

rr A rep LAF whose first item does not begin with a 'K,' or an 'A,' or a 'C,' or an 'N'

2 Sometimes we find it useful to explore the consequences of one or more alternatives even though we do not know which of the alternatives is the case or should be the case. What device in system F parallels this maneuver of natural reason?

3 System F can be described as a natural deduction formulation of sentential calculus. What is "natural" about system F? Why do we call system F a sentential calculus? Would "connecting-word calculus" be a good description of system F?

4 Sometimes when we have difficulty in establishing some thesis directly, we resort to showing that did the thesis not hold, a contradiction—that is, an absurdity—would result. So we argue that the thesis must hold even though we cannot establish it directly. This mode of "establishing" has been called traditionally "indirect proof," or "proof by reduction to the absurd," or sometimes simply *"reductio ad absurdum,"* or even more simply *"reductio."* What in system F reflects this traditional mode of arguing?

5 Suppose we think of system F as a class of classes of expressions—that is, as the class of these classes: class of symbols, class of WFFs, class of LAFs, class of proofs. What would be the advantages? The disadvantages?

6 System F is called a logical system because it offers a systematic treatment of LAFs. What is systematic about the treatment? What are the advantages of being systematic?

7 It seems difficult to deny that any argument that could be formalized by the AF

> | Cpq
> | Nq
> |— Np

is a valid argument, and so according to the definition of LAF in Part 2 the AF would be a LAF. But is this AF a LAF of system F? Is there in system F a proof that has as its only hypotheses WFFs like those above the '⊢' of this AF and has as last item a WFF like the WFF below the '⊢'? Relate your answers here to the notion of F as a *system.*

8 Why can we be sure we can always finally arrive at a decision as to whether or not a tail item has a good reason despite what might seem circular about saying that a tail item has a good reason if all the items of the tail item do—especially when some of these items themselves may be tail items?

9 Specify the symbols, WFFs, and LAFs in a system, call it PF, that resembles system F in every respect except that PF uses *Principia* notation. For instance, among the symbols of PF will be '&'s, '∨'s, '⊃'s, '~'s, '('s (left parentheses), and ')'s (right parentheses). Compare exercises 2, 3, 4 of Part 1 and exercises 9, 10 of Part 2.

10 Here is a proof in system PF:

1	(p ∨ q) ⊃ r	hyp
2	t & (~r)	hyp
3	s	hyp
4	4.1 q	hyp
	4.2 p ∨ q	4.1, ∨-in*
	4.3 r	1, 4.2, ⊃-out**
	4.4 ~r	2, &-out
	4.5 r & (~r)	4.3, 4.4, &-in
5	~q	4, ~-in

Write a parallel proof in system F.

(*In-LAFs might be called introduction LAFs or int LAFs. Compare F. B. Fitch, *Symbolic Logic*, chap. 2.)

(**Out-LAFs might be called elimination LAFs or elim LAFs. Compare F. B. Fitch, *Symbolic Logic*, chap. 2.)

11 Here is a proof in system F:

1	Crs	hyp
2	Ns	hyp
3	3.1 r	hyp
	3.2 s	1, 3.1, Co
	3.3 KsNs	3.2, 2, Ki
4	Nr	3, Ni

Write a parallel proof in system PF.

Achievement Test for Part 3

1   **a**   If the conclusion of an argument actually follows from the premisses of an argument, then the argument is valid.

     b   If an argument corresponds to a proof in system F, then the argument is valid.

     c   If an argument can be formalized by an argument formula that corresponds to a proof in system F, then that argument is valid.

     Which of the above are true? _____ _____

2   We specify system F by specifying:

         the _____ in system F,

         the _____ in system F,

         the _____ in system F, and

         the _____ in system F.

3   Every symbol in system F is either

         a _____ , or

         a _____ , or

         a '_____'-indicator

4   Put a check ($\sqrt{}$) in front of each of the following which is a sentence variable in system F, and put a cross ($\times$) in front of each of the following which is not a sentence variable in system F.

     a ____ R   **c** ____ i   **e** ____ K   **g** ____ ⊦   **i** ____ t

     b ____ r   **d** ____ o   **f** ____ q   **h** ____ C   **j** ____ s

5   Put a check ($\sqrt{}$) in front of each of the following which is a connective in system F, and put a cross ($\times$) in front of each of the following which is not a connective in system F.

     a ____ R   **c** ____ ⊦   **e** ____ A   **g** ____ N   **i** ____ E

     b ____ C   **d** ____ s   **f** ____ t   **h** ____ K   **j** ____ i

6   Put a check ($\sqrt{}$) in front of each of the following which is a symbol in system F, and put a cross ($\times$) in front of each of the following which is not a symbol in system F.

     a ____ p   **c** ____ r   **e** ____ t   **g** ____ K   **i** ____ C

     b ____ q   **d** ____ s   **f** ____ ⊦   **h** ____ A   **j** ____ N

7   Put a check ($\sqrt{}$) in front of each of the following which is a WFF in system F, and put a cross ($\times$) in front of each of the following which is not a WFF in system F.

     a ____ q   **d** ____ Cqt   **g** ____ st   **j** ____ p ⊃ q

     b ____ CpCrs   **e** ____ Npq   **h** ____ NNACKptqr   **k** ____ Np ∨ r

     c ____ Nr   **f** ____ NArp   **i** ____ (p) ∨ & t   **l** ____ KApqNr

8 What are the nine kinds of logical argument formulas in system F?

_____   _____

_____   _____

_____   _____

_____

9 **a** Name the kinds of LAFs with exactly one item. _____

 b Name the kinds of LAFs with exactly two items. _____

 c Name the kinds of LAFs with exactly three items. _____

 d Name the kinds of LAFs with exactly four items. _____

 e Name the kinds of LAFs with more than four items. _____

 f Name the kinds of LAFs that have no tail items. _____

 g Name the kinds of LAFs that have exactly one tail item. _____

 h Name the kinds of LAFs that have exactly two tail items. _____

 i Name the kinds of LAFs that have more than two tail items. _____

 j Name the kinds of LAFs that have exactly one tail item such that the last item of the tail item must begin with a 'K.' _____

 k Name the kinds of LAFs whose last item *could* begin with a 'K.' _____

 l Name the only kinds of LAFs whose last item *could not* begin with an 'A.' _____

 m Name the kinds of LAFs whose first item *could* begin with a 'C.' _____

 n Name the only kinds of LAFs whose first item *could not* begin with an 'N.'

_____

10 An argument is a sequence of _____, whereas a proof is a sequence of

_____ .

11 **a** A proof is a sequence of WFFs.

 b A proof is a sequence of items.

 c A tail item is a sequence of WFFs.

 d A tail item is a sequence of items.

 Which of the above are true? _____ _____

12 **a**

1	CPQ	hyp
2	p	hyp
3	r	hyp
4	q	1, 4, Co
5	Kqr	4, 3, Ki

 Why is the above sequence not a proof? _____

 b

1	Kpq	hyp
2	2.1 | r	hyp
	2.2 | t	
3	Crt	2, Ci

 Why is the above sequence not a proof? _____

13 Put a check (√) in front of each of the following which is a WFF in system F, and put a cross (×) in front of each of the following which is not a WFF in system F.

 a _____ AqKrt   **c** _____ NCpqr   **e** _____ CKApqNtr

 b _____ KtCpCqs   **d** _____ NNKNrt   **f** _____ CtAtKNpq

14 For each of these LAFs supply a good reason for the last item.

a 1 | p
    2 | q
    3 | Kpq   _____

b 1 | Kpq
    2 | p   _____

c 1 | AKpqKqr
    2 | 2.1 | Kpq
        | 2.2 | q   2.1, Ko
    3 | 3.1 | Kqr
        | 3.2 | q   3.1, Ko
    4 | q   _____

d 1 | p
    2 | Apq   _____

e 1 | 1.1 | p
        | 1.2 | Apq   1.1, Ai
    2 | CpApq   _____

f 1 | Cpq
    2 | p
    3 | q   _____

g 1 | 1.1 | NCpKpp
        | 1.2 | 1.2.1 | p
        | | 1.2.2 | Kpp   1.2.1, 1.2.1, Ki
        | 1.3 | CpKpp   1.2, Ci
        | 1.4 | KCpKppNCpKpp   1.3, 1.1, Ki
    2 | CpKpp   _____

h 1 | 1.1 | KpCpKqNq
        | 1.2 | p   1.1, Ko
        | 1.3 | CpKqNq   1.1, Ko
        | 1.4 | KqNq   1.3, 1.2, Co
    2 | NKpCpKqNq   _____

i 1 | p
    2 | p   _____

j 1 | Krs
    2 | Krs   _____

15 Put a check (√) in front of each of the following which is a *contradictory WFF*.
Put a cross (×) in front of each of the following which is not a contradictory WFF.

a _____ Sue sings and it is false that Sue sings.

b _____ KpNp

c _____ KNpNNp

d _____ KpNNp

e _____ Sue sings or it is false that Sue sings.

16 Which of the following are contradictions?

    a Sue sings and it is false that Sue sings.

    b KpNp

    c KNpNNp

    d KpNNp

    e Sue sings or it is false that Sue sings.

_____

17 Consider the following proof:

```
1 │ KApKqps      hyp
2 │ ApKqp        1, Ko
3 │ 3.1 │ p      hyp
  │ 3.2 │ p      3.1, rep
4 │ 4.1 │ Kqp    hyp
  │ 4.2 │ p      4.1, Ko
5 │ p            2, 3, 4, Ao
```

    a The WFF items of this proof are item _____, item _____, and item _____.

    b The tail items of this proof are item _____ and item _____.

    c Is item 4.2 an item of the proof? _____

18 Complete the following:

    a
```
1 │ r            _____
2 │ CrKpt        _____
3 │ Kpt          _____, _____, _____
4 │ p            _____, _____
```

    b
```
1 │ t            _____
2 │ Ksr          _____
3 │ CKstKpq      _____
4 │ s            _____, _____
5 │ Kst          _____, _____, _____
6 │ Kpq          _____, _____, _____
```

19 Every WFF item of a proof is either

    a above the 'Ⱶ' of the proof and has as a good reason a _____; or

    b below the 'Ⱶ' of the proof and can be thought of as the _____ item of a LAF.

20 A WFF item of a tail item has a good reason if the WFF item is above the 'Ⱶ' of the _____ item and has as a reason a '_____.'

21 A WFF item of a tail item can be given a good reason if the WFF item is below the 'Ⱶ' of the tail item and can be thought of as the last item of a LAF whose other items are

    a preceding items of the _____ item, or

    b preceding items of the sequence of which the tail item is an _____.

22 Complete the following:

a 1 | CCpKppq _____

2 | 2.1 | p _____

2.2 | Kpp 2.1, 2.1, _____

3 | CpKpp _____ , _____

4 | q _____ , _____ , _____

b 1 | p _____

2 | CApqt _____

3 | _____ _____

4 | t 2, 3, _____

23 Put a check (√) before each of the following which is a formalization of a sentence. Put a cross (×) in front of each of the following which is a sentence.

a _____ Tim thinks.

b _____ q

c _____ CKrsCtq

d _____ qt

e _____ Charles the Bald

24 **a** There are sentences in system F.

b There are formalizations of sentences in system F.

c There are WFFs in system F.

d There are sentences in system F and there are formalizations of sentences in system F.

Which of the above are true? _____ _____

25 **a** There are WFFs in the LAFs of system F.

b There are sentences in the LAFs of system F.

c There are WFFs in the proofs of system F.

d There are sentences in the proofs of system F.

Which of the above are true? _____ _____

Part **4**

Applying System F Definition of Validity: Search for Correspondent Proofs

AFs and Correspondent Proofs

4-1 An argument is valid if it has at least one AF that corresponds to a proof in system F. We know what an AF is, and we know what a proof in system F is. Now let's see how an AF can _____ to a proof in system F.

correspond

4-2 An AF is an argument formula, that is, a formalization of an argument. In an AF

1. The formalizations of the premisses are _____ the 'Ⱶ' for tho ΛF, and

above

2. Below the 'Ⱶ' for the AF is the formalization of the _____ of the argument.

conclusion

4-3 An AF corresponds to a proof in system F if

1. The items above the 'Ⱶ' for the AF are just like the items above the 'Ⱶ' for the proof, and
2. The item below the 'Ⱶ' for the AF is just like the last item of the _____ .

proof

4-4 Write an AF that corresponds to the proof

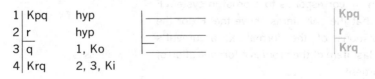

1	Kpq	hyp
2	r	hyp
3	q	1, Ko
4	Krq	2, 3, Ki

Kpq
r
Krq

4-5   The AF

> Kpq
>
> r
> ⊢
> Krq

corresponds to the proof

1	Kpq	hyp
2	r	hyp
3	q	1, Ko
4	Krq	2, 3, Ki

because

1. The items above the '⊢' for the AF are just like the items
   _____ the '⊢' for the _____ , and
2. The item below the '⊢' for the AF is just like the _____
   item of the _____ .

4-6   Write an AF that corresponds to the proof

1	Krs	hyp	_____
2	Csp	hyp	_____
3	s	1, Ko	⊢ _____
4	p	2, 3, Co	

4-7   Write an AF that corresponds to the proof

1	r	hyp	_____
2	p	hyp	_____
3	CKprq	hyp	_____
4	Kpr	2, 1, Ki	⊢ _____
5	q	3, 4, Co	
6	Aqs	5, Ai	

4-8   An argument is valid if it has at least one AF that
_____ to a proof in system F.

4-9   To say that an AF corresponds to a proof in system F
amounts to saying that the only items above the '⊢' for the
proof are formalizations of the formalized argument's
_____ and the last item of the proof is a formalization of
the formalized argument's _____ .

Plodding Search for
Correspondent Proofs

4-10   We can tell when a sequence of items is a proof, for we can tell if each of the items has a good reason. And we can tell when an AF corresponds to a proof, for we can tell if

1. The items above the 'Ⱶ' for the AF are just like the items above the 'Ⱶ' for the _____ , and

proof

2. The item below the 'Ⱶ' for the AF is just like the _____ item of the _____ .

last

proof

4-11   An argument is valid if it can be formalized by an AF that corresponds to a proof in system F. Given an AF and *given* a proof, we can tell if the AF corresponds to the proof. But there is another question that must be considered: Given an AF, how can we tell whether or not there *is* a proof in system F that _____ to that AF?

corresponds

4-12   Given an AF, we know there is a proof that corresponds to that AF if we can produce some sequence of items such that

1. Items like the items above the 'Ⱶ' for the AF are the only items _____ the 'Ⱶ' for the sequence, and

above

2. The last item of the sequence is like the item _____ the 'Ⱶ' for the AF,

below

and such that

3. Every _____ of the sequence has a good _____ .

item; reason

4-13   Next we learn an appropriate strategy to follow in trying to use system F to decide an argument's validity. That is, we need to know how to proceed when, given a formalization of that argument—an AF—we are trying to produce a proof that corresponds to that _____ .

AF

4-14   Let's see how we go about discovering whether there is a proof that corresponds to the AF

> | Cpq
> | p
> | Cqs
> |— q

Any proof that corresponds to this AF will have as the only items above its '⊢'

1. a 'Cpq,' then
2. a '_____,' and then
3. a '_____.'

Moreover, the proof would have as its last item a '_____.'

p

Cqs

q

4-15   Consider the AF

> | Cpq
> | p
> | Cqs
> |— q

Now consider the sequence of items

> 1 | Cpq
> 2 | p
> 3 | Cqs
> |——
> last | q

We will know that there is a proof corresponding to the above AF if

1. We can give a good reason for every item of the sequence and so know that the sequence is a _____, or else
2. We can produce a sequence that is a proof corresponding to the AF by adding items to the sequence but without adding any items _____ the '⊢' for the sequence nor below the _____ item of the sequence.

proof

above

last

4-16   Consider the sequence

```
1 | Cpq
2 | p
3 | Cqs
  |
last | q
```

We want to discern if this sequence is a proof or, if not, whether we can add items below the 'ⱶ' but above the last item to produce a sequence that is a proof and moreover a proof that corresponds to the AF given above. We will know this sequence is a proof if every _____ of the sequence can be given a good _____ .

item

reason

4-17
```
1 | Cpq
2 | p
3 | Cqs
  |
last | q
```

Item 1 is a WFF item of the sequence and is above the 'ⱶ' for the sequence; so, a good reason for item 1 is a '_____.'   hyp
Item 2 is a WFF item of the sequence and is above the 'ⱶ' for the sequence; so, a good reason for item 2 is a '_____.'   hyp
Item 3 is a WFF item of the sequence and is above the 'ⱶ' for the sequence; so, a good reason for item 3 is a '_____.'   hyp
The last item is a WFF item of the sequence and is below the 'ⱶ' for the sequence; so, we can give a good reason for the last item if we can think of it as the last item of a _____   LAF
whose other items are

1. _____ items of the sequence, or   Preceding
2. Preceding items of the sequence of which the sequence is an item. (But of course, in this instance there are no such items.)

4-18

$$\begin{array}{ll} 1 & \text{Cpq} \quad \text{hyp} \\ 2 & \text{p} \quad\ \ \ \text{hyp} \\ 3 & \text{Cqs} \quad \text{hyp} \\ \text{last} & \text{q} \end{array}$$

To give a good reason for the last item we must be able to think of it as the last item of a LAF of one of these nine kinds:

rep LAFs

Ki LAFs	Ko LAFs		
_____ LAFs	_____ LAFs	Ai	Ao
_____ LAFs	_____ LAFs	Ci	Co
_____ LAFs	_____ LAFs	Ni	No

4-19

$$\begin{array}{lll} 1 & \text{Cpq} & \text{hyp} \\ 2 & \text{p} & \text{hyp} \\ 3 & \text{Cqs} & \text{hyp} \\ \text{last} & \text{q} & ? \end{array}$$

We could think of the last item of the sequence as the last item of a rep LAF if there were in the sequence a WFF item that

1. Precedes the '____' (the last item),   q
2. Is an item just like a '____,' and   q
3. Has a good _____ .   reason

Is there any such item in the sequence? _____ Can we,   no
then, think of the last item of this sequence as the last item
of a rep LAF? _____   no

4-20

$$\begin{array}{lll} 1 & \text{Cpq} & \text{hyp} \\ 2 & \text{p} & \text{hyp} \\ 3 & \text{Cqs} & \text{hyp} \\ \text{last} & \text{q} & ? \end{array}$$

We could think of the last item of the sequence as the last item of a Ki LAF if the last item were a '____' followed by two   K
WFFs each of which is like some preceding item of the sequence and these preceding items have good reasons. But without even looking at the preceding items we know we

cannot think of the 'q' as the last item of a Ki LAF, because the
last item of every Ki LAF begins with a connective '_____' and   K
a 'q' does not begin with a connective '_____.'   K

4-21 1 | Cpq   hyp
     2 | p   hyp
     3 | Cqs   hyp

   last | q   ?

We could think of the last item of the sequence as the last
item of an Ai LAF if the last item were an '_____' followed by   A
two WFFs one of which is like some preceding item of the
sequence and that preceding item has a good reason. But
without even looking at the preceding items we know we
cannot think of the 'q' as the last item of an Ai LAF, because
the last item of every Ai LAF begins with a connective '_____'   A
and a 'q' does not begin with a connective '_____.'   A

4-22 1 | Cpq   hyp
     2 | p   hyp
     3 | Cqs   hyp

   last | q   ?

We could think of the last item of the sequence as the last
item of a Ci LAF if the last item were a '_____' followed by two C
WFFs and there were in the sequence a tail item that

1. Precedes the last item of the sequence,
2. Has as its only item above the 'ⱶ' for the tail item a WFF
like the _____ WFF following the 'C,'   first
3. Has as its last item a WFF like the _____ WFF follow-   second
ing the 'C', and
4. Each _____ of the tail item has a good _____ .   item; reason

But without looking at any preceding items we know that we
cannot think of the 'q' as the last item of a Ci LAF, because
the last item of every Ci LAF begins with a connective '_____'   C
and a 'q' does not begin with a connective '_____.'   C

4-23   1 | Cpq   hyp
    2 | p   hyp
    3 | Cqs   hyp

last | q   ?

We could think of the last item of the sequence as the last
item of an Ni LAF if the last item were an '____' followed by   N
one WFF and there were in the sequence a tail item that

1. _____ the last item of the sequence,   Precedes
2. Has as its only item above the 'Ⱶ' for the tail item a WFF
like the WFF following the '____' in the last item,   N
3. Has as its last item a _____ WFF, and   contradictory
4. Each _____ of the tail item has a good _____.   item; reason

But without even looking at the preceding items we know we
cannot think of the 'q' as the last item of an Ni LAF, because
the last item of every Ni LAF begins with a connective '____'   N
and a 'q' does not begin with a connective '____.'   N

4-24   1 | Cpq   hyp
    2 | p   hyp
    3 | Cqs   hyp

last | q   ?

We could not think of the last item of the sequence as the last
item of a rep LAF or of any in-LAF, for the only kinds of in-LAFs
are Ki, Ai, Ci, and Ni LAFs. So, if we are to give a good reason
for the last item of the sequence we must be able to think of
the item as the last item of some _____ -LAF. There are   out
four kinds of out-LAFs—____o LAFs, ____o LAFs, ____o   K; A; C
LAFs, and ____o LAFs.   N

4-25   1 | Cpq   hyp
    2 | p   hyp
    3 | Cqs   hyp

last | q   ?

We could think of the last item of the sequence as the last
item of a Ko LAF if there were in the sequence a WFF item that

1. _____ the last item of the sequence,   Precedes
2. Is a 'K' followed by two WFFs one of which is just like the
_____ item of the sequence, and   last
3. Has a good _____ .   reason
Is there such an item in the sequence? _____ Can we,   no
then, think of the last item of the sequence as the last item of
a Ko LAF? _____   no

4-26 $\;$ 1 | Cpq $\quad$ hyp
$\qquad$ 2 | p $\qquad$ hyp
$\qquad$ 3 | Cqs $\quad$ hyp

$\quad$ last | q $\qquad$?

We could think of the last item of the sequence as the last
item of an Ao LAF if there were in the sequence a WFF item
and two tail items such that

1. The three items all _____ the last item,   precede
2. The WFF item is an '____' followed by two WFFs,   A
3. The *first* tail item has as its only item above the '⊢' for the
tail item a WFF like the _____ WFF following the 'A' and   first
has as its last item a WFF like the _____ item of the   last
sequence,
4. The *second* tail item has as its only item above the '⊢' for
the tail item a WFF like the _____ WFF following the 'A'   second
and has as its last item a WFF like the _____ item of the   last
sequence, and
5. The WFF item has a good reason, and every item of the two
_____ items has a good _____ .   tail; reason

Are there any such three items in the sequence? _____   no
Can we, then, think of the last item of the sequence as the last
item of an Ao LAF? _____   no

4-27

```
   1 | Cpq    hyp
   2 | p      hyp
   3 | Cqs    hyp
     └
last | q      ?
```

We have been unable to think of the last item of the sequence as the last item of any

rep LAF

    Ki LAF   Ko LAF

    Ai LAF   Ao LAF

    Ci LAF

    Ni LAF

So, to give a good reason for the last item of the sequence we must be able to think of the last item as the last item of a _____ LAF or of an _____ LAF.

Co; No

4-28

```
   1 | Cpq    hyp
   2 | p      hyp
   3 | Cqs    hyp
     └
last | q      ?
```

We could think of the last item of the sequence as the last item of a Co LAF if there were in the sequence two WFF items such that

1. One item is a '_____' followed by two WFFs the second of which is like the _____ item of the sequence,

C
last

2. The other item is a WFF like the _____ WFF following the 'C,'

first

3. Both items precede the _____ item of the sequence, and

last

4. Both WFF _____ have good _____.

items; reasons

Are there any such two items in the sequence? _____
Can we, then, think of the last item of the sequence as the last item of a Co LAF? _____ So, a good reason for the last item of the sequence is a '_____.'

yes
yes
1, 2, Co

4-29

```
   1 | Cpq    hyp
   2 | p      hyp
   3 | Cqs    hyp
   4 | q      1, 2, Co
```

Every item of this sequence of items has a good reason; so the sequence is a _____.

proof

4-30

```
1 | Cpq      hyp
2 | p        hyp
3 | Cqs      hyp
4 | q        1, 2, Co
```

The above sequence is a proof, so every argument that can be
formalized by the AF

```
| Cpq
| p
| Cqs
|‾q
```

is a valid argument because this AF _____ to a   corresponds

_____ in system F.   proof

4-31 Given an AF, we discovered a proof that corresponds
to that AF. It turned out that the proof was just like the AF, but
this is not always the case. More often a proof has many more
items than the AF to which the proof corresponds. For an AF
to correspond to a proof, it is necessary only that

1. The items above the 'Ⱶ' for the AF are just like the items
above the 'Ⱶ' for the _____ , and   proof
2. The item below the 'Ⱶ' for the _____ is just like the AF
_____ item of the proof.   last

4-32 Let's try now to discern whether there is in system F
a proof that corresponds to the AF

```
| Cpq
| p
| Cqs
|‾s
```

Any proof that corresponds to this AF will have as the only
items above its 'Ⱶ'

1. a '_____,' then   Cpq
2. a '_____,' and then   p
3. a '_____.'   Cqs

Moreover, the proof would have as its last item an '_____.'   s

4-33 Consider the sequence

```
1 | Cpq
2 | p
3 | Cqs

last | s
```

We want to discern whether this sequence is a proof, or if not,
whether we can add items _____ the 'ⱶ' but above the   below
_____ item to produce a sequence that is a proof and   last
still corresponds to the AF we were given.
We will know this sequence or the sequence we produce is a
proof if every _____ of the sequence can be given a good   item
_____ .   reason

4-34
```
1 | Cpq
2 | p
3 | Cqs

last | s
```

Item 1 is a WFF item of the sequence and is above the 'ⱶ' for
the sequence; so, a good reason for item 1 is a '_____.'   hyp
Item 2 is a WFF item of the sequence and is above the 'ⱶ' for
the sequence; so, a good reason for item 2 is a '_____.'   hyp
Item 3 is a WFF item of the sequence and is above the 'ⱶ' for
the sequence; so, a good reason for item 3 is a '_____.'   hyp
The last item is a WFF item of the sequence and is _____   below
the 'ⱶ' for the sequence; so, we can give a good reason for the
last item if we can think of it as the last item of a _____   LAF
whose other items are

1. _____ items of the sequence, or   Preceding
2. Preceding items of the sequence of which the sequence is
an item. (But of course, in this instance again there are no
such items.)

4-35

```
    1 | Cpq    hyp
    2 | p      hyp
    3 | Cqs    hyp

last | s       ?
```

To give a good reason for the last item we must be able to think of it as the last item of a LAF of one of these nine kinds:

rep LAFs

Ki LAFs   Ko LAFs

_____ LAFs   _____ LAFs   Ai   Ao

_____ LAFs   _____ LAFs   Ci   Co

_____ LAFs   _____ LAFs   Ni   No

4-36

```
    1 | Cpq    hyp
    2 | p      hyp
    3 | Cqs    hyp

last | s       ?
```

We could think of the last item of the sequence as the last item of a rep LAF if there were in the sequence a WFF item that

1. Precedes the '_____,'   s
2. Is an item just like an '_____,' and   s
3. Has a good _____.   reason

Is there any such item in the sequence? _____ Can we,   no
then, think of the last item of this sequence as the last item
of a rep LAF? _____   no

4-37

```
    1 | Cpq    hyp
    2 | p      hyp
    3 | Cqs    hyp

last | s       ?
```

We were not able to think of the last item of the sequence as the last item of a rep LAF; so, if we are to give a good reason for the 's' we must be able to think of it as the last item of some in-LAF or of some out-LAF. The last item of every Ki LAF begins with a connective '_____.' The last item of every Ai   K
LAF begins with a connective '_____.' The last item of every   A
Ci LAF begins with a connective '_____.' The last item of   C
every Ni LAF begins with a connective '_____.' Can we think   N
of the 's' as the last item of any in-LAF? _____   no

4-38

```
  1 | Cpq      hyp
  2 | p        hyp
  3 | Cqs      hyp
 ___|
last | s        ?
```

Since an 's' does not begin with a connective, we cannot think of an 's' as the last item of any in-LAF. So, if we are to give a good reason for the 's' we must be able to think of it as the last item of some out-LAF. The *first* item of every Ko LAF begins with a connective '_____.' The *first* item of every Ao LAF begins with a connective '_____.' The *first* item of every Co LAF begins with a connective '_____.' Can we—without adding any items to the above sequence—think of the 's' as the last item of a Ko LAF? _____ Of an Ao LAF? _____

K

A

C

no; no

4-39

```
  1 | Cpq      hyp
  2 | p        hyp
  3 | Cqs      hyp
 ___|
last | s        ?
```

We could think of the last item of the sequence as the last item of a Co LAF if there were in the sequence two WFF items such that

1. One item is a '_____' followed by two WFFs the second of which is like the _____ item of the sequence,
2. The other item is a WFF like the _____ WFF following the 'C,'
3. Both items precede the _____ item of the sequence, and
4. Both WFF _____ have good _____.

C

last

first

last

items; reasons

Can we—without adding any items to the above sequence— think of the 's' as the last item of a Co LAF? _____

no

4-40

```
  1 | Cpq      hyp
  2 | p        hyp
  3 | Cqs      hyp
 ___|
last | s        ?
```

Is there as an item with a good reason and preceding 's' in the sequence a WFF which is a 'C' followed by two WFFs the second of which is like the 's'? _____ Is there as an item

yes

with a good reason and preceding 's' in the sequence a WFF item which is like the first WFF following the 'C'? _____ We could, then, think of the 's' as the last item of a Co LAF if we could add in the sequence as an item preceding the 's' a WFF item '_____' for which we can give a good reason.

no

q

4-41

1	Cpq	hyp
2	p	hyp
3	Cqs	hyp
?	q	?
last	s	_____, ?, Co

3

Notice that we use a '?' before an item to indicate that we would like to add that item, *provided* a good reason can be given.

4-42

1	Cpq	hyp
2	p	hyp
3	Cqs	hyp
?	q	?
last	s	3, ?, Co

We can give a good reason for the 's' if we can give a good reason for the 'q.' Can we without adding items think of the 'q' as the last item of a rep LAF? _____ We cannot think of the 'q' as the last item of any in-LAF, because the 'q' does not begin with any _____ . There is not in the sequence as an item with a good reason and preceding the 'q' a WFF item beginning with a 'K'; so we cannot, as the sequence stands, think of the 'q' as the last item of a _____o LAF. There is not in the sequence as an item with a good reason and preceding the 'q' a WFF item beginning with an 'A'; so we cannot, as the sequence stands, think of the 'q' as the last item of an _____o LAF. There is as an item preceding the 'q' in the sequence a WFF 'Cpq,' which is a 'C' followed by two WFFs the second of which is like a '_____.' There is also as an item preceding the 'q' in the sequence a WFF item 'p.' Do both these items have good reasons? _____ We can, then, think of the 'q' as the last item of a _____o LAF whose first item is item _____ and whose second item is item _____ .

no

connective

K

A

q

yes

C

1; 2

4-43

1	Cpq	hyp
2	p	hyp
3	Cqs	hyp
4	q	_____, _____, _____
last	s	3, ?, Co

1; 2; Co

4-44

1 | Cpq   hyp
2 | p   hyp
3 | Cqs   hyp
4 | q   1, 2, Co
5 | s   3, _____, Co   4

4-45

1 | Cpq   hyp
2 | p   hyp
3 | Cqs   hyp
4 | q   1, 2, Co
5 | s   3, 4, Co

Every item of this sequence of items has a good reason; so
the sequence is a _____.   proof

4-46

1 | Cpq   hyp
2 | p   hyp
3 | Cqs   hyp
4 | q   1, 2, Co
5 | s   3, 4, Co

The above sequence is a proof in system F; so every argument that can be formalized by the AF

                                               Cpq
                                               p
                                               Cqs
                                               s

is a valid argument because the _____ corresponds to   AF
a proof in system F.

4-47 We have just discovered a proof that corresponds to
an AF we were given. When trying to discover a proof that will
correspond to a given AF:

1. We begin a sequence
     by writing above the 'Ⱶ' for the sequence items just
     like the items _____ the 'Ⱶ' for the _____,   above; AF
     and
     by writing as the last item of the sequence an item
     just like the item _____ the 'Ⱶ' for the AF.   below

Then,

2. We try to discern if this sequence is a _____ or if we   proof
can produce a sequence that is a proof by adding items

_____ the '⊢' for the sequence but above the _____   below; last
item of the sequence.

And finally,

3. We know the initial sequence or the sequence we produce
is a proof if every _____ of this sequence can be given   item
a good _____ .   reason

4-48   Given an AF, we are interested to know whether there
is in system F a proof that corresponds to that AF, because an
argument is valid if it can be _____ by an AF that cor-   formalized
responds to a _____ in system F.   proof

Initial Search Strategies

4-49   Given an AF and given a proof, it is an easy matter to decide if the AF corresponds to the proof. But it is a less mechanical procedure given an AF to try to produce a _____ that corresponds to that AF.

proof

4-50   Given an AF we know that for any proof that corresponds to that AF

1. The only items above the 'ⱶ' for the proof will be like the items above the 'ⱶ' for the _____ , and

AF

2. The last item of the proof will be like the only item _____ the 'ⱶ' for the AF.

below

4-51   Not *all* arguments are valid arguments, and similarly, not *every* AF—every formalization of an argument—corresponds to a proof in system F. But given an AF, *if* there is in system F a proof that corresponds to that AF, we know simply by looking at the given AF

1. What will be the kinds of items above the 'ⱶ' for the _____ , and

proof

2. What will be the kind of last item in the _____ .

proof

4-52   Given an AF we begin a sequence using the appropriate kinds of items above the 'ⱶ' for the sequence and the appropriate kind of item as the last item of the sequence. And a sequence of items is a proof if every item has a good reason. We know that for any WFF item above the 'ⱶ' for a sequence, a good reason is a '_____.' We know further that for any WFF item below the 'ⱶ' for a sequence to have a good reason we must be able to think of the item as the last item of a LAF. But even so, is there any *one* kind of reason that is a good reason for *every* WFF item below a 'ⱶ' for a sequence? _____

hyp

no

4-53   A WFF item below the 'ⱶ' for a sequence must be thought of as the last item of a LAF of one of the _____ kinds.

nine

4-54   Since a WFF item below the 'ⱶ' for a sequence has a good reason if and only if the item can be thought of as the last item of a LAF of one of the nine kinds, when we are looking for a good reason for a WFF item below the 'ⱶ' for a sequence, we *could* (and when we can think of no other way to proceed, we *should*) for each kind of LAF in turn try to think of the WFF item as the _____ item of a LAF of that kind.

last

4-55   When we are looking for a good reason for a WFF item below the 'ⱶ' for a sequence, we *could* (and when we can think of no other way to proceed we *should*) for each kind of LAF in turn try to think of the WFF item as the last item of a LAF of that kind. But our knowledge of LAFs allows us to make certain observations which suggest more economical ways for proceeding when we are looking for a good reason for a WFF item _____ the 'ⱶ' for a sequence.

below

4-56   The *last* item of every *in*-LAF begins with a _____ .
The *first* item of every *out*-LAF—except No LAFs—begins with a _____ .

connective

connective

4-57   The last item of every Ki LAF begins with a connective '_____.' The last item of every Ai LAF begins with a connective '_____.' The last item of every Ci LAF begins with a con-
nective '_____.' The last item of every Ni LAF begins with a
connective '_____.'

K

A

C

N

4-58   Since the last item of every in-LAF begins with a connective, it is useless to try to think of a WFF item as the last
item of an in-LAF if the WFF item does not begin with
a _____ . Moreover, it is useless to try to think of the
WFF item as the last item of a Ki LAF if the WFF item does not
begin with a connective '_____.' It is useless to try to think of
the WFF item as the last item of an Ai LAF if the WFF item does
not begin with a connective '_____.' It is useless to try to think
of the WFF item as the last item of a Ci LAF if the WFF item
does not begin with a connective '_____.' And it is useless to
try to think of the WFF item that does not begin with a connective 'N' as the last item of an _____ LAF.

connective

K

A

C

Ni

4-59 Every WFF item either begins with a connective or does not begin with a connective. When trying to give a good reason for a WFF item below the 'Ⱶ' for a sequence, if the item begins with a connective it is a good strategy, rather than trying each kind of LAF in turn, first of all to try to think of the WFF item as the last item of the appropriate kind of _____-LAF.

in

4-60 When trying to give a good reason for a WFF item below the 'Ⱶ' for the sequence, if the item begins with a 'K' it is a good strategy, rather than trying each kind of LAF in turn, first of all to try to think of the WFF item as the last item of a _____ LAF.

Ki

4-61 When trying to give a good reason for a WFF item below the 'Ⱶ' for the sequence, if the item begins with an 'A' it is a good strategy, rather than trying each kind of LAF in turn, first of all to try to think of the WFF item as the last item of an _____ LAF.

Ai

4-62 When trying to give a good reason for a WFF item below the 'Ⱶ' for the sequence, if the item begins with a 'C' it is a good strategy, rather than trying each kind of LAF in turn, first of all to try to think of the WFF item as the last item of a _____ LAF.

Ci

4-63 If a WFF item of the sequence begins with an 'N,' it is a good strategy to try first of all to think of the WFF item as the last item of an Ni LAF—provided the WFF item is _____ the 'Ⱶ' for the sequence.

below

4-64 The last item of every in-LAF begins with a _____. The first item of every out-LAF—except No LAFs— begins with a _____.

connective

connective

4-65 The first item of every Ko LAF begins with a connective '____.' The first item of every Ao LAF begins with a connective '____.' The first item of every Co LAF begins with a connective '____.'

K

A

C

4-66 Since the first item of every out-LAF—except No LAFs —begins with a connective, it is useless to try to think of a WFF item as the last item of an out-LAF if no preceding item begins with a _____. Moreover, it is useless to try to think of a WFF item as the last item of a Ko LAF if no preceding item begins with a '_____.' It is useless to try to think of a WFF item as the last item of an Ao LAF if no preceding item begins with an '_____.' It is useless to try to think of a WFF item as the last item of a Co LAF if no preceding item begins with a '_____.'

connective

K

A

C

4-67 Every WFF item either begins with a connective or does not begin with a connective. When trying to give a good reason for a WFF item below the 'Ⱶ' for the sequence, if the item does not begin with a connective it is a good strategy, rather than trying each kind of LAF in turn, first of all to try to think of the WFF item as the last item of an _____-LAF.

out

4-68 Every WFF item of a sequence is either above the 'Ⱶ' for the sequence or else _____ the 'Ⱶ' for the sequence; and every WFF item either begins with a connective or does not begin with a _____.

below

connective

4-69 Any WFF item above the 'Ⱶ' for the sequence, whether or not the item begins with a connective, has as a good reason a '_____.' Any WFF item below the 'Ⱶ' for the sequence must be thought of as the _____ item of a _____. If the item begins with a connective then a good strategy is first of all to try to think of the WFF item as the last item of the appropriate _____-LAF. If the item does not begin with a connective then a good strategy is first of all to try to think of the WFF item as the last item of some _____-LAF.

hyp

last; LAF

in

out

4-70 An argument is valid if it can be formalized by an AF that corresponds to a proof in system F. And a sequence of items is a proof in system F if every _____ of the sequence has a good _____.

item

reason

Particular Search Strategies

A Likely Good Reasons for WFFs Beginning with a 'K'

4-71 Given an AF, we know there is a proof that corresponds to that AF if we can produce some sequence of items such that

1. Items like the items above the 'ʜ' for the AF are the only items _____ the 'ʜ' for the sequence, and
2. The last item of the sequence is like the only item _____ the 'ʜ' for the AF,

and such that

3. Every _____ of the sequence has a good _____.

above

below

item; reason

4-72 A 'hyp' is a good reason for any WFF item of a sequence _____ the 'ʜ' for that sequence.

above

4-73 To give good reasons for WFF items below the 'ʜ' for a sequence, we must be familiar with the nine kinds of LAFs in system F. If at any time in trying to discover proofs you feel need for a further reminder of the LAFs, you may want to turn to Appendix A, where the LAFs are described and exemplified; or you may turn to Unit 5 of Part 3; or you may reread the appropriate parts of Unit 4 of Part 3. Return then to discovering proofs in system F, once you feel comfortable with the LAFs in _____ _____.

system F

4-74 Write a Ki LAF whose last item is a 'Kqp.'

```
1 | q
2 | p
3 | Kqp     1, 2, Ki
```

4-75 Write a Ki LAF whose last item is a 'KsKrt.'

```
1 | s
2 | Krt
3 | KsKrt      1, 2, Ki
```

4-76 Write a Ko LAF whose first item is a 'Kpq.'

1	Kpq	
2	p	1, Ko

or

1	Kpq	
2	q	1, Ko

4-77 Write a Ko LAF whose first item is a 'KKrst.'

1	KKrst	
2	Krs	1, Ko

or

1	KKrst	
2	t	1, Ko

4-78 Write a Co LAF whose first item is a 'Cpq' and whose second item is a 'p.'

1	Cpq	
2	p	
3	q	1, 2, Co

4-79 Write a Co LAF whose first item is a 'Cst' and whose last item is a 't.'

1	Cst	
2	s	
3	t	1, 2, Co

4-80 Consider the AF

|s
|Csp
|Csr
|Kpr

If there is in system F a proof that corresponds to that AF that proof

will have _____ items above its '⊢', and   three

will have as its last item a WFF '_____.'   Kpr

4-81 Consider the AF

$$
\begin{array}{|l}
s \\
Csp \\
Csr \\
Kpr
\end{array}
$$

and consider the sequence

$$
\begin{array}{r|l}
1 & s \\
2 & Csp \\
3 & Csr \\
\\
\text{last} & Kpr
\end{array}
$$

We will know that there is a proof corresponding to the above AF if

1. We can give a good reason for every item of the sequence and so know that the sequence is a _____, or else
2. We can add items but without adding items _____ the 'Ⱶ' for the sequence nor _____ the last item of the sequence so as to produce a sequence of items each of which has a good reason—that is, produce a _____ that still corresponds to the _____ .

proof

above

below

proof

AF

4-82

$$
\begin{array}{r|l}
1 & s \\
2 & Csp \\
3 & Csr \\
\\
\text{last} & Kpr
\end{array}
$$

A 'hyp' is a good reason for item 1, item 2, and item 3, since each of these items is _____ the 'Ⱶ' for the sequence.

above

4-83

$$
\begin{array}{r|ll}
1 & s & \text{hyp} \\
2 & Csp & \text{hyp} \\
3 & Csr & \text{hyp} \\
\\
\text{last} & Kpr
\end{array}
$$

Since the last item of the sequence is _____ the 'Ⱶ' for the sequence and begins with a connective '_____,' a good strategy is to try to think of the 'Kpr' as the last item of a _____ LAF.

below

K

Ki

4-84 A Ki LAF has _____ items. The last item is a 'K'
followed by two WFFs the first of which is just like the
_____ item of the LAF and the second of which is like
the _____ item of the LAF.

three

first

second

4-85

1	s	hyp
2	Csp	hyp
3	Csr	hyp
last	Kpr	?

We could think of the 'Kpr' as the last item of a Ki LAF if

1. There were already in the sequence as items with good
reasons and preceding the 'Kpr' both a '_____' and an
'_____,' or
2. We could add in the sequence (below the 'ⱨ' for the
sequence but above the last item) a WFF item '_____' for
which we could give a good reason and a WFF item '_____' for
which we could give a good _____.

p

r

p

r

reason

4-86

1	s	hyp
2	Csp	hyp
3	Csr	hyp
last	Kpr	?

Are there already as items in the sequence with good reasons
and preceding the 'Kpr' both a 'p' and an 'r'? _____

no

4-87

1	s	hyp
2	Csp	hyp
3	Csr	hyp
?	p	
?	r	
last	Kpr	?, ?, Ki

Let's tentatively add a 'p' and an 'r' but put '?'s in front of
them to indicate we have as yet no good reasons for them.
Then if we can give good reasons for both a 'p' and an 'r,' we
can think of the 'Kpr' as the last item of a _____ LAF
whose first item is a '_____' and whose second item is an 'r.'
Notice that we put question marks rather than numbers of
items in front of the Ki following the 'Kpr' to indicate that we
would like to think of the 'Kpr' as the last item of a Ki LAF
provided we can give good reasons for the appropriate
preceding items.

Ki

p

4-88

1	s	hyp
2	Csp	hyp
3	Csr	hyp
?	p	?
?	r	
last	Kpr	?, ?, Ki

But what could we give as a good reason for the WFF item 'p'? Since the 'p' is a WFF item below the 'Ͱ' for the sequence and does *not* begin with a connective, a good strategy is to try to think of the 'p' as the last item of some _____-LAF. There is preceding the 'p' no item beginning with a 'K' nor with an 'A,' but there is an item (in fact two) beginning with a connective '_____.' So we may be able to think of the 'p' as the last item of a _____o LAF.

out

C

C

4-89   A Co LAF has _____ items. The first item is a 'C' followed by two WFFs, the first of which is like the _____ item of the LAF and the second of which is like the last item of the _____ .

two

second

LAF

4-90

1	s	hyp
2	Csp	hyp
3	Csr	hyp
?	p	?
?	r	
last	Kpr	?, ?, Ki

If 'p' is to be thought of as the last item of a Co LAF, the first item of the LAF must be a 'C' followed by two WFFs the second of which is a WFF '_____.' Notice that item 2 is such a WFF. If item 2 were the first item of a Co LAF, the second item of the LAF would be a WFF '_____.' Notice that item 1 is such a WFF. Do item 2 and item 1 both precede the 'p' in the sequence? _____ Do item 2 and item 1 each have a good reason? _____ So, we can think of the 'p' as the last item of a Co LAF whose first item is item _____ and whose second item is item _____ .

p

s

yes

yes

2

1

4-91

1	s	hyp
2	Csp	hyp
3	Csr	hyp
4	p	_____ , _____ , _____
?	r	
last	Kpr	?, ?, Ki

2; 1; Co

4-92

1	s	hyp
2	Csp	hyp
3	Csr	hyp
4	p	2, 1, Co
?	r	?
last	Kpr	?, ?, Ki

The 'p' now has a good reason. If we can give a good reason
for the 'r,' then we can think of the 'Kpr' as the last item of a
Ki LAF whose first item is a 'p' and whose second item is an
'r.' Since the 'r' is a WFF item below the '⊢' for the sequence
and does *not* begin with a connective, a good strategy is to try
to think of the 'r' as the last item of some _____-LAF.   out
There is preceding the 'r' no item beginning with a 'K' nor
with an 'A,' but there is an item (in fact there are two) beginning with a connective '_____.' So we may be able to think of   C
the 'r' as the last item of a _____o LAF.   C

4-93

1	s	hyp
2	Csp	hyp
3	Csr	hyp
4	p	2, 1, Co
?	r	?
last	Kpr	?, ?, Ki

If 'r' is to be thought of as the last item of a Co LAF, the first
item of the LAF must be a 'C' followed by two WFFs the second
of which is a WFF '_____.' Notice that item 3 is such a WFF.   r
If item 3 were the first item of a Co LAF, the second item of
the LAF would be a WFF '_____.' Notice that item 1 is such a   s
WFF. Do item 3 and item 1 both precede the 'r' in the
sequence? _____ Do item 3 and item 1 each have a good   yes
reason? _____ So, we can think of the 'r' as the last item   yes
of a Co LAF whose first item is item _____ and whose second   3
item is item _____ .   1

4-94

1	s	hyp
2	Csp	hyp
3	Csr	hyp
4	p	2, 1, Co
5	r	_____ , _____ , _____
last	Kpr	?, ?, Ki

3; 1; Co

4-95

1	s	hyp	
2	Csp	hyp	
3	Csr	hyp	
4	p	2, 1, Co	
5	r	3, 1, Co	
6	Kpr	_____ , _____ , Ki	4; 5

Since we have given good reasons for a 'p' and an 'r' as items preceding 'Kpr' in the sequence, we can now think of the 'Kpr' as the last item of a Ki LAF whose first item is item _____ and whose second item is item _____ .

4

5

4-96 Show that the following sequence of items is a proof by giving good reasons for each item in the sequence.

1	s	_____	hyp	
2	Csp	_____	hyp	
3	Csr	_____	hyp	
4	p	_____ , _____ , _____	2; 1; Co	
5	r	_____ , _____ , _____	3; 1; Co	
6	Kpr	_____ , _____ , _____	4; 5; Ki	

4-97

1	s	hyp	
2	Csp	hyp	
3	Csr	hyp	
4	p	2, 1, Co	
5	r	3, 1, Co	
6	Kpr	4, 5, Ki	

Since the above sequence is a proof, we know that an argument is valid if it can be formalized by the AF

s
Csp
Csr
Kpr

for this AF corresponds to a _____ in system F.

proof

4-98 Let's see if we can discover a proof that corresponds to the AF

Csp
Krq
s
Kpq

First, we begin the sequence

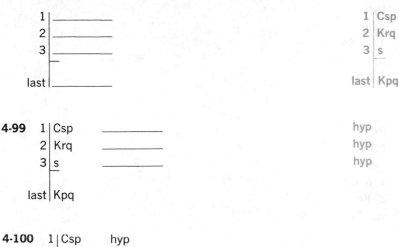

1	_____
2	_____
3	_____
last	_____

1	Csp
2	Krq
3	s
last	Kpq

4-99
1	Csp	_____
2	Krq	_____
3	s	_____
last	Kpq	

hyp
hyp
hyp

4-100
1	Csp	hyp
2	Krq	hyp
3	s	hyp
last	Kpq	?

We know what is always a good reason for any item above the 'ⱶ' for a sequence. But what about the last item, which is below the 'ⱶ' for the sequence? Since the last item begins with a '_____,' let's follow the strategy of trying to think of the 'Kpq' as the last item of a _____ LAF.

K
Ki

4-101
1	Csp	hyp
2	Krq	hyp
3	s	hyp
?	____	
?	____	
last	Kpq	?, ?, Ki

p
q

4-102
1	Csp	hyp
2	Krq	hyp
3	s	hyp
?	p	____ , ____ , ____
?	q	
last	Kpq	?, ?, Ki

1; 3; Co

4-103 A Ko LAF has _____ items. The first item is a 'K' followed by two WFFs one of which is like the _____ item of the LAF.

two
last

4-104

1	Csp	hyp	
2	Krq	hyp	
3	s	hyp	
4	p	1, 3, Co	
?	q	2, _____	Ko
last	Kpq	?, ?, Ki	

4-105

1	Csp	hyp	
2	Krq	hyp	
3	s	hyp	
4	p	1, 3, Co	
5	q	2, Ko	
6	Kpq	_____, _____, Ki	4; 5

4-106

1	Csp	_____	hyp
2	Krq	_____	hyp
3	s	_____	hyp
4	p	____, ____, ____	1; 3; Co
5	q	____, ____	2; Ko
6	Kpq	____, ____, ____	4; 5; Ki

4-107   Produce a proof that corresponds to the AF

t
Ctq
Kpr
Kqr

and give your good reasons.

*1	t	hyp
2	Ctq	hyp
3	Kpr	hyp
4	q	2, 1, Co
5	r	3, Ko
6	Kqr	4, 5, Ki

4-108   Let's see if we can discover a proof that corresponds to the AF

Krt
s
KsKrt

First, we begin the sequence

1	_____
2	_____
last	_____

1	Krt
2	s
last	KsKrt

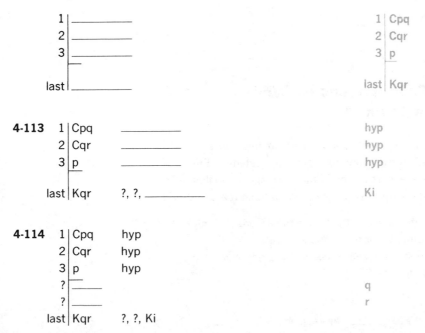

4-109　1 | Krt　　　 ──────　　　　　　　　　hyp
　　　　　2 | s　　　　　──────　　　　　　　　　hyp

　　　　last | KsKrt　　?, ?, ──────　　　　　　Ki

4-110　1 | Krt　　　hyp
　　　　　2 | s　　　　hyp
　　　　　3 | KsKrt　　──── , ──── , Ki　　　　　2; 1

4-111　Produce a proof that corresponds to the AF

　　　　| r
　　　　| Kqt
　　　　──
　　　　| Krt

*1 | r　　　hyp
　2 | Kqt　hyp
　3 | t　　　2, Ko
　4 | Krt　1, 3, Ki

and give good reasons. Notice that the last item of the proof
will be a WFF beginning with a 'K.'

4-112　To try to discover a proof that corresponds to the AF

　　　　| Cpq
　　　　| Cqr
　　　　| p
　　　　| Kqr

we first begin the sequence

　　　　　1 | ──────
　　　　　2 | ──────
　　　　　3 | ──────
　　　　　──
　　　　last | ──────

　　　　　1 | Cpq
　　　　　2 | Cqr
　　　　　3 | p
　　　　last | Kqr

4-113　1 | Cpq　　　──────　　　　　　　　hyp
　　　　　2 | Cqr　　　──────　　　　　　　　hyp
　　　　　3 | p　　　　──────　　　　　　　　hyp

　　　　last | Kqr　　?, ?, ──────　　　　　Ki

4-114　1 | Cpq　　hyp
　　　　　2 | Cqr　　hyp
　　　　　3 | p　　　hyp
　　　　　? | ────　　　　　　　　　　　　　q
　　　　　? | ────　　　　　　　　　　　　　r
　　　　last | Kqr　　?, ?, Ki

4-115

1	Cpq	hyp	
2	Cqr	hyp	
3	p	hyp	
?	q	____, ____, ____	1; 3; Co
?	r		
last	Kqr	?, ?, Ki	

4-116

1	Cpq	hyp	
2	Cqr	hyp	
3	p	hyp	
4	q	1, 3, Co	
5	r	2, ____, Co	4
last	Kqr	?, ?, Ki	

4-117

1	Cpq	hyp	
2	Cqr	hyp	
3	p	hyp	
4	q	1, 3, Co	
5	r	2, 4, Co	
6	Kqr	____, ____, Ki	4; 5

4-118

1	q	_____	hyp
2	Cqp	_____	hyp
3	Cps	_____	hyp
4	____	____, ____, ____	p; 2; 1; Co
5	s	____, ____, ____	3; 4; Co
6	Kps	____, ____, ____	4; 5; Ki

B Likely Good Reasons for WFFs Beginning with an 'A'

4-119 Not every argument is a valid argument, and similarly not every AF corresponds to a proof in system F. But given an AF, we know there is a proof that corresponds to that AF if we can produce some sequence of items such that

1. Items like the items above the 'Ⱶ' for the AF are the only items _____ the 'Ⱶ' for the sequence, and

above

2. The last item of the sequence is like the only item _____ the 'Ⱶ' for the AF,

below

and such that

3. Every item of the _____ has a good _____ .

sequence; reason

4-120 Write an Ai LAF whose last item is an 'Ast.'

1	s	
2	Ast	1, Ai

or

1	t	
2	Ast	1, Ai

4-121 Write an Ai LAF whose last item is an 'AKpqCrs.'

1	Kpq	
2	AKpqCrs	1, Ai

or

1	Crs	
2	AKpqCrs	1, Ai

4-122 Consider the AF

|q
|Cqs
|Ast

and consider the sequence

1	q
2	Cqs
last	Ast

We will know that there is a proof corresponding to the above AF if

1. We can give a good reason for every item of the sequence and so know that the sequence is a _____ , or else

proof

2. We can add items but without adding items above the '_____' for the sequence nor below the _____ item of the sequence so as to produce a sequence of items each of which has a good reason—that is, produce a proof that _____ to the AF.

⊢; last

corresponds

4-123

1	q
2	Cqs
last	Ast

A 'hyp' is a good reason for item 1 and item 2 since each of these items is above the '_____' for the sequence.

⊢

4-124　　1 | q　　　　hyp
　　　　　2 | Cqs　　hyp

　　　　last | Ast

Since the last item of the sequence is below the '_____' for the
sequence and begins with a connective '_____,' a good
strategy is to try to think of the 'Ast' as the last item of an
_____ LAF.

4-125　　An Ai LAF has _____ items. The last item is an
'A' followed by two WFFs one of which is just like the
_____ item of the LAF.

4-126　　1 | q　　　　hyp
　　　　　2 | Cqs　　hyp

　　　　last | Ast　　?

We could think of the 'Ast' as the last item of an Ai LAF if

1. There were already in the sequence as an item with a good
reason and preceding the 'Ast' either an '_____' or a '_____,' or
2. We could add in the sequence (below the '⊢' for the
sequence but above the last item) a WFF item '_____' for
which we could give a good reason *or* a WFF item '_____' for
which we could give a good _____ .

4-127　　1 | q　　　　hyp
　　　　　2 | Cqs　　hyp

　　　　last | Ast　　?

Is there already as an item in the sequence with a good reason
and preceding the 'Ast' either an 's' or a 't'? _____

4-128　　1 | q　　　　hyp
　　　　　2 | Cqs　　hyp
　　　　　? | s
　　　　last | Ast　　?, Ai

Let's tentatively add an 's' but put a '?' in front of it to indicate
we have as yet no good reason for the 's.' Then *if* we can give
a good reason for the 's,' we can think of the 'Ast' as the last
item of an Ai LAF whose first item is an '_____.' Notice that
we put question marks rather than numbers of items in front

of the Ai following the 'Ast' to indicate that we would like to think of the 'Ast' as the last item of an Ai LAF *provided* we can give a good reason for the appropriate preceding item.

4-129
1	q	hyp
2	Cqs	hyp
?	s	?
last	Ast	?, Ai

But what could we give as a good reason for the WFF item 's?' Since the 's' is a WFF item below the 'Ⱶ' for the sequence and does *not* begin with a connective, a good strategy is to try to think of the 's' as the last item of some _____-LAF. There is preceding the 's' no item beginning with a 'K' nor with an 'A' but there is an item beginning with a connective '_____.' So we may be able to think of the 's' as the last item of a _____o LAF.

out

C

C

4-130
1	q	hyp
2	Cqs	hyp
3	s	_____, _____, _____
last	Ast	?, Ai

2; 1; Co

4-131
1	q	hyp
2	Cqs	hyp
3	s	2, 1, Co
4	Ast	_____, Ai

3

Since we have given a good reason for an 's' as an item preceding 'Ast' in the sequence, we can now think of the 'Ast' as the last item of an Ai LAF whose first item is item _____.

3

4-132
1	q	hyp
2	Cqs	hyp
3	s	2, 1, Co
4	Ast	3, Ai

Since every item in this sequence has a good reason the sequence is a proof. So any argument is valid if it can be formalized by the AF

_____
_____
Ⱶ_____

q
Cqs
Ast

for this AF _____ to a proof in system F.

corresponds

4-133 Now let's see if we can find a proof that corresponds to the AF

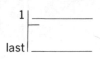

First we begin the sequence

$$1\ \underline{\qquad\qquad}$$
$$\mathrm{last}\ \underline{\qquad\qquad}$$

1 | Kqt

last | Art

4-134 1 | Kqt $\underline{\qquad\qquad}$

last | Art   ?, $\underline{\qquad\qquad}$

                hyp

                Ai

Since the 'Art' is a WFF item below the '⊦' for the sequence and begins with a connective 'A,' we follow the strategy of trying to think of the 'Art' as the last item of an $\underline{\qquad\qquad}$ Ai
LAF. We could think of the 'Art' as the last item of an Ai LAF if there were as an item with a good reason and preceding the 'Art' in the sequence either an '$\underline{\qquad}$' or a '$\underline{\qquad}$.'   r; t

4-135 1 | Kqt   hyp

     ? | r

last | Art   ?, Ai

Let's tentatively add an 'r' but put a '$\underline{\qquad}$' in front of it to   ?
indicate we have as yet given no good reason. Then if we can give a good reason for an 'r' we can think of the 'Art' as the last item of an Ai LAF whose first item is an '$\underline{\qquad}$.' But even   r
if we cannot find a good reason for the 'r,' we could still think of the 'Art' as the last item of an Ai LAF whose first item is a 't' *provided* we could give a good reason for a '$\underline{\qquad}$.'   t

4-136 1 | Kqt   hyp

     ? | r   ?

last | Art   ?, Ai

Since the 'r' is a WFF item below the '⊦' for the sequence and does not begin with a connective, a good strategy is to try to think of the 'r' as the last item of some out-LAF. There is preceding the 'r' no item beginning with an 'A' or with a 'C.' But item 1 begins with a 'K,' so we may be able to think of the 'r' as the last item of a $\underline{\qquad\qquad}$ LAF. But can an 'r' be   Ko
thought of as the last item of a Ko LAF whose first item con-

tains no 'r' but is a 'Kqt'? _____ We cannot think of the
'r' as the last item of a rep LAF because there is no preceding
item which is an '_____.' We cannot think of the 'r' as the last
item of any in-LAF because an 'r' does not begin with a
_____. We cannot as the sequence stands think of the
'r' as the last item of a Ko, Ao, or Co LAF. We could try adding
further items so as to try to think of the 'r' as the last item of
an No LAF, but it may be simpler to try the other alternative
open to us. For we noted that even if we were unable to give
a good reason for an 'r,' we could still think of the 'Art' as the
last item of an Ai LAF if we had as an item with a good reason
and preceding the 'Art' in the sequence a '_____.'

4-137 $\quad$ 1 | Kqt $\quad$ hyp

$\qquad$ last | Art $\quad$?, Ai

We had added an 'r' and were trying to find a good reason.
But we are free to remove the 'r' and try adding some other
item. Whenever we add an item for which we do not yet have
a good reason, it is important to put a '____' in front of that
item until we find a good reason for the item or else remove
the item.

4-138 $\quad$ 1 | Kqt $\quad$ hyp

$\quad$? | t $\qquad$?

last | Art $\quad$?, Ai

We could think of the 'Art' as the last item of an Ai LAF if we
can give a good reason for the '_____.' Since the 't' is a WFF
item below the '⊢' for the sequence and does not begin with a
connective, it is a good strategy to try to think of the 't' as the
last item of an _____-LAF.

4-139 $\quad$ 1 | Kqt $\quad$ hyp

$\quad$ 2 | t $\qquad$ _____, _____

last | Art $\quad$?, Ai

4-140 $\quad$ 1 | Kqt $\quad$ hyp

$\quad$ 2 | t $\quad$ 1, Ko

$\quad$ 3 | Art $\qquad$ _____, _____

We have now produced a proof that corresponds to the AF

⊢ _____

⊢ _____

| Kqt
| Art

Margin answers:

no

r

connective

t

?

t

out

1, Ko

2; Ai

4-141   Produce a proof that corresponds to the AF

| Ksp |
| AsCqr |

and give your good reasons.

*1	Ksp	hyp
2	s	1, Ko
3	AsCqr	2, Ai

4-142   Produce a proof that corresponds to the AF

| Csr |
| s |
| Apr |

and give your good reasons.

*1	Csr	hyp
2	s	hyp
3	r	1, 2, Co
4	Apr	3, Ai

4-143   To discover a proof that corresponds to the AF

| r |
| Crp |
| Crq |
| AKpqt |

first we begin the sequence

1	_____
2	_____
3	_____

last	_____

1	r
2	Crp
3	Crq

last	AKpqt

4-144

1	r	_____	hyp
2	Crp	_____	hyp
3	Crq	_____	hyp
last	AKpqt	?, _____	Ai

4-145

1	r	hyp	
2	Crp	hyp	
3	Crq	hyp	
?	_____		Kpq
last	AKpqt	?, Ai	

4-146

1	r	hyp	
2	Crp	hyp	
3	Crq	hyp	
?	Kpq	?, ?, _____	Ki
last	AKpqt	?, Ai	

4-147

1	r	hyp	
2	Crp	hyp	
3	Crq	hyp	
?	_____		p
?	_____		q
?	Kpq	?, ?, Ki	
last	AKpqt	?, Ai	

4-148

1	r	hyp	
2	Crp	hyp	
3	Crq	hyp	
4	p	_____, _____, _____	2; 1; Co
?	q		
?	Kpq	?, ?, Ki	
last	AKpqt	?, Ai	

4-149

1	r	hyp	
2	Crp	hyp	
3	Crq	hyp	
4	p	2, 1, Co	
5	q	_____, _____, _____	3; 1; Co
?	Kpq	?, ?, Ki	
last	AKpqt	?, Ai	

4-150

1	r	hyp	
2	Crp	hyp	
3	Crq	hyp	
4	p	2, 1, Co	
5	q	3, 1, Co	
6	Kpq	_____, _____, Ki	4; 5
last	AKpqt	?, Ai	

4-151

1	r	hyp	
2	Crp	hyp	
3	Crq	hyp	
4	p	2, 1, Co	
5	q	3, 1, Co	
6	Kpq	4, 5, Ki	
7	AKpqt	_____, Ai	6

4-152 Produce a proof that corresponds to the AF

$$\begin{array}{l} \text{Csq} \\ \text{s} \\ \text{Cst} \\ \hline \text{ApKtq} \end{array}$$

and give your good reasons.

*1	Csq	hyp
2	s	hyp
3	Cst	hyp
4	t	3, 2, Co
5	q	1, 2, Co
6	Ktq	4, 5, Ki
7	ApKtq	6, Ai

C   Likely Good Reasons for WFFs Beginning with a 'C'

4-153 Write a Ci LAF whose first item is like this tail item:

1.1	Kpq	hyp
1.2	p	1.1, Ko

1	1.1	Kpq	hyp
	1.2	p	1.1, Ko
2	CKpqp		1, Ci

4-154 Write a Ci LAF whose first item is like this tail item:

1.1	p	hyp
1.2	p	1.1, rep

1	1.1	p	hyp
	1.2	p	1.1, rep
2	Cpp		1, Ci

4-155 Consider the AF

$$\begin{array}{l} \text{Kpq} \\ \hline \text{Crq} \end{array}$$

and consider the sequence

$$\begin{array}{ll} 1 & \text{Kpq} \\ \\ \text{last} & \text{Crq} \end{array}$$

We will know there is a proof corresponding to the above AF if

1. We can give a good reason for every item of the sequence and so know it is a proof, or
2. We can add items so as to produce a sequence each of whose items has a good reason but add the items in such a way that the resulting proof _____ to the AF.

corresponds

4-156

```
  1  | Kpq
     ┌─
last | Crq
```

A 'hyp' is a good reason for item 1 since item 1 is above the
'⊢' for the _____ .

sequence

4-157

```
  1  | Kpq      hyp
     ┌─
last | Crq
```

Since the last item of the sequence is below the '⊢' for the
sequence and begins with a connective '_____,' a good
strategy is to try to think of the 'Crq' as the last item of
a _____ LAF.

C

Ci

4-158 A Ci LAF has two items—the first of which is a
sequence of items, that is, a _____ item. The last item
of a Ci LAF is a 'C' followed by two WFFs the first of which is
just like the only item _____ the '⊢' for the first item and
the second of which is just like the _____ item of the
first item.

tail

above

last

4-159

```
  1  | Kpq      hyp
     ┌─
last | Crq      ?
```

We could think of the 'Crq' as the last item of a Ci LAF if

1. There were already in the sequence as an item with a good
reason a tail item whose only item above the '⊢' for the tail
item was an '_____' and whose last item was a '_____,' or
2. We could add in the sequence (below the '⊢' for the
sequence but above the last item) a tail item for which we
could give a good reason, and whose only item above the '⊢'
for the tail item was an '_____' and whose last item was
a '_____.'

r; q

r

q

4-160

```
  1  | Kpq      hyp
     ┌─
last | Crq      ?
```

Is there already as an item in the sequence with a good reason
and preceding the 'Crq' a tail item whose only item above the
'⊢' for the tail item is an 'r' and whose last item is a 'q'?

_____

no

4-161

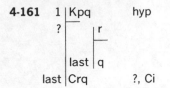

1 | Kpq   hyp

?

     | r

     last | q

last | Crq   ?, Ci

Let's tentatively add to the sequence a tail item with an 'r' as the only item above the 'ⱶ' for the tail item and a 'q' as the last item. Then if we can give a good reason for the tail item, that is

1. If we can give a good reason for every item of the tail item just as it now stands, or
2. If we can add items to the tail item in such a way that every item of the tail item has a good reason, but we have added no item above the 'ⱶ' for the tail item nor below the last item 'q' of the tail item,

then we can think of the 'Crq' as the last item of a _____   Ci
LAF whose first item is the _____ item.   tail

4-162   A tail item has a good reason if each of its items has a good reason. A WFF item above the 'ⱶ' for the sequence can be given as a good reason a '_____.' A WFF item below   hyp
the 'ⱶ' for the sequence can be given a good reason if the item can be thought of as the last item of a LAF whose other items are

1. Preceding items of the same _____, or   sequence
2. Preceding items of the sequence of which the _____   sequence
is an item—especially relevant when the WFF item for which we are giving a reason is an item of a tail item.

4-163   1 | Kpq   hyp

?

     | r

     last | q

last | Crq   ?, Ci

Since the 'r' is a WFF item above the 'ⱶ' for the tail item, we can give a '_____' as a good reason for the 'r.'   hyp

4-164

```
1 | Kpq           hyp
 ? |     | r       hyp
   |     |—
   |     | last | q    ?
   last | Crq         ?, Ci
```

Since the 'q' is a WFF item below the '⊢' for the tail item and does not begin with a connective, it is a good strategy to try to think of the 'q' as the last item of some _____-LAF whose other items are   out

1. Preceding items of the _____ item, or   tail
2. Preceding items of the sequence of which the _____   tail
item is an item.

4-165

```
1 | Kpq           hyp
 ? |     | r       hyp
   |     |—
   |     | last | q    ?
   last | Crq         ?, Ci
```

Item 1 is a '_____pq.' Is item 1 an item of the tail item?   K
_____ Is item 1 an item of the sequence of which the   no
tail item is an item? _____ Does item 1 have a good   yes
reason? _____ Can we think of the 'q' as the last item   yes
of a Ko LAF whose first item is item 1? _____   yes

4-166

```
1 | Kpq              hyp
2 | 2.1 | r          hyp
  | 2.2 | q          _____ , _____      1; Ko
  last | Crq         ?, Ci
```

4-167

```
1 | Kpq              hyp
2 | 2.1 | r          hyp
  | 2.2 | q          1, Ko
3 | Crq              _____ , _____      2; Ci
```

Notice the whole tail item 2 (not just item 2.1 or item 2.2) is cited in the reason for item 3. For, loosely speaking, from an 'r' as hypothesis a 'q' "follows." So if 'r,' then 'q'—or '_____rq.'   C

4-168

```
1 | Kpq        hyp
2 | 2.1 | r    hyp
  | 2.2 | q    1, Ko
3 | Crq        2, Ci
```

Since every item in this sequence has a good reason (item 2 has a good reason because each of the items in item 2 has a good reason) the sequence is a proof. So any argument is valid if it can be formalized by the AF

|—————
|—————

for this AF _____ to a proof in system F.

Kpq
Crq

corresponds

4-169   Produce a proof that corresponds to the AF

|KAstr
|Csr

and give your good reasons. Notice that the last item of the proof will be a WFF beginning with a 'C.'

```
*1 | KAstr       hyp
 2 | 2.1 | s     hyp
   | 2.2 | r     1, Ko
 3 | Csr         2, Ci
```

4-170   Produce a proof that corresponds to the AF

|s
|Csq
|Ctq

and give your good reasons. Notice that the last item of the proof will be a WFF beginning with a 'C.'

```
*1 | s              hyp
 2 | Csq            hyp
 3 | 3.1 | t        hyp
   | 3.2 | q        2, 1, Co
 4 | Ctq            3, Ci
```

4-171   To try to discover a proof that corresponds to the AF

|Cps
|Cpr
|CpKrs

we begin the sequence

```
1 |—————
2 |—————

last |—————
```

```
1 | Cpq
2 | Cpr

last | CpKrs
```

4-172 1 | Cps   —————   hyp
      2 | Cpr   —————   hyp
   last | CpKrs   ?, —————   Ci

4-173 1 | Cps   hyp
      2 | Cpr   hyp
      ? ⌈ —————   p
  last ⌊ —————   Krs
  last | CpKrs   ?, Ci

4-174 1 | Cps   hyp
      2 | Cpr   hyp
      ? | p   —————   hyp
  last | Krs   ?, ?, —————   Ki
  last | CpKrs   ?, Ci

4-175 1 | Cps   hyp
      2 | Cpr   hyp
      ? | p   hyp
       ? —————   r
       ? —————   s
  last | Krs   ?, ?, Ki
  last | CpKrs   ?, Ci

4-176 1 | Cps   hyp
      2 | Cpr   hyp
      3 | 3.1   p   hyp
        3.2   r   2, ————— , Co   3.1
        ?   s
  last | Krs   ?, ?, Ki
  last | CpKrs   ?, Ci

4-177 1 | Cps   hyp
      2 | Cpr   hyp
      3 | 3.1   p   hyp
        3.2   r   2, 3.1, Co
        3.3   s   ———— , ———— , ————   1; 3.1; Co
        last   Krs   ?, ?, Ki
  last | CpKrs   ?, Ci

4-178

```
1 | Cps              hyp
2 | Cpr              hyp
3 | 3.1 |  p         hyp
    3.2 |  r         2, 3.1, Co
    3.3 |  s         1, 3 1, Co
    3.4 |  Krs       ____, ____, ____        3.2; 3.3; Ki
last | CpKrs         ?, Ci
```

4-179

```
1 | Cps              hyp
2 | Cpr              hyp
3 | 3.1 | p          hyp
    3.2 | r          2, 3.1, Co
    3.3 | s          1, 3.1, Co
    3.4 | Krs        3.2, 3.3, Ki
4 | CpKrs            ____, ____             3; Ci
```

4-180 Produce a proof that corresponds to the AF

```
| Cqt
| CqAts
```

and give your good reasons.

```
*1 | Cqt                   hyp
 2 | 2.1 | q               hyp
     2.2 | t               1, 2.1, Co
     2.3 | Ats             2.2, Ai
 3 | CqAts                 2, Ci
```

4-181 To try to discover a proof that corresponds to the AF

```
| Cpq
| Kpt
| CpAKqts
```

we begin the sequence

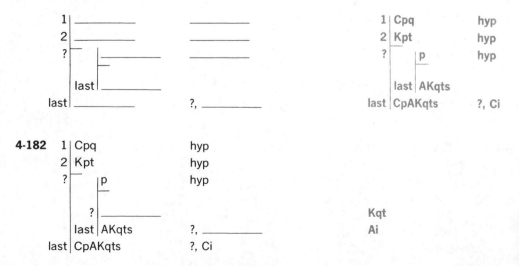

```
1 | _____        _____
2 | _____        _____
? |    | _____       _____
   last | _____
last | _____        ?, _____
```

```
1 | Cpq                hyp
2 | Kpt                hyp
? |    | p             hyp
   last | AKqts
last | CpAKqts         ?, Ci
```

4-182

```
1 | Cpq                hyp
2 | Kpt                hyp
? |    | p             hyp

   ? | _____
   last | AKqts        ?, _____            Kqt
last | CpAKqts         ?, Ci                  Ai
```

4-183

1	Cpq	hyp	
2	Kpt	hyp	
?	⌐ p	hyp	
?	——		q
?	——		t
?	Kqt	?, ?, ——	Ki
last	AKqts	?, Ai	
last	CpAKqts	?, Ci	

4-184

1	Cpq	hyp	
2	Kpt	hyp	
3	3.1 ⌐ p	hyp	
	3.2 q	——, ——, ——	1; 3.1; Co
	3.3 t	——, ——	2; Ko
?	Kqt	?, ?, Ki	
last	AKqts	?, Ai	
last	CpAKqts	?, Ci	

4-185

1	Cpq	hyp	
2	Kpt	hyp	
3	3.1 ⌐ p	hyp	
	3.2 q	1, 3.1, Co	
	3.3 t	2, Ko	
	3.4 Kqt	——, ——, Ki	3.2; 3.3
	3.5 AKqts	——, Ai	3.4
4	CpAKqts	——, Ci	3

4-186 Produce a proof that corresponds to the AF

```
| Kqp
| Cqr
| CqAtKrp
```

and give your good reasons.

*1	Kqp	hyp	
2	Cqr	hyp	
3	3.1 ⌐ q	hyp	
	3.2 r	2, 3.1, Co	
	3.3 p	1, Ko	
	3.4 Krp	3.2, 3.3, Ki	
	3.5 AtKrp	3.4, Ai	
4	CqAtKrp	3, Ci	

D   Likely Good Reasons for WFFs Beginning with an 'N'

4-187 Write an Ni LAF whose first item is like this tail item:

```
1.1 | KpKrNr    hyp
1.2 | KrNr      1.1, Ko
```

1	1.1 KpKrNr	hyp	
	1.2 KrNr	1.1, Ko	
2	NKpKrNr	1, Ni	

4-188 Write an Ni LAF whose first item is like this tail item:

```
1.1| KrNr     hyp
1.2| KrNr     1.1, rep
```

```
1| 1.1| KrNr     hyp
   1.2| KrNr     1.1, rep
2| NKrNr         1, Ni
```

4-189 Could a 'Kst' be the last item of an Ni LAF? _____

no

4-190 Consider the AF

```
|Cpq
|Nq
|Np
```

and consider the sequence

```
1| Cpq
2| Nq

last| Np
```

We will know there is a proof corresponding to the above AF if

1. We can give a good reason for every item of the sequence and so know it is a _____, or

proof

2. We can add items so as to produce a sequence each of whose items has a good reason but add the items in such a way that the resulting proof _____ to the AF.

corresponds

4-191

```
1| Cpq
2| Nq

last| Np
```

A 'hyp' is a good reason for item 1 and for item 2 since both are items of the sequence and are above the 'Ⱶ' for the

_____ .

sequence

4-192

```
1| Cpq     hyp
2| Nq      hyp

last| Np    ?
```

Since the last item of the sequence is below the 'Ⱶ' for the sequence and begins with a connective '_____,' a good strategy is to try to think of the 'Np' as the last item of an _____ LAF.

N

Ni

4-193   An Ni LAF has two items, the first of which is a
_____ item. The last item of an Ni LAF is an 'N' followed   tail
by a WFF just like the only item above the '____' for the first   ⊢
item. The last item of the first item is a _____ WFF.   contradictory

4-194   KrNr   KpNp   KKqrNKqr   KANrsNANrs

The above are all contradictory WFFs. A contradictory WFF is
a '____' followed by two WFFs the second of which is an   K
'____' followed by a WFF just like the _____ WFF.   N; first

4-195   1 | Cpq   hyp
            2 | Nq   hyp

      last | Np   ?

We could think of the 'Np' as the last item of an Ni LAF if

1. There were already in the sequence as an item with a good
reason a tail item such that the only item above the '⊢' for
the tail item was a '____' and the last item of the tail item was   p
a _____ WFF, or   contradictory
2. We could add in the sequence (below the '⊢' for the
sequence but above the last item) a tail item
       with as the only item above the '⊢' for the tail item
       a '____,'   p
       with as last item a _____ WFF, and   contradictory
       with a good reason, that is, such that every
       _____ of the _____ item had a good   item; tail
       reason.

4-196   1 | Cpq
            2 | Nq   hyp

      last | Np   ?

Is there already as an item in the sequence with a good reason
and preceding the 'Np' a tail item whose only item above the
'⊢' for the tail item is a 'p' and whose last item is a contradictory WFF? _____   no

4-197   1 | Cpq   hyp
    2 | Nq   hyp
    ? | | p
      | ⊢
      | last | K···N···
  last | Np   ?, Ni

Let's tentatively add to the sequence a tail item with a 'p' as
the only item above the '⊢' and let's indicate that we would
like the last item of the tail item to be a contradictory WFF by
writing a '_____···_____···' where the last item would go.   K; N
Then if we can add items to the tail item so that every
_____ has a good reason and the last item is a   item
_____ WFF, we can think of the 'Np' as the last item of   contradictory
an _____ LAF whose first item is the _____ item.   Ni; tail

4-198   1 | Cpq   hyp
    2 | Nq   hyp
    ? | | p
      | ⊢
      | last | K···N···
  last | Np   ?, Ni

So far we have specified for the last item of the tail item only
that it be a contradictory WFF without saying *which* contradictory WFF. A reason cannot, of course, always be found for
a contradictory WFF; but even suppose it can be found,
a reason is not found with equal ease for all contradictory
WFFs. In general, if there is as an item with a good reason a
WFF item beginning with an 'N' as

1. Preceding item of the tail item whose last item is to be a
contradictory WFF, or
2. Preceding item of the sequence of which the tail item is
an item,

then it is a good strategy to try to give a good reason for
a contradictory WFF such that the second WFF following the
'K' in the contradictory WFF is like the WFF beginning with
an 'N.' Thus in the above sequence, since an 'Nq' has a good
reason and is an item of the sequence of which the tail item
is an item, it would be a good strategy to try to give a good
reason for a contradictory WFF '_____.'   KqNq

4-199

```
  1 | Cpq          hyp                                    hyp
  2 | Nq           hyp
  ?  |    | p      _____                           2
     | last | KqNq    ?, _____ , Ki
last | Np           ?, Ni
```

Notice if we choose to try to find a good reason for a contradictory WFF 'KqNq' and are guided in our choice by the
presence of an 'Nq' with a good reason, then we can think of
the contradictory WFF as the last item of a Ki LAF if we can
give a good reason for a WFF item '_____.'   q

4-200

```
  1 | Cpq          hyp
  2 | Nq           hyp
  ?  |    | p      hyp                                    q
     |  ? |___
     | last | KqNq    ?, 2, Ki
last | Np           ?, Ni
```


4-201

```
  1 | Cpq              hyp
  2 | Nq               hyp
  3 | 3.1 | p          hyp
    | 3.2 | q          ____ , ____ , ____              1; 3.1; Co
    | last | KqNq      ?, 2, Ki
last | Np              ?, Ni
```


4-202

```
  1 | Cpq              hyp
  2 | Nq               hyp
  3 | 3.1 | p          hyp
    | 3.2 | q          1, 3.1, Co
    | 3.3 | KqNq       ____ , ____ , ____              3.2; 2; Ki
  4 | Np               ?, Ni
```

4-203

1	Cpq	hyp
2	Nq	hyp
3	3.1 | p	hyp
	3.2 | q	1, 3.1, Co
	3.3 | KqNq	3.2, 2, Ki
4	Np	_____ , _____

3; Ni

Notice the whole tail item 3 (and not just item 3.1 or the last item 3.3) is cited in the reason for item 4. For, loosely speaking, from a 'p' as a hypothesis, a 'KqNq' "follows." But a 'KqNq' formalizes a contradiction. So under the hypotheses 'Cpq' and 'Nq,' a 'p' must be rejected as a hypothesis, and it must be the case that 'Np.'

4-204

1	Cpq	hyp
2	Nq	hyp
3	3.1 | p	hyp
	3.2 | q	1, 3.1, Co
	3.3 | KqNq	3.2, 2, Ki
4	Np	3, Ni

Since every item in this sequence has a good reason (item 3 has a good reason because each of the items in item 3 has a good reason) the sequence is a _____ . So any argument is valid if it can be formalized by the AF

      ⊢ _____
       _____
       _____

proof

Cpq
Nq
Np

for this AF corresponds to a _____ in system F.

proof

4-205 To try to discover a proof that corresponds to the AF

    ⊢ Nr
     NKrs

we begin the sequence

   1 ⊢ _____
       ___
last ⊢ _____

   1 ⊢ Nr
last ⊢ NKrs

4-206

1	Nr	_____	hyp
last	NKrs	?, _____	Ni

4-207 1│Nr   hyp

$\quad$?│ $\quad$ ┌─────────

$\qquad$ │ last│ K⋯N⋯

$\quad$ last│ NKrs $\qquad\qquad$?, Ni

$\hfill$ Krs

4-208 1│Nr   hyp

$\quad$?│ $\quad$ │Krs

$\qquad$ │ last│ K⋯N⋯

$\quad$ last│ NKrs $\qquad\qquad$?, Ni

Since we want as last item of the tail item a contradictory WFF and since item 1 is an '_____' and has a good reason, it would be a good strategy to try to give a good reason for a contradictory WFF '_____.'

$\hfill$ Nr

$\hfill$ KrNr

4-209 1│Nr $\qquad\qquad$ hyp $\hfill$ hyp

$\quad$?│ $\quad$ │Krs $\qquad$ _____ $\hfill$ 1

$\qquad$ │ last│ KrNr $\qquad$?, _____, Ki

$\quad$ last│ NKrs $\qquad\qquad$?, Ni

4-210 1│Nr $\qquad\qquad$ hyp

$\quad$?│ $\quad$ │Krs $\qquad$ hyp $\hfill$ r

$\qquad$?│ $\quad$ ─────

$\qquad$ │ last│ KrNr $\qquad$?, 1, Ki

$\quad$ last│ NKrs $\qquad\qquad$?, Ni

4-211 1│Nr $\qquad\qquad$ hyp

$\quad$ 2│ 2.1│ Krs $\qquad$ hyp $\hfill$ 2.1; Ko

$\qquad$ │ 2.2│ r $\qquad$ ____ , ____

$\qquad$ │ last│ KrNr $\qquad$?, 1, Ki

$\quad$ last│ NKrs $\qquad\qquad$?, Ni

4-212 1│Nr $\qquad\qquad$ hyp

$\quad$ 2│ 2.1│ Krs $\qquad$ hyp

$\qquad$ │ 2.2│ r $\qquad$ 2.1, Ko $\hfill$ 2.2; 1; Ki

$\qquad$ │ 2.3│ KrNr $\qquad$ ____ , ____ , ____

$\quad$ last│ NKrs $\qquad\qquad$?, Ni

4-213

```
1 | Nr               hyp
2 | 2.1 | Krs         hyp
  | 2.2 | r           2.1, Ko
  | 2.3 | KrNr        2.2, 1, Ki
3 | NKrs         _____ , _____        3; Ni
```

4-214 To try to discover a proof that corresponds to the AF

```
| p
| NNp
```

we begin the sequence

```
1    | _____      _____        p; hyp

last | _____   ?, _____        NNp; Ni
```

4-215

```
1 | p                        hyp
? |  ‾| _____                       Np
  |   |
  |  last | K···N···
last | NNp              ?, Ni
```

4-216

```
1 | p                        hyp
? |  ‾| Np        _____            hyp
  |   |
  |  last | K···N···
last | NNp              ?, Ni
```

Since we want as last item of the tail item a contradictory WFF
and since the first item of the tail item is an '_____' and   Np
can be given a '_____' as a good reason, it would be a   hyp
good strategy to try to give a good reason for a contradictory
WFF '_____.'   KpNp

4-217

```
1 | p                      hyp
2 | 2.1 | Np               hyp
  |  ‾|
  | last | KpNp       ?, _____ , Ki       2.1
last | NNp            ?, Ni
```

4-218

```
1 | p                      hyp
2 | 2.1 | Np               hyp
  | 2.2 | KpNp       _____ , _____ , _____      1; 2.1; Ki
last | NNp           ?, Ni
```

4-219

```
1 | p                    hyp
2 | 2.1 | Np            hyp
  | 2.2 | KpNp          1, 2.1, Ki
3 | NNp           _____ , Ni        2
```

4-220 Produce a proof that corresponds to the AF

|Kpq
|‾‾‾‾‾
|NNKpq

and give your good reasons.

```
*1 | Kpq                    hyp
 2 | 2.1 | NKpq           hyp
   | 2.2 | KKpqNKpq       1, 2.1, Ki
 3 | NNKpq               2, Ni
```

4-221 To try to discover a proof that corresponds to the AF

|NApq
|‾‾‾‾
|Np

we begin the sequence

```
 1   | NApq      _____          hyp

last | Np     ?, _____          Ni
```

4-222

```
 1    | NApq              hyp
 ?    |                                p; hyp
      |  |
      |  last | K···N···
last  | Np              ?, Ni
```

4-223

```
 1    | NApq              hyp
 ?    |  | p              hyp
      |  |
      |  last | _____   ?, 1, Ki     KApqNApq
last  | Np              ?, Ni
```

4-224

```
 1    | NApq              hyp
 ?    |  | p              hyp
      |  ? | _____                Apq
      | last | KApqNApq   ?, 1, Ki
last  | Np              ?, Ni
```

4-225

```
 1    | NApq              hyp
 2    | 2.1 | p           hyp
      | 2.2 | Apq      _____ , _____   2.1; Ai
      | last | KApqNApq   ?, 1, Ki
last  | Np              ?, Ni
```

4-226

1	NApq	hyp
2	2.1	p	hyp
	2.2	Apq	2.1, Ai
	2.3	KApqNApq	_____, _____, _____	2.2; 1; Ki
3	Np	_____, _____	2; Ni

4-227 To try to discover a proof that corresponds to the AF

| Nr
| Kpr
|‾ Nt

we begin the sequence

1	Nr	_____	hyp
2	Kpr	_____	hyp
last	Nt	?, _____	Ni

4-228

1	Nr		hyp
2	Kpr		hyp
?	|— _____	_____	t; hyp
	last	K···N···	
last	Nt		?, Ni

4-229

1	Nr		hyp
2	Kpr		hyp
?		t	hyp
	last	_____	?, _____, Ki	KrNr; 1
last	Nt		?, Ni

4-230

1	Nr		hyp
2	Kpr		hyp
?		t	hyp
	?	_____		r
	last	KrNr	?, 1, Ki
last	Nt		?, Ni

4-231

1	Nr	hyp
2	Kpr	hyp
3	3.1| t	hyp
	3.2| r	_____ , _____ 2; Ko
	3.3| KrNr	_____ , _____ , _____ 3.2; 1; Ki
4	Nt	_____ , _____ 3; Ni

4-232 Produce a proof that corresponds to the AF

KCqst
Nt
Np

and give your good reasons.

*1	KCqst	hyp
2	Nt	hyp
3	3.1| p	hyp
	3.2| t	1, Ko
	3.3| KtNt	3.2, 2, Ki
4	Np	3, Ni

4-233 In general, when trying to decide for which contradictory WFF to try to give a good reason, if there is as an item with a good reason a WFF item beginning with an 'N' and that item is a

1. Preceding item of the tail item whose last item is to be a contradictory WFF, or
2. Preceding item of the sequence of which the tail item is an item,

then it is a good strategy to try to give a good reason for a contradictory WFF such that the _____ WFF following the 'K' in the contradictory WFF is like the WFF beginning with an '_____ .'

second

N

4-234 When trying to give a good reason for a contradictory WFF, if there is no preceding item beginning with an 'N,' then if there is a WFF beginning with an 'N' as *part* of some preceding item it is a good strategy to try to give a good reason for a contradictory WFF such that the second WFF following the 'K' in the contradictory WFF is like the WFF beginning with an '_____ .' Thus, if there were some preceding item 'CpNt,' a good strategy might be to look for a good reason for a contradictory WFF '_____ .'

N

KtNt

4-235 To try to discover a proof that corresponds to the AF

> | CpNq
> | p
> |‾‾‾‾‾
> | NCpq

we begin the sequence

1	CpNq	————	hyp
2	p	————	hyp
last	NCpq	?, ————	Ni

4-236

1	CpNq		hyp	
2	p		hyp	
?		———— ————		Cpq; hyp
	last	K···N···		
last	NCpq		?, Ni	

4-237

1	CpNq		hyp
2	p		hyp
?		Cpq	hyp
	last	K···N···	
last	NCpq		?, Ni

No item of the tail item or item of the sequence preceding the tail item begins with an 'N.' But the second WFF following the 'C' in item 1 is an '————.' So a good strategy may be to try to give a good reason for a contradictory WFF '————.'

Nq
KqNq

4-238

1	CpNq		hyp
2	p		hyp
?		Cpq	hyp
	last	————	KqNq
last	NCpq		?, Ni

4-239

1	CpNq		hyp	
2	p		hyp	
3	3.1	Cpq	hyp	
	3.2	————	————, ————, ————	q; 3.1; 2; Co
	3.3	————	————, ————, ————	Nq; 1, 2, Co
	last	KqNq	?, ?, Ki	
last	NCpq		?, Ni	

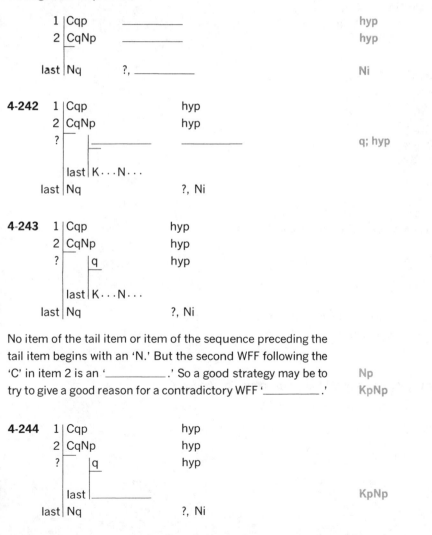

4-240

1	CpNq		hyp	
2	p		hyp	
3	3.1	Cpq	hyp	
	3.2	q	3.1, 2, Co	
	3.3	Nq	1, 2, Co	
	3.4	KqNq	_____ , _____ , _____	3.2; 3.3; Ki
4	NCpq		_____ , _____	3; Ni

4-241 To try to discover a proof that corresponds to the AF

Cqp
CqNp
Nq

we begin the sequence

1	Cqp	_____		hyp
2	CqNp	_____		hyp
last	Nq	?, _____		Ni

4-242

1	Cqp		hyp	
2	CqNp		hyp	
?	_____	_____		q; hyp
	last	K···N···		
last	Nq	?, Ni		

4-243

1	Cqp		hyp	
2	CqNp		hyp	
?	q		hyp	
	last	K···N···		
last	Nq	?, Ni		

No item of the tail item or item of the sequence preceding the tail item begins with an 'N.' But the second WFF following the 'C' in item 2 is an '_____.' So a good strategy may be to try to give a good reason for a contradictory WFF '_____.'   Np   KpNp

4-244

1	Cqp		hyp	
2	CqNp		hyp	
?	q		hyp	
	last	_____		KpNp
last	Nq	?, Ni		

4-245

```
1    | Cqp                    hyp
2    | CqNp                   hyp
?    |   | q                  hyp
     ?   | ____                        p
     ?   | ____                        Np
   last  | KpNp     ?, ?, ____         Ki
last | Nq           ?, Ni
```

4-246

```
1    | Cqp                    hyp
2    | CqNp                   hyp
3    | 3.1 | q                hyp
     | 3.2 | p      ____, ____, ____    1; 3.1; Co
     | 3.3 | Np     ____, ____, ____    2; 3.1; Co
     | last| KpNp   ?, ?, Ki
last | Nq           ?, Ni
```

4-247

```
1    | Cqp                    hyp
2    | CqNp                   hyp
3    | 3.1 | q                hyp
     | 3.2 | p      1, 3.1, Co
     | 3.3 | Np     2, 3.1, Co
     | 3.4 | KpNp   ____, ____, ____    3.2; 3.3; Ki
4    | Nq           ____, ____          3; Ni
```

4-248 Produce a proof that corresponds to the AF

```
| CrNs
| Crs
| Nr
```

and give your good reasons. Notice that the last item of the
proof will be a WFF beginning with an 'N.'

```
*1   | CrNs                   hyp
2    | Crs                    hyp
3    | 3.1 | r                hyp
     | 3.2 | s       2, 3.1, Co
     | 3.3 | Ns      1, 3.1, Co
     | 3.4 | KsNs    3.2, 3.3, Ki
4    | Nr            3, Ni
```

4-249 To try to discover a proof that corresponds to the AF

```
| p
| NKrNp
```

we begin the sequence

```
1    | p          _____              hyp

last | NKrNp   ?, _____              Ni
```

4-250

```
1 | p                                      hyp
? |———          ————                                    KrNp; hyp

  last | K...N...
last | NKrNp              ?, Ni
```

4-251

```
1 | p                                      hyp
? |  | KrNp                                 hyp

  last |————                                               KpNp
last | NKrNp              ?, Ni
```

4-252

```
1 | p                          hyp
? |  | KrNp                     hyp

   ? |———                                    Np
  last | KpNp        ———, ?, Ki               1
last | NKrNp         ?, Ni
```

4-253

```
1 | p                    hyp
2 | 2.1 | KrNp           hyp
    2.2 | Np         ———, ———                 2.1; Ko
    2.3 | KpNp       ———, ———, ———            1; 2.2; Ki
3 | NKrNp           ———, ———                  2; Ni
```

4-254   Produce a proof that corresponds to the AF

```
| Cpt
| NKrNCpt
```

and give your good reasons.

```
*1 | Cpt                    hyp
 2 | 2.1 | KrNCpt           hyp
     2.2 | NCpt             2.1, Ko
     2.3 | KCptNCpt         1, 2.2, Ki
 3 | NKrNCpt                2, Ni
```

4-255   To try to discover a proof that corresponds to the AF

```
| CpKrNr
| NKsp
```

we begin the sequence

```
1 | CpKrNr       hyp

last | NKsp       ?, ———                       Ni
```

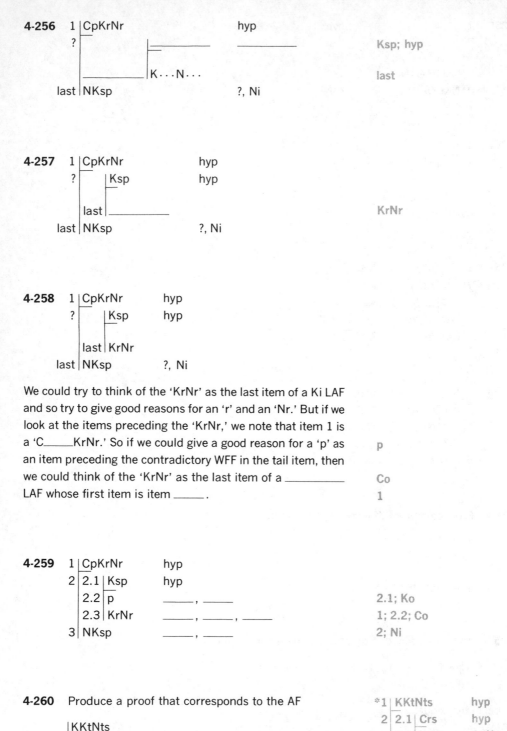

4-256 1 | CpKrNr   hyp   Ksp; hyp

       ?

                       K...N...   last

   last | NKsp   ?, Ni

4-257 1 | CpKrNr   hyp

       ? | Ksp   hyp   KrNr

          last |_____

   last | NKsp   ?, Ni

4-258 1 | CpKrNr   hyp

       ? | Ksp   hyp

          last | KrNr

   last | NKsp   ?, Ni

We could try to think of the 'KrNr' as the last item of a Ki LAF and so try to give good reasons for an 'r' and an 'Nr.' But if we look at the items preceding the 'KrNr,' we note that item 1 is a 'C_____KrNr.' So if we could give a good reason for a 'p' as   p an item preceding the contradictory WFF in the tail item, then we could think of the 'KrNr' as the last item of a _____   Co LAF whose first item is item _____.   1

4-259 1 | CpKrNr   hyp

    2 | 2.1 | Ksp   hyp

          2.2 | p   _____ , _____   2.1; Ko

          2.3 | KrNr   _____ , _____ , _____   1; 2.2; Co

    3 | NKsp   _____ , _____   2; Ni

4-260   Produce a proof that corresponds to the AF   *1 | KKtNts   hyp

                                          2 | 2.1 | Crs   hyp

   | KKtNts   2.2 | KtNt   1, Ko

   | NCrs   3 | NCrs   2, Ni

and give your good reasons.

4-261   When trying to give a good reason for a WFF item below the 'Ⱶ' for the sequence

1. If the item begins with a 'K,' try to think of the item as the last item of a _____ LAF;   Ki

2. If the item begins with an 'A,' try to think of the item as the last item of an _____ LAF;   Ai

3. If the item begins with a 'C,' try to think of the item as the last item of a _____ LAF;   Ci

4. If the item begins with an 'N,' try to think of the item as the last item of an _____ LAF.   Ni

When trying to think of an item as the last item of an Ni LAF, there must be a preceding tail item whose last item is a contradictory WFF. When trying to decide for which contradictory WFF to try to give a good reason

1. If a preceding item begins with an 'N,' try to give a good reason for a contradictory WFF such that the _____ WFF   second
following the 'K' in the contradictory WFF is like the item beginning with an 'N';

2. If no preceding item begins with an 'N' but some part of some preceding item is a WFF beginning with an 'N,' try to give a good reason for a contradictory WFF such that the second WFF following the 'K' in the contradictory WFF is like the WFF beginning with an '____';   N

3. If at a loss as to which WFF to pick, then try to give a good reason for a contradictory WFF such that the second WFF following the 'K' in the contradictory WFF is a sentence variable like some sentence variable occurring already in some preceding item.

E   WFFs as the Last Items of Ao LAFs

4-262   When trying to find a good reason for a WFF item below the 'Ⱶ' for a sequence

1. If the item begins with a connective, then a good strategy is to try to think of the item as the last item of the appropriate kind of _____-LAF, for the last item of every in-LAF   in
begins with a _____;   connective

2. If the item does not begin with a connective, then a good strategy is to try to think of the item as the last item of some _____-LAF, for the last item of an out-LAF need not   out
begin with a connective.

4-263   There are four kinds of out-LAFs; but so far, though
we have thought of some items as last items of Ko LAFs and
others as last items of Co LAFs, we have not tried to think of
any items as last items of _____ LAFs or of _____
LAFs.

Ao; No
(Either order)

4-264   The first item of every out-LAF—except No LAFs—
begins with a connective; the first item of a Ko LAF begins
with a '_____'; the first item of an Ao LAF begins with an
'_____'; and the first item of a Co LAF begins with a '_____.'
The first item of an No LAF is a tail item, and the first item of
the tail item begins with a connective '_____.'

K

A; C

N

4-265   Complete these out-LAFs by giving good reasons for
the last item in each case.

```
1| KKrsKpq      hyp
2| Krs          _____                          1, Ko

1| KKrsKpq      hyp
2| Kpq          _____                          1, Ko

1| AKrss        hyp
2| 2.1| Krs     hyp
   2.2| s       2.1, Ko
   2.3| Asp     2.2, Ai
3| 3.1| s       hyp
   3.2| Asp     3.1, Ai
4| Asp          _____                          1, 2, 3, Ao

1| CCpqCrs      hyp
2| Cpq          hyp
3| Crs          _____                          1, 2, Co

1| 1.1| NCpp          hyp
   1.2| 1.2.1| p      hyp
        1.2.2| p      1.2.1, rep
   1.3| Cpp           1.2, Ci
   1.4| KCppNCpp      1.3, 1.1, Ki
2| Cpp               _____                      1, No
```

4-266 Complete the following:

1	_____	hyp
2	2.1 ⌐ Kpt	hyp
	2.2 ⌐ p	2.1, Ko
3	3.1 ⌐ Kpr	hyp
	3.2 ⌐ p	3.2, Ko
4	_____	1, 2, 3, Ao

AKptKpr

p

4-267 Consider the AF

| Apq
| Cpr
| Cqr
⌐ r

and consider the sequence

1	Apq
2	Cpr
3	Cqr

last | r

We will know there is a proof corresponding to the above AF if

1. We can give a good reason for every item of the sequence
and so know it is a _____, or

proof

2. We can add items so as to produce a sequence each of
whose items has a good reason but add the items in such a
way that the resulting proof _____ to the AF.

corresponds

4-268

1	Apq
2	Cpr
3	Cqr

last | r

A 'hyp' is a good reason for item 1, item 2, and item 3, since
all three items are above the 'ⱶ' for the sequence and are
items of the _____.

sequence

4-269

```
     1 | Apq      hyp
     2 | Cpr      hyp
     3 | Cqr      hyp
         ┌
  last | r        ?
```

Since the last item of the sequence is below the 'ⱶ' for the sequence and does not begin with a connective, a good strategy is to try to think of the 'r' as the last item of some _____-LAF. There is as an item with a good reason and preceding the 'r' in the sequence no item beginning with a 'K,' but there is an item beginning with an 'A.' So a good strategy is to try to think of the 'r' as the last item of an _____ LAF.

out

Ao

4-270   An Ao LAF has four items, the second and third of which are _____ items. The first item of an Ao LAF is an 'A' followed by two WFFs the first of which is like the only item above the 'ⱶ' for the _____ tail item and the second of which is like the only item above the 'ⱶ' for the _____ tail item. The last item of both tail items is like the _____ item of the LAF.

tail

first

second

last

4-271

```
     1 | Apq      hyp
     2 | Cpr      hyp
     3 | Cqr      hyp
         ┌
  last | r        ?
```

We could think of the 'r' as the last item of an Ao LAF if there were in the sequence in addition to the 'Apq' two tail items with good reasons and such that

1. The first tail item had as the only item above the 'ⱶ' for the tail item a '_____' and had as its last item an '_____,' and
2. The second tail item had as the only item above the 'ⱶ' for the tail item a '_____' and had as its last item an '_____,' or

if we could add to the sequence and preceding the 'r' two such tail items for which we could give good _____ .

p; r

q; r

reasons

4-272

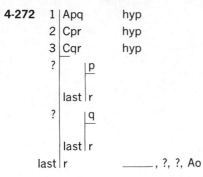

1	Apq	hyp
2	Cpr	hyp
3	Cqr	hyp
?	⌐ p	
	last ⌐ r	
?	⌐ q	
	last ⌐ r	
last ⌐ r	_____ , ?, ?, Ao	1

Since, though there is an 'Apq' with a good reason, no appropriate tail items were present in the sequence, let's tentatively add to the sequence two tail items and indicate what must be the only items above the 'Ⱶ's for the tail items and what must be the last items for the tail items. Then if we can add items to the tail items so that in each tail item every _____ has a good reason, then we can think of the 'r' as   item
the last item of an Ao LAF whose first item is item _____ and   1
whose other items are the _____ items.   tail

4-273

1	Apq	hyp	
2	Cpr	hyp	
3	Cqr	hyp	
?	⌐ p	_____	hyp
	last ⌐ r	?	
?	⌐ q		
	last ⌐ r		
last ⌐ r	1, ?, ?, Ao		

Since the 'p' is above the 'Ⱶ' for the tail item, a good reason for the 'p' is a '_____.'   hyp

4-274

1	Apq	hyp	
2	Cpr	hyp	
3	Cqr	hyp	
4	4.1 ⌐ p	hyp	
	4.2 ⌐ r	_____ , _____ , _____	2; 4.1; Co
?	⌐ q		
	last ⌐ r		
last ⌐ r	1, ?, ?, Ao		

A tail item has a good reason if each of its items has a good reason. Item 4 has how many items? _____ Does item   two
4 have a good reason? _____   yes

4-275

```
      1 | Apq              hyp
      2 | Cpr              hyp
      3 | Cqr              hyp
      4 | 4.1 | p          hyp
        | 4.2 | r          2, 4.1, Co
      5 | 5.1 | q          _____                      hyp
        | 5.2 | r          ____, ____, ____                 3; 5.1; Co
   last | r                1, ?, ?, Ao
```

4-276

```
      1 | Apq              hyp
      2 | Cpr              hyp
      3 | Cqr              hyp
      4 | 4.1 | p          hyp
        | 4.2 | r          2, 4.1, Co
      5 | 5.1 | q          hyp
        | 5.2 | r          3, 5.1, Co
      6 | r                ____, ____, ____, ____           1; 4; 5; Ao
```

Notice we cite three items (1, 4, 5) in the reason for item 6. Loosely speaking, item 1 ('Apq') says that either 'p' or else 'q,' and we have item 1 as an hypothesis. In item 4, from 'p' as hypothesis an 'r' "follows"; in item 5, from 'q' as hypothesis an 'r' "follows." So since an 'r' "follows" from a 'p' as well as from a 'q' and we have assumed (item 1) either 'p' or 'q,' it must be the case that 'r'; hence, item 6.

4-277

```
      1 | Apq              hyp
      2 | Cpr              hyp
      3 | Cqr              hyp
      4 | 4.1 | p          hyp
        | 4.2 | r          2, 4.1, Co
      5 | 5.1 | q          hyp
        | 5.2 | r          3, 5.1, Co
      6 | r                1, 4, 5, Ao
```

Since every item in the sequence has a good reason (item 4 and item 5 have good reasons since in each of them every item has a good reason) the sequence is a _____. So   proof
any argument is valid if it can be formalized by the AF

```
   | _____                                             | Apq
   | _____                                             | Cpr
   | _____                                             | Cqr
   | _____                                             | r
```

for this AF corresponds to a _____ in system F.   proof

4-278 To try to discover a proof that corresponds to the AF

| Aqt
| Ctq
|‾‾
| q

we begin the sequence

```
  1 | Aqt      hyp
  2 | Ctq      hyp
   ‾‾
last | q        ?
```

A 'hyp' is a good reason for the items above the 'Ͱ' for the sequence. The last item is below the 'Ͱ' for the sequence and does not begin with a connective. So a good strategy is to try to think of the 'q' as the last item of an _____-LAF. Is there any preceding item beginning with a 'K'? _____ With an 'A'? _____

out

no

yes

4-279
```
  1 | Aqt      hyp
  2 | Ctq      hyp
   ‾‾
last | r        _____, ?, ?, Ao
```

1

4-280
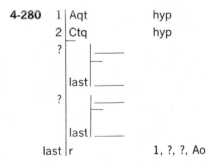
```
  1 | Aqt            hyp
  2 | Ctq            hyp
  ? | |‾‾ _____
    | |
    | last| _____
  ? | |‾‾ _____
    | |
    | last| _____
last | r            1, ?, ?, Ao
```

q

r
t

r

4-281
```
  1 | Aqt         hyp
  2 | Ctq         hyp
  3 | 3.1 | q     _____
    | 3.2 | q     _____, _____
  4 | 4.1 | t     _____
    | 4.2 | q     _____, _____, _____
last | q          1, ?, ?, Ao
```

hyp
3.1; rep
hyp
2; 4.1; Co

4-282

```
1 | Aqt          hyp
2 | Ctq          hyp
3 | 3.1 | q       hyp
  | 3.2 | q̄      3.1, rep
4 | 4.1 | t̄      hyp
  | 4.2 | q       2, 4.1, Co
5 | q           ____, ____, ____, ____        1; 3; 4; Ao
```

Does item 1 have a good reason? _____ Does item 3
have a good reason? _____ Does item 4 have a good
reason? _____ Does item 5 have a good reason, then?
_____

yes

yes

yes

yes

4-283   Produce a proof that corresponds to the AF

```
| Cps
| Asp
| Cst
|‾t
```

and give your good reasons.

```
*1 | Cps              hyp
 2 | Asp              hyp
 3 | Cst              hyp
 4 | 4.1 | s          hyp
   | 4.2 | t          3, 4.1, Co
 5 | 5.1 | p          hyp
   | 5.2 | s          1, 5.1, Co
   | 5.3 | t          3, 5.2, Co
 6 | t                2, 4, 5, Ao
```

4-284   To try to discover a proof that corresponds to the AF

```
| AApqKts
| CApqr
| CKtsr
|‾r
```

we begin the sequence

```
1 | AApqKts      hyp
2 | CApqr        hyp
3 | CKtsr        hyp

last | r         1, ?, ?, _____        Ao
```

4-285

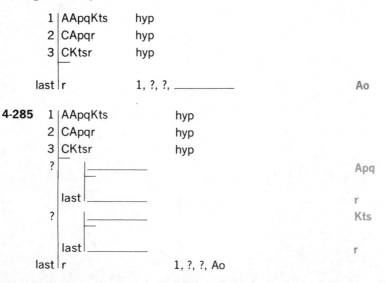

```
1 | AApqKts              hyp
2 | CApqr                hyp
3 | CKtsr                hyp
? |   | _____                           Apq
  |   |
  | last | _____                        r
? |   | _____                           Kts
  |   |
  | last | _____                        r
last | r          1, ?, ?, Ao
```

4-286

1	AApqKts	hyp	
2	CApqr	hyp	
3	CKtsr	hyp	
4	4.1 | Apq	_____	hyp
	4.2 | r	____ , ____ , ____	2; 4.1; Co
5	5.1 | Kts	_____	hyp
	5.2 | r	____ , ____ , ____	3; 5.1; Co
last	r	1, ?, ?, Ao	

4-287

1	AApqKts	hyp	
2	CApqr	hyp	
3	CKtsr	hyp	
4	4.1 | Apq	hyp	
	4.2 | r	2, 4.1, Co	
5	5.1 | Kts	hyp	
	5.2 | r	3, 5.1, Co	
6	r	____ , ____ , ____ , ____	1; 4; 5; Ao

4-288   To try to discover a proof that corresponds to the AF

|	Ats
|	p
|	CKtpr
|	Csr
|‾	r

we begin the sequence

1	Ats	hyp
2	p	hyp
3	CKtpr	hyp
4	Csr	hyp
last	r	____ , ?, ?, ____ 1; Ao

The 'r' is _____ the 'ⱶ' for the sequence, does not begin   below
with a _____ , and item 1 is an '_____.' So we may   connective; Ats
be able to think of the 'r' as the last item of an _____ LAF.   Ao

4-289

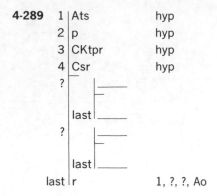

```
4-289   1 | Ats          hyp
        2 | p            hyp
        3 | CKtpr        hyp
        4 | Csr          hyp
        ? |    _____                                    t
          | last|_____                                  r
        ? |    _____                                    s
          | last|_____                                  r
     last |r          1, ?, ?, Ao
```

```
4-290   1 | Ats          hyp
        2 | p            hyp
        3 | CKtpr        hyp
        4 | Csr          hyp
        ? |    |t
          | last|r
        ? |    |s
          | last|r
     last |r          1, ?, ?, Ao
```

To give a good reason for the first tail item, we must be able to give a good reason for each of the items and we must not add any items _____ the 'Ⱶ' for the tail item or _____ the 'r' (otherwise the tail item would not be a proper second item of an Ao LAF of which item 1 is the first item and the 'r' the last item). Since the 't' is above the 'Ⱶ' for the tail item, the 't' can have as a good reason a '_____.' The 'r' is below the 'Ⱶ' for the tail item and does not begin with a connective. So we should try to think of the 'r' as the last item of some out-LAF. No preceding item begins with a 'K,' so we won't try a _____ LAF. Item 1 is an 'Ats,' but we are already trying to think of the 'r' as the last item of an Ao LAF whose first item is the 'Ats.' *In general* it is not a good idea to try to think of a given item beginning with an 'A' as the first item of more than one Ao LAF (though we may want to do this with an item beginning with a 'C' or with a 'K'). But item 3 begins with a 'C' and the _____ WFF following the 'C' is like the WFF for which we are trying to give a good reason. So we could think of the 'r' which is the last item of the first tail

Right margin answers:

above; below

hyp

Ko

second

item as the last item of a Co LAF whose first item is item 3 if there were as an item with a good reason and preceding 'r' in the tail item or preceding the tail item in the sequence a WFF item '_____.'

Ktp

4-291

```
1 | Ats          hyp
2 | p            hyp
3 | CKtpr        hyp
4 | Csr          hyp
? |      | t      hyp
     ? | Ktp
     last | r    3, ?, _____          Co
? |      | s

     last | r
last | r          1, ?, ?, Ao
```

Since there was no item 'Ktp,' let's tentatively add a 'Ktp' preceding the 'r.' Then if we can give a good reason for the 'Ktp,' we can think of the 'r' as the last item of a _____   Co
LAF which has as its second item a '_____.'   Ktp

4-292

```
1 | Ats          hyp
2 | p            hyp
3 | CKtpr        hyp
4 | Csr          hyp
5 | 5.1 | t      hyp
    5.2 | Ktp    ____, ____, ____          5.1; 2; Ki
    last | r     3, ?, Co
? |      | s

     last | r
last | r          1, ?, ?, Ao
```

Does the 't' have a good reason? _____ Does the 'p'   yes
have a good reason? _____ Is the 't' an item preceding   yes
the 'Ktp' in the tail item? _____ Is the 'p' an item   yes
preceding the 'Ktp' in the tail item? _____ Is the 'p' an   no
item preceding the tail item but in the same sequence of
which the tail item is an item? _____   yes

4-293

1	Ats	hyp
2	p	hyp
3	CKtpr	hyp
4	Csr	hyp
5	5.1	t	hyp
	5.2	Ktp	5.1, 2, Ki
	5.3	r	____, ____, ____ 3; 5.2; Co
?		s	____ hyp
	last	r	
last	r	1, ?, ?, Ao

4-294

1	Ats	hyp
2	p	hyp
3	CKtpr	hyp
4	Csr	hyp
5	5.1	t	hyp
	5.2	Ktp	5.1, 2, Ki
	5.3	r	3, 5.2, Co
6	6.1	s	hyp
	6.2	r	____, ____, ____ 4; 6.1; Co
last	r	1, ?, ?, Ao

4-295

1	Ats	hyp
2	p	hyp
3	CKtpr	hyp
4	Csr	hyp
5	5.1	t	hyp
	5.2	Ktp	5.1, 2, Ki
	5.3	r	3, 5.2, Co
6	6.1	s	hyp
	6.2	r	4, 6.1, Co
7	r	____, ____, ____, ____ 1; 5; 6; Ao

4-296   Produce a proof that corresponds to the AF

> | Csp
> | Crp
> | AKqrKst
> | p

and give your good reasons.

*1	Csp	hyp
2	Crp	hyp
3	AKqrKst	hyp
4	4.1	Kqr	hyp
	4.2	r	4.1, Ko
	4.3	p	2, 4.2, Co
5	5.1	Kst	hyp
	5.2	s	5.1, Ko
	5.3	p	1, 5.2, Co
6	p	3, 4, 5, Ao

F WFFs as the Last Items of No LAFs

4-297   Just as it is useless to try to think of an item as the last item of an in-LAF if the item does not begin with a connective, so it is useless to try to think of an item as the last item of a Ko, Ao, or Co LAF if no preceding item begins with the appropriate connective. But even if no preceding item begins with an 'N,' it may still be possible to think of an item as the last item of an ___ ___ LAF.

No

4-298   Complete the following:

1	1.1	NCKpqp	hyp
	1.2	1.2.1	Kpq	hyp
		1.2.2	p	1.2.1, Ko
	1.3	CKpqq	1.2, Cɪ
	1.4	KCKpqpNCKpqp	1.3, 1.1, Ki
2	_____		1, No

CKpqp

4-299   Consider the AF

```
p
Cpq
CpNq
r
```

and consider the sequence

```
1 | p
2 | Cpq
3 | CpNq

last | r
```

We will know there is a proof corresponding to the above AF if

1. We can give a good reason for every item of the sequence and so know it is a _____ , or

proof

2. We can add items so as to produce a sequence each of whose items has a good reason but add the items in such a way that the resulting proof _____ to the AF.

corresponds

4-300

```
1 | p
2 | Cpq
3 | CpNq

last | r
```

A 'hyp' is a good reason for item 1, item 2, and item 3 since
all three are items of the sequence and are above the 'Ⱶ' for
the _____ .

sequence

4-301

```
1 | p        hyp
2 | Cpq      hyp
3 | CpNq     hyp

last | r
```

A good strategy is to think of the last item as the last item of
some out-LAF since the 'r' is _____ the 'Ⱶ' for the   below
sequence and does not begin with a _____ . Any item in   connective
the sequence preceding the 'r' and beginning with a 'K'?
_____ Then should we try to think of the 'r' as the last   no
item of a Ko LAF? _____ Any preceding item beginning   no
with an 'A'? _____ Should we try an Ao LAF? _____   no; no
Any preceding item beginning with a 'C'? _____ Any   yes
preceding item beginning with a 'C' and such that the second
WFF following the 'C' is like the WFF 'r' for which we are trying
to give a good reason? _____ So should we try to think   no
of the 'r' as the last item of a Co LAF? _____ So if we are   no
to think of the 'r' as the last item of an out-LAF, we must think
of the 'r' as the last item of an _____ LAF.   No

4-302   An No LAF has two items, the first of which is a
_____ item. The only item above the 'Ⱶ' for the tail item   tail
is an '____' followed by a WFF like the _____ item of the   N; last
LAF. The last item of the tail item is a _____ WFF.   contradictory

4-303

```
1 | p        hyp
2 | Cpq      hyp
3 | CpNq     hyp

last | r     ?
```

We could think of the 'r' as the last item of an No LAF if

1. There were already in the sequence as an item with a good
reason a tail item such that the only item above the 'Ⱶ' for
the tail item was an '_____' and the last item of the tail   Nr
item was a _____ WFF, or   contradictory
2. We could add in the sequence (below the 'Ⱶ' for the
sequence but above the last item) a tail item
      with as the only item above the 'Ⱶ' for the tail item
      an '_____,'   Nr
      with as last item a _____ WFF, and   contradictory
      with a good reason, that is, such that every
      _____ of the _____ item had a good   item; tail
      reason.

4-304
```
  1 | p        hyp
  2 | Cpq      hyp
  3 | CpNq     hyp

last | r        ?
```

Is there already as an item in the sequence with a good reason
and preceding the 'r' a tail item whose only item above the
'Ⱶ' for the tail item is an 'Nr' and whose last item is a contradictory WFF? _____   no

4-305
```
  1 | p              hyp
  2 | Cpq            hyp
  3 | CpNq           hyp
  ?  |    | Nr
     | last | K···N···
last | r              ?, No
```

Let's tentatively add to the sequence a tail item with an 'Nr'
as the only item above the 'Ⱶ' and let's indicate that we would
like the last item of the tail item to be a contradictory WFF by
writing a '_____···_____···' where the last item would go.   K; N

Then if we can add items to the tail item so that every
_____ has a good reason and the last item is a   item
_____ WFF, then we can think of the 'r' as the last item   contradictory
of an _____ LAF whose first item is the _____ item.   No; tail

4-306 When trying to give a good reason for a contradictory WFF as last item of a tail item, whether for an Ni LAF or an No LAF:

1. If an item of the sequence and preceding the tail item begins with an 'N,' try to give a good reason for a contradictory WFF such that the _____ WFF following the 'K' in the contradictory WFF is like the item beginning with an '_____';

second

N

2. If no preceding item in the sequence begins with an 'N' but some part of some preceding item is a WFF beginning with an 'N,' let this WFF guide the choice of the _____ WFF for which you try to give a good reason;

contradictory

3. If no preceding item nor any part of a preceding item begins with an 'N,' then if the first item of the tail item begins with an 'N,' let this item guide your choice of _____ WFF.

contradictory

4-307

1	p		hyp
2	Cpq		hyp
3	CpNq		hyp
?		Nr	
	last	_____	
last	r		?, No

KqNq

Ignore the 'Nr' (first item of tail item) unless there is nothing else to guide choice of contradictory WFF.

4-308

1	p		hyp
2	Cpq		hyp
3	CpNq		hyp
?		Nr	_____
	?	_____	
	?	_____	
	last	KqNq	?, ?, Ki
last	r		?, No

hyp
q
Nq

4-309

1	p		hyp
2	Cpq		hyp
3	CpNq		hyp
4	4.1	Nr	hyp
	4.2	q	___, ___, ___
	4.3	Nq	___, ___, ___
	4.4	KqNq	___, ___, ___
last	r		?, No

2; 1; Co
3; 1; Co
4.2; 4.3; Ki

4-310

1	p	hyp
2	Cpq	hyp
3	CpNq	hyp
4	4.1 | Nr	hyp
	4.2 | q	2, 1, Co
	4.3 | Nq	3, 1, Co
	4.4 | KqNq	4.2, 4.3, Ki
5	r	_____ , _____ 4; No

Notice the whole tail item 4 (and not just item 4.1 or the last item 4.4) is cited in the reason for item 4. For, loosely speaking, from an 'Nr' as an hypothesis, a 'KqNq' "follows." But a 'KqNq' formalizes a contradiction. So under the hypotheses 'p,' 'Cpq,' 'CpNq,' and 'Nr' must be rejected as an hypothesis; and if we reject an 'Nr,' then it must be the case that 'r'—for an 'N' represents an 'it is false that.'

4-311

1	p	hyp
2	Cpq	hyp
3	CpNq	hyp
4	4.1 | Nr	hyp
	4.2 | q	2, 1, Co
	4.3 | Nq	3, 1, Co
	4.4 | KqNq	4.2, 4.3, Ki
5	r	4, No

Since every item in this sequence has a good reason the sequence is a _____. So any argument is valid if it can be formalized by the AF

for this AF _____ to a _____ in system F.

proof

```
p
Cpq
CpNq
r
```

corresponds; proof

4-312 To try to discover a proof that corresponds to the AF

> | CNpq
> | Nq
> | p

we begin the sequence

> 1 | CNpq   hyp
> 2 | Nq   hyp
>
> last | p   ?

A 'hyp' is a good reason for the items above the 'Ⱶ' for the sequence. The 'p' is below the 'Ⱶ' for the sequence and does not begin with a connective. Should we try to think of it as the last item of an in-LAF? _____ Should we try to think of the 'p' as the last item of a Ko LAF? _____ As the last item of an Ao LAF? _____ Of a Co LAF? Perhaps. But does the item beginning with a 'C' have as the second WFF following the 'C' a 'p'? _____ Should we, then, try to think of the 'p' as the last item of a Co LAF? _____

     no
     no
     no

     no
     no

4-313   1 | CNpq   hyp
        2 | Nq   hyp

    last | p   ?, _____

     No

4-314   1 | CNpq   hyp
        2 | Nq   hyp
        ? | Ⱶ_____   _____

        last | K···N···
    last | p   ?, No

     Np; hyp

4-315 In choosing a contradictory WFF, we ignore the first item of the tail item *if* some other item can guide our choice of contradictory WFF.

> 1 | CNpq   hyp
> 2 | Nq   hyp
> ? | | Np   hyp
>
> | last | _____
> last | p   ?, No

     KqNq

4-316

1	CNpq	hyp	
2	Nq	hyp	
?	Np	hyp	
?	_____		q
last	KqNq	?, 2, Ki	
last	p	?, No	

4-317

1	CNpq	hyp	
2	Nq	hyp	
3	3.1	Np	hyp	
	3.2	q	_____ , _____ , _____	1; 3.1; Co
	3.3	KqNq	_____ , _____ , _____	3.2; 2; Ki
last	p	?, No	

4-318

1	CNpq	hyp	
2	Nq	hyp	
3	3.1	Np	hyp	
	3.2	q	1, 3.1, Co	
	3.3	KqNq	3.2, 2, Ki	
4	p	_____ , _____	3; No

4-319 To try to discover a proof that corresponds to the AF

| NKpNq |
| Cpq |

we begin the sequence

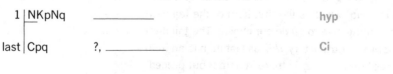

1	NKpNq	_____	hyp
last	Cpq	?, _____	Ci

4-320

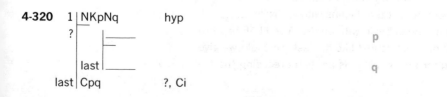

1	NKpNq	hyp	
?	_____		p
last	_____		q
last	Cpq	?, Ci	

4-321

```
1 | NKpNq        hyp
? |   | p          _____            hyp
  |   |
  | last | q
last | Cpq        ?, Ci
```

A 'hyp' is a good reason for the first item of the tail item since
the 'p' is above the 'Ⱶ' for the _____ item. Since the 'q'   tail
is _____ the 'Ⱶ' for the tail item and does not begin with   below
a connective, we should think of the 'q' as the last item of an
out-LAF. No preceding item begins with a 'K,' an 'A,' or a 'C';
so we should try to think of the 'q' as the last item of
an _____o LAF.   N

4-322

```
1 | NKpNq                    hyp
? |   | p                    hyp
  |   | ? |                               _____      Nq; hyp
  |   |   | Ⱶ_____
  |   | last | K···N···
  | last | q                  ?, No
last | Cpq                    ?, Ci
```

4-323

```
1 | NKpNq                    hyp
2 |   | p                    hyp
  |   | ? |   | Nq           hyp
  |   |   | Ⱶ
  |   | last | K···N···
  | last | q                  ?, No
last | Cpq                    ?, Ci
```

For which contradictory WFF as last item of the tail item
should we try to give a good reason? We should be guided in
our choice by the 'Nq' which is the first item of the tail item
only if there is nothing else to guide our choice. The tail item
for which we want a contradictory WFF as last item is an item
of what sequence? Item _____. Is there in item 2 but preced-   2
ing the tail item in item 2 any
      item beginning with an 'N'? _____   no
      item with a part that begins with an 'N'? _____   no
But notice item 1 does begin with an 'N.' A rep LAF has two
items the first of which is just like the last. So could we give
a good reason for an 'NKpNq' as an item preceding the tail
item in item 2? _____   yes

4-324

```
1 | NKpNq                        hyp
2 | 2.1 | p                      hyp
  | 2.2 | NKpNq        _____, _____   1; rep
  |  ?  |    | Nq               hyp
  |     |    |
  |     last | K···N···
  | last | q                    ?, No
last | Cpq                       ?, Ci
```

4-325 The rep LAF is very useful in, loosely speaking, allowing us to make *repeated* use of a hypothesis. When considering what preceding items are available to cite in reasons for any given item, it is a good idea to consider along with appropriate preceding items also what added preceding items can be made available by means of the _____ LAF.   rep

4-326

```
1 | NKpNq                        hyp
2 | 2.1 | p                      hyp
  | 2.2 | NKpNq                  1, rep
  |  ?  |    | Nq
  |     |    |
  |     last | _____        ?, 2.2, Ki        KKpNqNKpNq
  | last | q                     ?, No
last | Cpq                       ?, Ci
```

4-327

```
1 | NKpNq                        hyp
2 | 2.1 | p                      hyp
  | 2.2 | NKpNq                  1, rep
  |  ?  |    | Nq
  |     |  ? |_____                           KpNq
  |     last | KKpNqNKpNq        ?, 2.2, Ki
  | last | q                     ?, No
last | Cpq                       ?, Ci
```

4-328

```
1 | NKpNq                        hyp
2 | 2.1 | p                      hyp
  | 2.2 | NKpNq                  1, rep
  | 2.3 | 2.3.1 | Nq             hyp
  |     | 2.3.2 | KpNq           ____, ____, ____   2.1; 2.3.1; Ki
  |     | 2.3.3 | KKpNqNKpNq     ____, ____, ____   2.3.2; 2.2; Ki
  | 2.4 | q                      ?, No
last | Cpq                       ?, Ci
```

4-329

1	NKpNq			hyp
2	2.1	p		hyp
	2.2	NKpNq		1, rep
	2.3	2.3.1	Nq	hyp
		2.3.2	KpNq	2.1, 2.3.1, Ki
		2.3.3	KKpNqNKpNq	2.3.2, 2.2, Ki
	2.4	q		____ , ____ 2.3; No
3	Cpq			____ , ____ 2; Ci

4-330 Produce a proof that corresponds to the AF

|NKNrt
|CCpqCtr

and give your good reasons.

*1	NKNrt				hyp
2	2.1	Cpq			hyp
	2.2	NKNrt			1, rep
	2.3	2.3.1	t		hyp
		2.3.2	NKNrt		2.2, rep
		2.3.3	2.3.3.1	Nr	hyp
			2.3.3.2	KNrt	2.3.3.1, 2.3.1, Ki
			2.3.3.3	KKNrtNKNrt	2.3.3.2, 2.3.2, Ki
		2.3.4	r		2.3.3, No
	2.4	Ctr			2.3, Ci
3	CCpqCtr				2, Ci

Recapitulation of Strategies

4-331   *Given* an AF and *given* a proof, there is no difficulty in deciding whether or not they correspond. But to establish that there is in fact some proof that corresponds to a given AF is another matter.

Given the AF, we know immediately what must be the only items above the 'ⱶ' for the would-be proof and we know too what the last item of the desired proof would have to be. Moreover, a 'hyp' will always be a good reason for the items above the 'ⱶ' for the would-be correspondent proof (so that the formalizations of the premisses of the argument formalized by the AF become the only hypotheses of the proof that is to establish the formalized argument's validity). The difficulty of discovering corresponding proofs reduces then to the problem of giving a good reason for the WFF formalizing the conclusion of the argument whose validity is in question. We have been considering some strategies for dealing with this problem.

A strategy is a plan for the systematic exploration of possible solutions to a problem in the hope of hitting on and recognizing an adequate solution to the problem. Suppose you have a problem to solve and "see" your way to an adequate solution. Is there then any point in resorting to strategy?

—————————   no

4-332   We resort to strategy not always but only when we do not immediately "see" our way to a solution. Specifics aside, the strategies we have considered direct attention to the relation between the item for which we seek a reason— that is, an item whose place in the sequence is as yet unjustified—and the items already justified as members of the sequence. So to speak, we consider where we want to go in relation to what is available for getting there.

For items above a 'ⱶ' for a sequence justification is no problem. And if the item is below a 'ⱶ' for a sequence, we ask first: Does the item needing a reason begin with a connective?

If so, we ask: What preceding justified items must the sequence have to allow us to justify the given item as the last item of an appropriate in-LAF? We look at the justified members of the sequence. If the appropriate items are there, our problem is solved. If not, we can choose either to put in the needed items and try to justify them, or to try to justify the given item as the last item of some out-LAF.

To decide which out-LAF to try, we consider the initial connectives in the already justified items as well as considering the unjustified item in relation to significant parts of justified items. If appropriate items are present, then the problem is solved. If appropriate items are not already present but a justified item begins with an 'A,' we add and try to justify appropriate tail items that we may justify the questioned item as the last item of an Ao LAF. If no justified item begins with an 'A,' we consider what items can be added and justified as last items of Ko, Co, or rep LAFs.

If this additional store of justified items still provides no justification for the questioned item, we can still try to think of that item as the last item of an No LAF—provided we can add and justify a proper tail item.

In brief, then, we justify a questioned item either in terms of already justified items or else in terms of justified items already present plus items that can be added preceding the questioned item and justified. For any item can be added but not every item can be justified; and, of course, unless an item can be justified in a sequence—that is, given a good reason—that item cannot be an item of a proof.

Sometimes the items we add are tail items. Roughly speaking, tail items are devices for exploring what follows from a hypothesis when added to the already justified items. Realizing the nature of a tail item makes clear that we are free to take as hypothesis of a tail item any WFF we please (though in practice the hypotheses of tail items we try to justify are dictated by the justification we want to give for a questioned item). But our freedom to choose a hypothesis must not obscure this fact: What follows from justified items *plus* a hypothesis does not necessarily follow from those items without that hypothesis; moreover, what follows from the justified items plus some one hypothesis does not necessarily follow from the justified items plus some different hypothesis. This observation can be made in another way: Within a sequence merely following *after* must be distinguished from following *from*, even though an item must follow after in order to follow from. This observation is the counterpart of the familiar restriction in system F: An item of a sequence can be justified as the last item of a LAF provided that there are appropriate items which are already justified *either as preceding items of the same sequence or else as preceding items of the sequence which has as an item the tail item of which the questioned item is an item.* The restriction, although rather elaborate to state, is perhaps not so difficult to follow once its plausibility is appreciated in terms of exploring consequences of hypotheses given for a proof or of these hypotheses supplemented by an exploratory hypothesis.

In terms of this discussion, let's consider the following sequence

```
1 │ Csp            hyp
2 │ AsKqp          hyp
3 │ 3.1 │ s        hyp
  │ 3.2 │ p        1, 3.1, Co
4 │ 4.1 │ Kqp      hyp
  │ 4.2 │ p
5 │ p              2, 3, ?, Ao
```

What would be a good reason for item 4.2? Given that item 3.2 is a 'p' and is a justified item, we might be tempted to give a '3.2, rep' as a good reason for item 4.2. But item 4.2 is an item of item 4. Is item 3.2 an item of item 4? Is item 3.2 an item of the sequence of which the tail item 4 is an item? Since we give a negative answer to both questions, a '3.2, rep' cannot be a good reason for item 4.2. But item 4.1 is a 'Kqp' and item 4.1 precedes item 4.2 in one and the same sequence; so a '4.1, Ko' is a good reason for item 4.2.

Notice that the improper giving of a '3.2, rep' as a reason for item 4.2 would amount to maintaining that a 'p' follows from a 'Csp,' an 'AsKqp,' and a 'Kqp' taken together *simply because* a 'p' follows from the first two hypotheses along with the hypothesis 's.' And notice further that we are trying to think of item 5 as the last item of an Ao LAF whose first item is an 'AsKqp.' So we must show that a 'p' follows whether we take an 's' as the only additional hypothesis *or* take a 'Kqp' as the only additional hypothesis. That is, roughly speaking, we want to show that a 'p' follows whichever of the two alternatives 's' or 'Kqp' is the case, since we know only that at least one of them is the case; clearly then we must show what follows from 'Kqp' quite *independently* of what may follow from 's.'

Trying to discover whether there is a proof that corresponds to a given AF is facilitated, then, if

1. We are actively aware of the possible kinds of LAFs and of the structure of a LAF of any given kind,
2. We have in mind strategies to follow explicitly when a solution is not immediately obvious, and
3. We are alert to certain moves that must be avoided and certain signs that an alternative being explored is unfruitful.

Going Beyond Initial

Strategies

4-333   In this unit we look at proofs interesting from two points of view: The proofs "establish" in system F certain laws or patterns of inference to which logic has given special names, and the discovery of the proof illustrates the use of techniques which supplement initial strategies.

Suppose we are trying to find a proof that corresponds to the AF

|Cpq
|CNqNp

(To find such a proof amounts to establishing the "Law of Contraposition": If from one thing we can infer a second, then from the falsity of the second we can infer the falsity of the first.)

Almost automatically we write

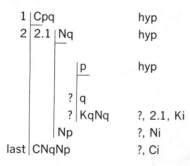

and our problem is reduced to finding a good reason for a 'q.' As the sequence stands the only justified items within range for use are the 'Nq' and the 'p'—neither of which suggests itself as helpful. But item 1, which is neither an item of the tail item of which 'q' is an item nor an item of the sequence of which that tail item is an item, is a 'Cpq.' Were such an item in the proper sequence, the item could be used along with the 'p' as first items of a Co LAF whose last item is a '_____.'   q

Can we somehow enlarge the store of justified items available for justifying the 'q' so as to include among these justified items a 'Cpq'? Yes, because we can write as item 2.2 a 'Cpq' and give as a good reason for this item a '_____.'

1, rep

4-334   In trying to discover proofs we have essentially two devices at hand. The problem is always one of trying to justify an item in terms of previously justified items; so, if the problem is not immediately solved we move towards its solution either

1. By choosing and trying to justify as preceding items simpler items which if justified would be sufficient to justify the questioned item, or
2. By legitimately enlarging the store of appropriately placed and justified items—by use of Ko, Co, or _____ LAFs.

rep

4-335   Suppose we are trying to find a proof that corresponds to the AF

  |CpCqr
  |CCpqCpr

(Finding this proof amounts to establishing in F a so-called "transitivity of implication": If from one thing we can infer that a second implies a third, then if the first implies the second, then the first implies the third.) We begin

```
 1 | CpCqr           hyp
 2 | 2.1 | Cpq       hyp

            | p        hyp

            | r        ?
       | Cpr           ?, Ci
last | CCpqCpr         ?, Ci
```

The problem reduces easily to finding a reason for the 'r' in the innermost tail item. As the sequence stands the only justified items within range for use in giving this reason are a 'p' and a '_____,' neither of which is immediately use-ful. Can we then add to the store of justified items usable for giving a reason for the 'r'? Since item 1 has a good reason we can add as item 2.2 a 'CpCqr' and give as a good reason for this item a '_____.' Then since both a 'CpCqr' and a 'p' are justified items within range for use in justifying items in the innermost tail item, we can add to that tail item an item

Cpq

1, rep

'Cqr,' which we can think of as the last item of a _____ LAF. But there are also as justified items within range for use in giving reasons for items within the innermost tail item both a 'Cpq' and a 'p'; so we can add as an item of the tail item a 'q' and think of it as the last item of a _____ LAF.

Co

Co

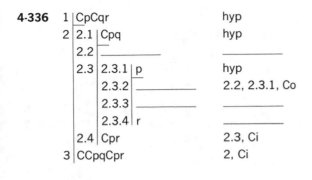

4-336

1	CpCqr		hyp
2	2.1 Cpq		hyp
	2.2 _____	_____	CpCqr; 1, rep
	2.3 2.3.1 p	hyp	
	2.3.2 _____	2.2, 2.3.1, Co	Cqr
	2.3.3 _____	_____	q; 2.1, 2.3.1, Co
	2.3.4 r	_____	2.3.2, 2.3.3, Co
	2.4 Cpr	2.3, Ci	
3	CCpqCpr	2, Ci	

4-337 When the justified items within range for use are not yet sufficient to justify a questioned item, a constructive move toward giving a reason for the questioned item is to enlarge the store of usable justified items by considering how we can use the justified items to allow us to justify additional items as last items of rep, Ko, or _____ LAFs. Then, given the enlarged stock of justified items, we reassess the possibility of justifying the questioned item in terms of appropriately placed items for which _____ have been given.

Co

reasons

4-338 Write a proof that corresponds to the AF

| CpCqr |
| CKpqr |

(Your proof amounts to establishing in system F the so-called "Law of Importation": If a first thing implies that the second implies a third, then the first two together imply the third.)

*1	CpCqr		hyp
2	2.1 Kpq		hyp
	2.2 p		2.1, Ko
	2.3 Cqr		1, 2.2, Co
	2.4 q		2.1, Ko
	2.5 r		2.3, 2.4, Co
3	CKpqr		2, Ci

4-339 Write a proof that corresponds to the AF

    |CKpqr
    |CpCqr

(to establish in system F the so-called "Law of Exportation":
If two things together imply a third, then the first implies that
the second implies the third.)

*1	CKpqr		hyp
2	2.1	p	hyp
	2.2	CKpqr	1, rep
	2.3	2.3.1	q	hyp
		2.3.2	Kpq	2.1, 2.3.1, Ki
		2.3.3	r	2.2, 2.3.2, Co
	2.4	Cqr	2.3, Ci
3	CpCqr		2, Ci

4-340 Write a proof that corresponds to the AF

    |NApq
    |KNpNq

[a so-called "De Morgan rule": If it is false that at least one of
two things is the case, then both are false. Augustus De
Morgan (1806–1871) was an English logician.]

*1	NApq		hyp
2	2.1	p	hyp
	2.2	Apq	2.1, Ai
	2.3	KApqNApq	2.2, 1, Ki
3	3.1	q	hyp
	3.2	Apq	3.1, Ai
	3.3	KApqNApq	3.2, 1, Ki
4	Np		2, Ni
5	Nq		3, Ni
6	KNpNq		4, 5, Ki

4-341   Another "De Morgan rule" is suggested by the AF

> ANpNq
> NKpq

(If at least one of two things is false, then it is false that both are true.)

To discover a proof that corresponds to this AF we begin

1	ANpNq	_____	hyp
last	NKpq	_____	?, Ni

4-342   Initial strategies would suggest that we try to think of the 'NKpq' as the last item of an Ni LAF. But oftentimes an easier, shorter, or more direct proof may be found if where we have an item that starts with an 'A' as a justified item we try to think of the questioned item as the last item of an Ao LAF. Following this tip, find a proof that corresponds to the AF

> ANpNq
> NKpq

*1	ANpNq			hyp
2	2.1	Np		hyp
	2.2	2.2.1	Kpq	hyp
		2.2.2	p	2.2.1, Ko
		2.2.3	KpNp	2.2.2, 2.1, Ki
	2.3	NKpq		2.2, Ni
3	3.1	Nq		hyp
	3.2	3.2.1	Kpq	hyp
		3.2.2	q	3.2.1, Ko
		3.2.3	KqNq	3.2.2, 3.1, Ki
	3.3	NKpq		3.2, Ni
4	NKpq			1, 2, 3, Ao

4-343 Consider the AF

> | ApKqr
> | KApqApr

(The so-called "Law of Distribution of Disjunction over Conjunction" or of 'or' over 'and': If either a first thing or else both a second and a third, then both, on the one hand, the first or else the second is the case and, on the other hand, either the first or else the third is the case.)

To find a proof that corresponds to this AF we begin

> 1 | ApKqr   hyp
>
> last | KApqApr   ?

Exploiting the tip that it is often advantageous to think of a questioned item—even if the item begins with a 'K,' an 'A,' or an 'N'—as the last item of an Ao LAF provided only there is an already justified item beginning with an 'A,' find a proof that corresponds to the AF.

*1	ApKqr		hyp
2	2.1	p	hyp
	2.2	Apq	2.1, Ai
	2.3	Apr	2.1, Ai
	2.4	KApqApr	2.2, 2.3, Ki
3	3.1	Kqr	hyp
	3.2	q	3.1, Ko
	3.3	r	3.1, Ko
	3.4	Apq	3.2, Ai
	3.5	Apr	3.3, Ai
	3.6	KApqApr	3.4, 3.5, Ki
4	KApqApr		1, 2, 3, Ao

4-344 The so-called "Law of Distribution of Conjunction over Disjunction" is suggested by the AF

> | KpAqr
> | AKpqKpr

(If both a first and either a second or a third, then either, on the one hand, both the first and the second or else, on the other hand, both the first and the third.)

To find a proof that corresponds to this AF we begin

> 1 | KpAqr   —————   hyp
>
> last | AKpqKpr   —————   ?, Ai

4-345   Initial strategies would suggest we try to think of the 'AKpqKpr' as the last item of an Ai LAF. But oftentimes we can give a reason for an 'A' followed by two WFFs when we could not give a reason for either of the two WFFs standing alone. This observation suggests this tip: Try to think of a questioned item beginning with an 'A' as the last item of an Ai LAF *only if* no other possibility presents itself. Taking note of this tip, remembering that we may have to enlarge the store of justified items by use of rep, Ko, or Co LAFs, and recalling the tip that whenever possible we should try to think of a questioned item as the last item of an Ao LAF, find a proof that corresponds to the AF

> | KpAqr
> | AKpqKpr

*1	KpAqr			hyp
2	2.1	NAKpqKpr		hyp
	2.2	p		1, Ko
	2.3	Aqr		1, Ko
	2.4	2.4.1	q	hyp
		2.4.2	Kpq	2.2, 2.4.1, Ki
		2.4.3	AKpqKpr	2.4.2, Ai
	2.5	2.5.1	r	hyp
		2.5.2	Kpr	2.2, 2.5.1, Ki
		2.5.3	AKpqKpr	2.5.2, Ai
	2.6	AKpqKpr		2.3, 2.4, 2.5, Ao
	2.7	KAKpqKprNAKpqKpr		2.6, 2.1, Ki
3	AKpqKpr			2, No

4-346   The AF

> | ANpq
> | Cpq

suggests the so-called "definition of material implication," where the qualification "material" is used to distinguish the type of implication associated with the connective 'C' (or in *Principia* notation, with the '⊃') from the rich notion of 'implication' in ordinary language and from formal implication as defined within some system of logic: If either a first thing is false or else a second thing is the case, then the first (materially) implies the second. To find a proof that corresponds to the AF, we begin

```
  1 | ANpq      hyp
    |
last| Cpq       ?
```

Initial strategy suggests we try to think of the 'Cpq' as the last item of a Ci LAF; a recent tip might suggest, given the justified 'ANpq,' that we try to think of the 'Cpq' as the last item of an Ao LAF. But the one alternative we should try even before the Ao LAF is the Ci LAF. So when an item begins with a 'C,' try a Ci LAF even though an item beginning with an 'A' is already justified. Thus we begin

```
  1 | ANpq        hyp
  2 | 2.1| p      hyp
    |    |
    |    | q      ?
last| Cpq         ?, Ci
```

We must be able to think of the 'q' as the last item of an out-LAF. Not only in this problem but in general, it may be advantageous to avoid use of the No LAF (or for that matter, Ni LAF) unless no other out-LAF can be used or until other possibilities have been explored. With these tips in mind, find a proof that corresponds to the AF

```
| ANpq
| Cpq
```

```
*1 | ANpq                                   hyp
 2 | 2.1 | p                                hyp
   |     | 2.2 | 2.2.1 | Np                  hyp
   |     |     | 2.2.2 | p                   2.1, rep
   |     |     | 2.2.3 | 2.2.3.1 | Nq        hyp
   |     |     |       | 2.2.3.2 | KpNp      2.2.2, 2.2.1, Ki
   |     |     | 2.2.4 | q                   2.2.3, No
   |     | 2.3 | 2.3.1 | q                   hyp
   |     |     | 2.3.2 | q                   2.3.1, rep
   |     | 2.4 | q                           1, 2.2, 2.3, Ao
 3 | Cpq                                     2, Ci
```

4-347 Another AF closely related to the "definition of material implication" is

$$\frac{\mid CNpq}{\mid Apq}$$

(if the falsity of a first thing (materially) implies a second, then either the first is not false or else the second is the case.)

To find a proof that corresponds to the AF we begin

1	CNpq		hyp
2	2.1	NApq	hyp
		p	
		Apq	?, Ai
		KApqNApq	?, 2.1, Ki
last	Apq		?, No

Since even though item 1 is a 'CNpq' there is no way to use rep, Ko, Ao, or Co LAFs to get an 'Np' as a justified item of the tail item, we resort to trying to justify the contradictory WFF suggested by item 2.1, for there is no other possibility suggested. But why try to think of the 'Apq' in the tail item as the last item of an Ai LAF when a recent tip suggests trying even No before Ai? Notice that trying to justify the 'Apq' in the tail item as last item of an No LAF would require our adding a tail item whose only hypothesis would be an '_____' —an   NApq

item that merely duplicates the justified item _____.   2.1

4-348 In general, add a tail item whose hypothesis duplicates an already justified item only when no alternative presents itself. Bearing in mind this and former tips, find a proof that corresponds to the AF

$$\frac{\mid CNpq}{\mid Apq}$$

*1	CNpq			hyp
2	2.1	NApq		hyp
	2.2	CNpq		1, rep
	2.3	2.3.1	Np	hyp
		2.3.2	q	2.2, 2.3.1, Co
		2.3.3	Apq	2.3.2, Ai
		2.3.4	KApqNApq	2.3.3, 2.1, Ki
	2.4	p		2.3, No
	2.5	Apq		2.4, Ai
	2.6	KApqNApq		2.5, 2.1, Ki
3	Apq			2, No

$$\frac{\vert t}{\vert ApNp}$$

suggests the so-called "Law of Excluded Middle": A thing is either true or else not true—there is no middle ground. This "law" is reflected in system F by the above AF: Given any one thing, any second thing is either true or else not true, no matter how the first is related to the second or whether the first is related at all to the second. To "establish" this "law" in system F, find a proof that corresponds to the above AF.

*1	t			hyp
2	2.1	NApNp		hyp
	2.2	2.2.1	Np	hyp
		2.2.2	ApNp	2.2.1, Ai
		2.2.3	KApNpNApNp	2.2.2, 2.1, Ki
	2.3	p		2.2, No
	2.4	ApNp		2.3, Ai
	2.5	KApNpNApNp		2.4, 2.1, Ki
3	ApNp			2, No

4-350   Another version of excluded middle is suggested by the AF

$$\frac{\vert t}{\vert ApCpq}$$

(If any first thing is the case, then a second thing is the case or else that second thing *materially* implies some third thing.)

Find a proof that corresponds to the above AF.

*1	t			hyp
2	2.1	NApCpq		hyp
	2.2	2.2.1	p	hyp
		2.2.2	NApCpq	2.1, rep
		2.2.3	2.2.3.1	Nq	hyp
			2.2.3.2	ApCpq	2.2.1, Ai
			2.2.3.3	KApCpqNApCpq	2.2.3.2, 2.2.2, Ki
		2.2.4	q		2.2.3, No
	2.3	Cpq		2.2, Ci
	2.4	ApCpq		2.3, Ai
	2.5	KApCpqNApCpq		2.4, 2.1, Ki
3	ApCpq			2.1, No

4-351 In sum, when trying to find proofs that correspond to given AFs, the following tips may be helpful as supplements to general strategies:

1. New possibilities for justifying a questioned item may present themselves if we increase the store of already justified items by use of rep, Ko, Ao, and Co LAFs.

2. If some justified item begins with an 'A,' try to think of a questioned item as the last item of an Ao LAF, unless the 'A' item is currently guiding addition of items or the questioned item begins with a 'C.'

3. If the questioned item begins with an 'A,' try to think of the questioned item as the last item of an Ai LAF only if no other viable alternative presents itself.

4. Shorter proofs may result if the use of Ni and No LAFs is deferred until after the stock of justified items is increased by suitable uses of rep, Ko, Ao, and Co LAFs.

5. Only when no viable alternative presents itself should we resort to trying to justify a tail item whose hypothesis duplicates an already justified item.

6. Abandon attempts to use No or Ni LAFs if the questioned item itself contains no 'N' and *even after* all attempts to enlarge the store of justified items by uses of rep, Ko, Ao, and Co LAFs no justified item begins with an 'N.'

Summary of Part 4

4-352   Given an AF we are interested to show whether there is in system F a proof that corresponds to that AF, for we say an argument is valid if it can be _____ by an AF that corresponds to a _____ in system F.

formalized
proof

4-353   When trying to discover a proof that will correspond to a given AF

1. We begin a sequence

   by writing above the 'ㅏ' for the sequence items just like the items _____ the 'ㅏ' for the _____, and

   above; AF

   by writing as the last item of the sequence an item just like the item _____ the 'ㅏ' for the AF.

   below

Then

2. We try to discern if this sequence is already a _____ or else if we can produce a sequence that is a proof by adding items _____ the 'ㅏ' for the sequence but above the _____ item for the sequence.

proof

below
last

And finally

3. We know the initial sequence or the sequence we produce is a proof if every _____ of the sequence can be given a good _____.

item

reason

4-354   For any WFF item above the 'ㅏ' for a sequence, a good reason is a '_____.' A WFF item below the 'ㅏ' for a sequence has a good reason if we can think of the item as the last item of a LAF of one of these nine kinds:

hyp

_____ _____

_____ _____

_____ _____

_____ _____

_____

Ki   Ko
Ai   Ao
Ci   Co
Ni   No
   rep

A tail item has a good reason if there is a good reason for each _____ of the tail item.

item

4-355   When looking for a good reason for a WFF item below the 'Ⱶ' for a sequence we *could* (and when no other alternative presents itself we *should*) for each kind of LAF in turn try to think of the WFF item as the _____ item of a LAF of that kind. But rather than trying each kind of LAF in turn a good initial strategy is this: If the item begins with a connective, try to think of the questioned item as the last item of the appropriate kind of _____-LAF; and if the item does not begin with a connective, try to think of the item as the last item of an _____-LAF.

last

in

out

4-356   But initial strategies are not always sufficient guides in the discovery of proofs. As supplements to initial strategies, these generalizations will often prove helpful:

1. New possibilities for justifying a questioned item may present themselves if we increase the store of already justified items by use of _____, _____, _____, or _____ LAFs.

rep; Ko; Ao
Co
(In any order)

2. If some justified item begins with an 'A,' try to think of a questioned item as the last item of an Ao LAF unless the 'A' item is currently guiding addition of items or the questioned item begins with a '_____.'

C

3. If the questioned item begins with an 'A,' try to think of the questioned item as the last item of an Ai LAF only if _____ other viable alternative presents itself.

no

4. Shorter proofs may result if the use of Ni and No LAFs is deferred until _____ the stock of justified items is increased by suitable uses of rep, Ko, Ao, and Co LAFs.

after

5. Only when no other viable alternative presents itself should we resort to trying to justify a tail item whose _____ duplicates an already justified item.

hypothesis

6. Abandon attempts to use No or Ni LAFs if the questioned item itself contains no 'N' and even after all attempts to enlarge the store of justified items by uses of rep, Ko, Ao, and Co LAFs no justified item begins with an '_____.'

N

Exercises for Part 4

1   For each of the following AFs it is possible to write in system F a proof that corresponds to the AF. For each AF find such a proof. Where relevant, the traditional
name of a corresponding "law" or "principle" has been included.

a | AKrtKqr
    | CKrps
    | Crp
    | s

b | Cpq
    | Crs
    | Nt
    | Cqr
    | Cst
    | Np

c | CApqKrs
    | CrNs
    | CNpt
    | KtNq

d | Cpq
    | Crs
    | ANqNs
    | NKpr

*e | NKtp
    | Crt
    | CsNNp
    | ANsNr

f   A De Morgan law
    | NKpq
    | ANpNq

g   A De Morgan law
    | Kpq
    | NANpNq

h   Distribution of conjunction
    over disjunction
    | KApqApr
    | ApKqr

i   Distribution of disjunction
    over conjunction
    | AKpqKpr
    | KpAqr

j   Definition of material
    implication
    | Cpq
    | ANpq

k   Definition of material
    implication
    | ANpq
    | Cpq

l   Law of Contraposition
    | CNqNp
    | Cpq

m | Csp
    | Cqr
    | CCpCsqCsr

n   Law of Non-contradiction
    | t
    | NKpNp

o   Axiom 1 of Lukasiewicz 1929
    formulation of classical
    sentential calculus
    | t
    | CCpqCCqrCpr

p   Axiom 2 of Lukasiewicz 1929
    formulation of classical
    sentential calculus
    | t
    | CCNppp

q   Axiom 3 of Lukasiewicz 1929
    formulation of classical
    sentential calculus
    | t
    | CpCNpq

r   Definition of material
    implication
    | Kpq
    | NCpNq

s   Definition of material
    implication
    | NCpNq
    | Kpq

t   Axiom 1 of *Principia*

    t
    ⊢CAppp

v   Axiom 3 of *Principia*

    t
    ⊢CApqAqp

x   Axiom 5 of *Principia*

    t
    ⊢CCqrCApqApr

u   Axiom 2 of *Principia*

    t
    ⊢CqApq

w   Axiom 4 of *Principia*

    t
    ⊢CApAqrAqApr

y   KCpNqCNqp
    CKptr
    t
    ⎯
    Arq

*z   Axiom for Meredith's single-axiom formulation (1953) of classical sentential calculus

    t′ (See Appendix A)
    ⊢CCCpqArAstCCspArAtp

2   For each of the following AFs it is possible to write in system PF a proof that corresponds to that AF. For each AF find such a proof. (Compare exercises 9 and 10 in Part 3)

a   s ⊃ p
    q ⊃ (~r)
    p ⊃ ((s ⊃ q) ⊃ (s ⊃ (~r)))

b   p & q
    ~((~p) ∨ (~q))

c   p ⊃ q
    r ⊃ s
    (~q) ∨ (~s)
    (~p) ∨ (~r)

Achievement Test for Part 4

1 a If an argument corresponds to a proof in system F, then the argument is a valid argument.

b If an argument formula corresponds to a proof in system F, then the argument formalized by that AF is a valid argument.

Which of the above is true? _____

2 Consider the AF

$$\left|\begin{array}{l} r \\ \hline CArpKpq \\ \hline q \end{array}\right.$$

Place a check ($\sqrt{}$) in front of each of the following proofs which corresponds to this AF. Put a cross ($\times$) in front of each of the following proofs that does not correspond to this AF.

a

1	r	hyp
2	CArpKpq	hyp
3	Arp	hyp
4	Kpq	2, 3, Co
5	q	4, Ko

_____ (before 3)

b

1	r	hyp
2	CArpKpq	hyp
3	Arp	1, Ai
4	Kpq	2, 3, Co
5	p	4, Ko

_____ (before 3)

c

1	r	hyp
2	CArpKpq	hyp
3	Arp	1, Ai
4	Kpq	2, 3, Co
5	q	4, Ko

_____ (before 3)

3 An argument is valid if it has at least one argument formula that _____ to a proof in system F.

4 Write a proof that corresponds to the AF

$$\left|\begin{array}{l} Cpr \\ \hline CpArs \end{array}\right.$$

and give reasons.

5 Write a proof that corresponds to the AF

$$\left|\begin{array}{l} Ktr \\ Kqs \\ \hline Krs \end{array}\right.$$

and give reasons.

6 Write a proof that corresponds to the AF

$$\left|\begin{array}{l} CpKqNq \\ \hline Np \end{array}\right.$$

and give reasons.

7 Write a proof that corresponds to the AF

> Ars
> Csr
> ─
> r

and give reasons.

8 Write a proof that corresponds to the AF

> CNps
> Ns
> ─
> p

and give reasons.

9 **a** Write an argument that can be formalized by the AF in exercise 8 and whose first premiss is a sentence like

> *If it is false that Adams won, then Jackson won.*

   b Is the argument valid? _____

10 If an AF corresponds to a proof in system F, then any argument that can be _____ by that AF is a valid argument.

11 Write a proof that corresponds to the AF

> s
> ─
> CpCqCrs

and give reasons.

12 Write a proof that corresponds to the AF

> Cts
> ─
> NKtNs

and give reasons.

13 **a** Write an argument that can be formalized by the AF in exercise 12 and whose first premiss is a sentence like

> *If Jackson won, then Adams lost.*

   b Is the argument valid? _____

14 If an argument can be formalized by an AF which corresponds to a proof in system F, then the premisses of the argument are formalized by the items _____ the '⊢' of the proof and the conclusion is formalized by the _____ item of the proof.

15 Write a proof that corresponds to the AF

> CNpq
> ─
> Apq

and give reasons.

16 If an argument can be formalized by an AF

> Cqr
> q
> ─
> r

what is the conclusion of the argument? _____

17 Write a proof that corresponds to the AF

> CApqNp
> ─
> CpNq

and give reasons.

18 Write a proof that corresponds to the AF

> | CrAqp
> | Krt
> | Cqp
> |— p

and give reasons.

19 Write a proof that corresponds to the AF

> | q
> |— AArsNArs

and give reasons.

20 Write a proof that corresponds to the AF

> | CqArs
> | Ctp
> | ANArsNp
> |— ANqNt

and give reasons.

Part

Language, Validity, and

System F

Systematic Definition of
Validity Evaluated

5-1   In Part 2 we defined 'valid argument' as: An argument in which the conclusion not only is said to follow from but actually does follow from the premisses.

Then in Part 3 we redefined 'valid argument' as: An argument which can be formalized by an AF that corresponds to a proof in system F. The redefinition was proposed because the first definition, though it clarified the notion of valid argument, did not allow the easy discrimination of valid from invalid arguments—especially when an argument was complex or lengthy or when the argument's validity had to be shown for another person.

To see how the redefinition in terms of system F facilitates the practical task of deciding or establishing an argument's validity, let's look at two arguments whose validity or lack of it seems not to be apparent by immediate inspection.

5-2   Consider the argument:

> *If Florence Nightingale brought health to the Crimea, then Miss Nightingale was a gentle angel of mercy.*
> *If it is false that Nurse Nightingale spoke strongly against army medical policies, then Florence Nightingale brought health to the Crimea.*
> *It is false that Miss Nightingale was a gentle angel of mercy.*
> *Therefore, Nurse Nightingale spoke strongly against army medical policies.*

We will say that the argument is valid if it can be formalized by an AF that corresponds to a proof in system F. So first we must formalize the argument; but to be able to formalize it we must first represent it. The argument can be represented by the symbolic expression

CPQ	
CNRP	
———	NQ
⊢ ———	R

and so the argument can be formalized by the AF

Csq	
———	CNts
———	Nq
⊢ t	

5-3 Now find a proof that corresponds to the AF that you used to formalize the argument about Miss Nightingale.

*1	Csq		hyp
2	CNts		hyp
3	Nq		hyp
4	4.1	Nt	hyp
	4.2	s	2, 4.1, Co
	4.3	q	1, 2.4, Co
	4.4	KqNq	4.3, 3, Ki
5	t		4, No

5-4 Now consider the argument:

If it is false that if Caesar wooed Cleopatra then Antony withdrew his suit, then respect for Caesar was less strong in Antony's breast then was his love for Cleopatra.
Therefore, if it is false that respect for Caesar was less strong in Antony's breast than was his love for Cleopatra, then if it is false that Antony withdrew his suit then it is false that Caesar wooed Cleopatra.

The argument can be represented by

| CNCPQR | |
| ⊢ ——— | CNRCNQNP |

and so can be formalized by the AF

| CNCpqr | |
| ⊢ ——— | CNrCNqNp |

which corresponds to what proof?

```
 *1│ CNCpqr                               hyp
  2│ 2.1│ Nr                              hyp
   │ 2.2│ CNCpqr                          1, rep
   │ 2.3│ 2.3.1│ Nq                       hyp
   │    │ 2.3.2│ CNCpqr                   2.2, rep
   │    │ 2.3.3│ Nr                       2.1, rep
   │    │ 2.3.4│ 2.3.4.1│ p               hyp
   │    │      │ 2.3.4.2│ Nq              2.3.1, rep
   │    │      │ 2.3.4.3│ 2.3.4.3.1│ Cpq   hyp
   │    │      │        │ 2.3.4.3.2│ q     2.3.4.3.1, 2.3.4.1, Co
   │    │      │        │ 2.3.4.3.3│ KqNq  2.3.4.3.2, 2.3.4.2, Ki
   │    │      │ 2.3.4.4│ NCpq            2.3.4.3, Ni
   │    │      │ 2.3.4.5│ r               2.3.2, 2.3.4.4, Co
   │    │      │ 2.3.4.6│ KrNr            2.3.4.5, 2.3.3, Ki
   │    │ 2.3.5│ Np                       2.3.4, Ni
   │ 2.4│ CNqNp                           2.3, Ci
  3│ CNrCNqNp                             2, Ci
```

5-5 Saying that an argument is valid because it can be formalized by an AF that corresponds to a proof in system F amounts to accepting an argument as valid if from the premises we can argue to the conclusion by using only arguments formalizable by _____ of system Γ.

LAΓs

5-6 It seems hard to deny that the definition of validity in terms of system F is in a sense a more usable definition than the definition in terms of following from. But though ease of use—along with considerations of systematic economy— motivated the chosen redefinition of 'valid argument,' the redefinition was guided too by the wish that all and only those arguments valid according to the first definition would be valid according to the second definition. But do both definitions pass the tag of validity to the same arguments? Consider the argument

> Socrates was a Greek, but Cicero was a Roman.
> Therefore, Cicero was a Roman.

Does the conclusion follow from the premiss? Immediate inspection makes it hard to deny that the conclusion does follow from the premiss. So according to the following-from definition, the argument is valid. But can the argument be formalized by an AF that corresponds to a proof in system F? To answer this question we must represent the argument; then, in the light of this representation, formalize the argument; and finally, produce a proof that corresponds to the AF that formalizes the argument. But given the above argument, can we take the first step—that is, can we represent the argument? Consider the matter.

5-7   Our conventions for representing are as follows:

1. Sentences containing no connecting words are represented by capitals *other than* '____'s, '____'s, '____'s, or '____'s.

K; A; C
N
(In any order)

2. Connecting words are represented as follows:

    (*a*) A 'K' represents an '_____.'
    (*b*) An 'A' represents an '_____.'
    (*c*) A 'C' represents an '_____.'
    (*d*) An 'N' represents an '_____.'

and
or
if then
it is false that

3. When sentences that contain connecting words are represented, the symbol representing the connecting word precedes the symbols representing the sentences joined by the _____ word.

connecting

Conventions for representing must be explicitly agreed upon, since a representation is—in contrast to a formalization—a symbolic expression *every* symbol of which corresponds in a _____ way to a part of the represented expression.

known

5-8   *Socrates was a Greek, but Cicero was a Roman.*
    Therefore, Cicero was a Roman.

The premise of the argument contains a connecting word 'but.' We expect a connecting word to be represented by a connective. Which connective—a 'K,' an 'A,' a 'C,' or an 'N'—can represent a 'but'? Again, consider.

5-9   Strictly speaking, no connective of system F can represent a connecting word 'but.' Can we represent the premiss of the argument? _____ Can we represent the argument? _____ Can we formalize the argument? _____ Would the system F definition, then, label the argument about Cicero valid? _____

no
no; no

no

5-10   *Grant was an unsuccessful President.*
Grant was a great Civil War general.
Therefore, Grant was an unsuccessful President, though
Grant was a great Civil War general.

Upon inspection, does the conclusion follow from the
premisses? _____ But would the system F definition
allow us to call the argument valid? _____

yes

no

5-11   Clearly, then, there are some arguments whose conclusions seem to follow from the premisses but which the system F definition would not call valid. Moreover, some of these
arguments differ from arguments system F would call valid
simply by containing connecting words which cannot be
represented by any _____ of system F.

connective

5-12   We might be tempted to deal with such unrepresentable arguments by trying to formalize them not on the basis
of a representation but rather on some direct insight into the
"form" of the argument, as that insight is guided by understanding of unrepresentable connecting words. To attempt to
extend the usefulness of system F by following such a temp-
tation is, however, to subvert the whole procedure of resorting to system F. Even after realizing that validity depends
upon logical form, the question of what *is* a logical form of
some given argument still remains. For suppose that someone admits that an argument which has a form, say,

$$\begin{array}{|l} p \\ \underline{q} \\ Kpq \end{array}$$

is a valid argument but denies that the argument

> *Catherine gave Henry no sons.*
> *Henry VIII divorced Catherine of Aragon.*
> *Therefore, Catherine gave Henry no sons, and Henry*
> *VIII divorced Catherine of Aragon.*

has this logical form.

The dispute can be settled if we represent the argument
according to the conventions for representing and then for-

malize the argument on the basis of this representation. If, however, your "insight" directed that the argument

> Grant was an unsuccessful President.
> Grant was a great Civil War general.
> Therefore, Grant was an unsuccessful President, though Grant was a great Civil War general.

could be formalized by

$$\begin{array}{l} p \\ q \\ \hline Kpq \end{array}$$

and someone disagreed with your formalization of the conclusion, to what could you appeal? Notice that we are in exactly the same position we were in when one man "saw" the argument to be valid and the other did not. Only if there is some agreed-upon procedure for arriving at formalizations does system F offer us an agreed-upon means for establishing validity.

5-13   If, however, we consider unrepresentable connecting words and can come to some explicit agreement as to how for purposes of argument they can be related to representable connecting words, then we can use system F to comment on the validity of arguments containing those unrepresentable connecting words—at least for those persons who share the agreement as to the relatedness of connecting words. The task of relating unrepresentable connecting words to connecting words representable by the connectives of system F is not formidable. Nor is the task unrewarding, since such considerations can bring us to a new appreciation, perhaps, of the logical force of the little considered but much used words of the English language.

5-14   Given an argument that contains connecting words we cannot represent, we write an argument as close as possible in meaning to the unrepresentable argument but an argument we can _____ .

represent

5-15   In effect, instead of the unrepresentable argument we write one just like it except that an unrepresentable connecting word is replaced by one or more representable connecting words deemed to have the same force for argument as does the unrepresentable word. For unrepresentable connecting words are either connecting words which replace a complex of simpler connecting words, or else they are connecting words which have in addition to their force for argument also a commentorial meaning. This commentorial meaning may reveal, say, the speaker's attitude toward or comment on the joining effected by the connecting word. When, for example, the historian says

> *Grant was an unsuccessful President, though Grant was a great Civil War general.*

he is, in addition to telling us that Grant was a great general and a poor President, commenting that we might have expected a great general to have been a great President.

5-16 Given an unrepresentable argument, we write a related representable argument. Then if system F shows the representable argument valid, we claim that the unrepresentable argument is likewise valid—since our agreement relating unrepresentable connecting words to representable ones will be based in effect on an estimate of like argumentive force.

Unrepresentable Arguments

A Connecting Words Not Representable by Connectives in System F

CONNECTING WORDS WITH EXTRALOGICAL MEANING

5-17 A connecting word 'but' is related to what representable connecting word? We can answer this question once we decide which representable sentence is very close in meaning to a given '_____' sentence.

but

5-18 *The elephant is larger than the mouse,* but *the elephant fears the mouse.*

The above 'but' sentence is closest in meaning to which of the following sentences?

> It is false that *the elephant is larger than the mouse.*
> If *the elephant is larger than the mouse,* then *the elephant fears the mouse.*
> *The elephant is larger than the mouse,* or *the elephant fears the mouse.*
> *The elephant is larger than the mouse,* and *the elephant fears the mouse.*

The '_____' sentence.

and

5-19 We had to decide whether a 'but' sentence is closest in meaning to

> an 'and' sentence,
> an 'or' sentence,
> an 'if then' sentence, or
> an 'it is false that' sentence.

We saw that a 'but' sentence is closest in meaning to an '_____' sentence.

and

5-20 Since a 'but' sentence is very close in meaning to an 'and' sentence, a connecting word 'but' is related to a connecting word '_____.'

and

5-21 A 'but' sentence is very close in meaning to an 'and' sentence, but now let's see how a 'but' sentence differs in meaning from an '_____' sentence.

and

5-22 Suppose in addition to giving the nationality of two great thinkers, we wish to emphasize the *difference* in their nationalities. Which sentence would we use—the 'but' sentence or the 'and' sentence?

> *Socrates was a Greek,* but *Cicero was a Roman.*
> *Socrates was a Greek,* and *Cicero was a Roman.*

The '_____' sentence.

but

5-23 Suppose in addition to presenting two facts about elephants we wish to emphasize how different the second fact is from what the first fact leads us to expect. Which sentence would we use—the 'but' sentence or the 'and' sentence?

> *The elephant is larger than the mouse,* and *the elephant fears the mouse.*
> *The elephant is larger than the mouse,* but *the elephant fears the mouse.*

The '_____' sentence.

but

5-24 Suppose in addition to describing melodies and chords we want to emphasize the difference between melodies and chords. Which sentence would we use?

> *Melodies are tones sounded in succession,* but *chords are tones sounded together.*
> *Melodies are tones sounded in succession,* and *chords are tones sounded together.*

The '_____' sentence.

but

5-25 When we want a sentence that not only states two facts but also emphasizes some difference between the two facts, we join a sentence stating the one fact to a sentence stating the other fact not by a word 'and' but by a word '_____.'

but

5-26   We cannot represent a connecting word 'whereas.' So we must decide to which of the representable connecting words a connecting word 'whereas' is _____.

related

5-27   *Corot painted landscapes, whereas Reynolds painted portraits.*

The above 'whereas' sentence is closest in meaning to which of the following sentences?

> *It is false that Corot painted landscapes.*
> *If Corot painted landscapes, then Reynolds painted portraits.*
> *Corot painted landscapes, or Reynolds painted portraits.*
> *Corot painted landscapes, and Reynolds painted portraits.*

The '_____' sentence.

and

5-28   Since a 'whereas' sentence is very close in meaning to an 'and' sentence, a connecting word 'whereas' is related to a connecting word '_____.' But now let's see how a 'whereas' sentence differs in meaning from an '_____' sentence.

and

and

5-29   Suppose in addition to telling which instruments two great musicians played, we want to emphasize that they played different instruments. Which sentence would we use?

> *Bach was an organist, whereas Chopin was a pianist.*
> *Bach was an organist, and Chopin was a pianist.*

The '_____' sentence.

whereas

5-30   Suppose in addition to classifying the main works of two great painters, we want to emphasize the difference in their works. Which sentence would we use?

> *Corot painted landscapes, whereas Reynolds painted portraits.*
> *Corot painted landscapes, and Reynolds painted portraits.*

The '_____' sentence.

whereas

5-31 When we want a sentence that merely states two facts, we use an '_____' sentence. But we may use a 'whereas' sentence when we want a sentence that states two facts and in addition emphasizes some _____ between the two facts.

and

difference

5-32 Notice that a 'whereas' sentence differs in meaning from an 'and' sentence in much the same way as a '_____' sentence differs in meaning from an 'and' sentence.

but

5-33 When we want a sentence that merely states two facts, we use an '_____' sentence. But when we want a sentence that states two facts and in addition emphasizes some difference between the two facts, we may use either a '_____' sentence or a '_____' sentence.

and

but; whereas
(Either order)

5-34 A connecting word 'though' is related to what representable connecting word? Consider.

5-35 *Conrad was a master of English prose, though Polish was Conrad's native tongue.*

The above 'though' sentence is closest in meaning to which of the following sentences?

> *It is false that Conrad was a master of English prose.*
> *If Conrad was a master of English prose, then Polish was Conrad's native tongue.*
> *Conrad was a master of English prose, or Polish was Conrad's native tongue.*
> *Conrad was a master of English prose, and Polish was Conrad's native tongue.*

The '_____' sentence.

and

5-36 *Berlioz played no orchestral instrument, though Berlioz composed orchestral music.*

The above 'though' sentence is very close in meaning to what representable sentence?

_____

Berlioz played no orchestral instrument, and Berlioz composed orchestral music.

5-37   Since a 'though' sentence is very close in meaning to an 'and' sentence, a connecting word 'though' is _____ to a connecting word 'and.'

5-38   A 'though' sentence is very close in meaning to an 'and' sentence. But now let's see how a 'though' sentence *differs* in _____ from an 'and' sentence.

5-39   Suppose we want a sentence that not only states that a certain spring day was pleasant and that the day was wet but also emphasizes that the day was pleasant *in spite of* the day's being wet. That is, suppose we want a sentence that emphasizes that the wetness of the day did not prevent the day's being pleasant, or, in other words, that the wetness of the day did not affect the day's being pleasant. Which sentence would we use?

> *The spring day was pleasant, though the showers continued all day.*
> *The spring day was pleasant, and the showers continued all day.*

The '_____' sentence.

5-40   Suppose we want a sentence that in addition to stating two facts about Berlioz emphasizes that the first fact is not affected by the second. Which sentence would we use?

> *Berlioz composed orchestral music, though Berlioz played no orchestral instrument.*
> *Berlioz composed orchestral music, and Berlioz played no orchestral instrument.*

The '_____' sentence.

5-41   When we want a sentence that merely states two facts, we use an '_____' sentence. But when we want a sentence that not only states two facts but also emphasizes that the first fact is not affected by the second, then we use a '_____' sentence.

5-42   An 'and' sentence merely states two facts. A 'though' sentence states two facts and in addition emphasizes that the first fact is not _____ by the second.

5-43   *Grant was an unsuccessful President, although Grant was a great Civil War general.*

The above 'although' sentence is closest in meaning to which representable sentence?

> *It is false that Grant was an unsuccessful President.*
> *If Grant was an unsuccessful President, then Grant was a great Civil War general.*
> *Grant was an unsuccessful President, or Grant was a great Civil War general.*
> *Grant was an unsuccessful President, and Grant was a great Civil War general.*

The '_____' sentence.   and

5-44   *Grant was an unsuccessful President, even though Grant was a great Civil War general.*

The above 'even though' sentence is closest in meaning to which representable sentence?

> *It is false that Grant was an unsuccessful President.*
> *If Grant was an unsuccessful President, then Grant was a great Civil War general.*
> *Grant was an unsuccessful President, or Grant was a great Civil War general.*
> *Grant was an unsuccessful President, and Grant was a great Civil War general.*

The '_____' sentence.   and

5-45   When we want a sentence that not only states two facts but also emphasizes that the first fact is not affected by the second, we may use a '_____' sentence, an '_____' sentence, or an '_____' sentence.   though
although; even though

5-46   A connecting word 'because' is related to what representable connecting word? Consider.

5-47 *Henry VIII divorced Catherine of Aragon, because Catherine gave Henry no sons.*

The above 'because' sentence is closest in meaning to which of these representable sentences?

> *It is false that Henry VIII divorced Catherine of Aragon.*
> *If Henry VIII divorced Catherine of Aragon, then Catherine gave Henry no sons.*
> *Henry VIII divorced Catherine of Aragon, or Catherine gave Henry no sons.*
> *Henry VIII divorced Catherine of Aragon, and Catherine gave Henry no sons.*

The '_____' sentence.   and

5-48 A 'because' sentence is very close in meaning to an 'and' sentence. But now let's see how a 'because' sentence *differs* in _____ from an 'and' sentence.   meaning

5-49 Suppose in addition to noting two properties of cork, we wish to emphasize that cork's having the first property results from cork's having the second property. Which sentence would we use?

> *Cork floats on the ocean, because cork is less dense than brine.*
> *Cork floats on the ocean, and cork is less dense than brine.*

The '_____' sentence.   because

5-50 An 'and' sentence merely states two facts. A 'because' sentence states two facts and in addition emphasizes that the first fact _____ from the other.   results

5-51 Suppose in addition to telling of two events in English history we wish to emphasize that the one event results from the other. Which sentence would we use?

> *Henry VIII divorced Catherine of Aragon, for Catherine gave Henry no sons.*
> *Henry VIII divorced Catherine of Aragon, and Catherine gave Henry no sons.*

The '_____' sentence.   for

5-52 Suppose in addition to telling of two events in English history we wish to emphasize that the one event results from the other. Which sentence would we use?

> *Henry VIII divorced Catherine of Aragon, since Catherine gave Henry no sons.*
> *Henry VIII divorced Catherine of Aragon, and Catherine gave Henry no sons.*

The '_____' sentence.

since

5-53 When we want a sentence that in addition to stating two facts emphasizes that the first fact results from the other, we may use a '_____' sentence, a '_____' sentence, or a '_____' sentence.

because; for
since

5-54 The connecting words 'because,' 'for,' and 'since' are all related to a representable connecting word '_____.' Moreover, a 'because' sentence differs in meaning from an 'and' sentence in much the same way as does a '_____' sentence or a '_____' sentence.

and

for
since

5-55 List eight unlike connecting words all of which are unrepresentable but all of which are related to a connecting word 'and.'

but	though	because
_____	_____	_____
	_____	_____

whereas; although; even
  though
for; since

5-56

but	though	because
whereas	although	for
	even though	since

The above connecting words are all unrepresentable and are all related to a connecting word 'and.' But do all these connecting words have exactly the same function? _____

no

5-57 An 'and' sentence merely states two facts. A 'but' sentence or a 'whereas' sentence states two facts and emphasizes that the first fact _____ _____ the second fact. A 'though' sentence or an 'although' sentence or an 'even though' sentence states two facts and emphasizes that the first fact is _____ _____ by the second fact. A 'because' sentence, a 'for' sentence, or a 'since' sentence states two facts and emphasizes that the first fact _____ _____ the second fact.

differs from

not affected

results
from

5-58 A connecting word 'either or' is related to which representable connecting word?

5-59 *Either Frege was a logician, or Frege was a philosopher.*

The above 'either or' sentence is closest in meaning to which representable sentence?

> *It is false that Frege was a logician.*
> *If Frege was a logician, then Frege was a philosopher.*
> *Frege was a logician, or Frege was a philosopher.*
> *Frege was a logician, and Frege was a philosopher.*

The '_____' sentence.

or

5-60 An unrepresentable connecting word 'either or' is related to a representable connecting word '_____.'

or

5-61 Can we represent a connecting word 'provided then'? _____

no

5-62 The connecting word 'provided then' is related to what representable connecting word? We can answer this question once we decide to which _____ sentence a given 'provided then' sentence is very close in _____.

representable
meaning

5-63   *Provided Chaucer read Boccaccio, then* The Canterbury
Tales *are less remarkable.*

The above 'provided then' sentence is closest in meaning to
which of the following representable sentences?

> *It is false that Chaucer read Boccaccio.*
> *If Chaucer read Boccaccio, then* The Canterbury Tales
> *are less remarkable.*
> *Chaucer read Boccaccio, or* The Canterbury Tales *are
> less remarkable.*
> *Chaucer read Boccaccio, and* The Canterbury Tales *are
> less remarkable.*

The '_____' sentence.   if then

5-64   How many of the following six connecting words can
we represent?

> provided then   in the event that then
> on the condition that then   in case that then
> assuming that then   if then

_____   one

5-65   *If Socrates was an Athenian, then Socrates was a Greek.*

How many of the following five sentences are very close in
meaning to the above 'if then' sentence?

> Provided *Socrates was an Athenian, then Socrates was
> a Greek.*
> On condition that *Socrates was an Athenian, then
> Socrates was a Greek.*
> Assuming that *Socrates was an Athenian, then Socrates
> was a Greek.*
> In the event that *Socrates was an Athenian, then
> Socrates was a Greek.*
> In case that *Socrates was an Athenian, then Socrates was
> a Greek.*

_____   five

5-66 (1) provided then
(2) on the condition that then
(3) assuming that then
(4) in the event that then
(5) in case that then
(6) but

How many of the above connecting words are representable?
_____ How many of the above connecting words are   none
related to a representable connecting word 'if then'?
_____   five

5-67 Write five unlike connecting words each of which is
related to a connecting word 'if then.'   provided then
                                                               on condition that then
                                                               assuming that then
                                                               in the event that then
                                                               in case that then

5-68 We cannot represent a connecting word 'it is not the
case that' since the only connecting words we can represent
are connecting words just like

    and
    or
    if then

    _____   it is false that

5-69 *It is not the case that Socrates wrote books.*

The above sentence is closest in meaning to which of the
following representable sentences?

    It is false that Socrates wrote books.
    If Socrates wrote books, then Socrates wrote books.
    Socrates wrote books, or Socrates wrote books.
    Socrates wrote books, and Socrates wrote books.

The '_____' sentence.   it is false that

5-70 (1) it is not the case that
      (2) whereas
      (3) it is not true that
      (4) though

How many of the above connecting words are representable?
_____ How many of the above connecting words are   none
related to the representable connecting word 'it is false that'?

_____   two

5-71 Can we represent a connecting word 'not'? _____   no

5-72 *The whale is not a fish.*

The above sentence is closest in meaning to which of the
following representable sentences?

> *It is false that the whale is a fish.*
> *If the whale is a fish, then the whale is a fish.*
> *The whale is a fish, or the whale is a fish.*
> *The whale is a fish, and the whale is a fish.*

The '_____' sentence.   it is false that

5-73 *Mathematics is not more basic than logic.*

Write a representable sentence that is very close in meaning   It is false that
to the above unrepresentable sentence.   mathematics is more

_____   basic than logic.

5-74 (1) it is not the case that
      (2) whereas
      (3) not
      (4) it is not true that
      (5) although

How many of the above connecting words are representable?
_____ How many of the above connecting words are   none
related to 'it is false that'? _____   three

5-75 List eight unlike connecting words all of which are
related to a connecting word 'and.'

    but   because
    whereas   for
    though   since
    although
    even though

5-76 Write an unrepresentable connecting word which is related to the representable connecting word 'or.'

either or

5-77 Copy those of the following connecting words which are related to the representable connecting word 'if then.'

assuming that then	but
in case that then	though
not	provided then

assuming that then
in case that then
provided then

5-78 List three unlike connecting words all of which are unrepresentable and all of which are related to a connecting word 'it is false that.'

it is not the case that
it is not true that
not

5-79 Given an unrepresentable argument, we can write a related representable argument once we know how unrepresentable connecting words are _____ to _____ connecting words.

related; representable

5-80 *Jackson was not an unpopular President, but Jackson had displeased the commercial interests.*
Jackson had displeased the commercial interests, because Jackson allowed unstable money.
Therefore, it is not true that Jackson was an unpopular President, even though Jackson allowed unstable money.

Is the above argument representable? _____ The above argument has as a related representable argument the following:

no

_____ *Jackson was an unpopular President,*
_____ *Jackson had displeased the commercial interests.*
Jackson had displeased the commercial interests,
_____ *Jackson allowed unstable money.*
Therefore, _____ *Jackson was an unpopular President,* _____ *Jackson allowed unstable money.*

It is false that
and

and
it is false that
and

5-81   *Either John killed Tom, or Peter lied in court.*
In the event that John killed Tom, then John committed
a crime.
Assuming that Peter lied in court, then Peter committed
a crime.
Therefore, either John committed a crime, or Peter committed a crime.

Since the above argument contains connecting words we cannot represent, the argument is an _____ argument. The above argument has as a related representable argument the following:

John killed Tom, _____ Peter lied in court.
_____ John killed Tom, _____ John committed a crime.
_____ Peter lied in court, _____ Peter committed a crime.
Therefore, John committed a crime, _____ Peter committed a crime.

5-82   *Provided Bach wrote for the piano, then the piano was invented before Bach's death.*
The piano was not invented before Bach's death, whereas the organ was in use in the eighteenth century.
Therefore, it is not the case that Bach wrote for the piano.

Is the above argument representable? _____ The above argument has as a related representable argument the following:

_____ Bach wrote for the piano, _____ the piano was invented before Bach's death.
_____ the piano was invented before Bach's death, _____ the organ was in use in the eighteenth century.
Therefore, _____ Bach wrote for the piano.

5-83   Given an unrepresentable argument, we write a related representable argument. Then if we can use system F to _____ that the related representable argument is valid, we _____ that the unrepresentable argument is also valid.

5-84 We have seen how certain unrepresentable connecting words can be fairly simply related to one or another kind of representable connecting words. But other unrepresentable connecting words are related to representable connecting words in a perhaps less obvious way. Can we represent a connecting word 'only if'? _____

no

5-85 Before deciding how an 'only if' is related to representable connecting words, let's explore the meaning of an 'only if' sentence.

Phil has a daughter only if Phil has a child.

Given the above sentence, then if we know that Phil has a child do we necessarily know that Phil has a daughter? _____

no

5-86 *Phil has a daughter only if Phil has a child.*

If we know that Phil has a child, we do not necessarily know that Phil has a daughter. For we know only that Phil has a son *or a* _____ .

daughter

5-87 *Phil has a daughter only if Phil has a child.*

If we know that Phil has a daughter, then do we know that Phil has a child? _____

yes

5-88 *Phil has a daughter only if Phil has a child.*

To which of the following 'if then' sentences is the above 'only if' sentence closer in meaning?

    (1) If Phil has a daughter, then Phil has a child.
    (2) If Phil has a child, then Phil has a daughter.

Sentence _____ .

1

5-89 The following two sentences are close in meaning:

Phil has a daughter only if Phil has a child.
If Phil has a _____ *, then Phil has a* _____ .

daughter; child

5-90 *Phil has a daughter* only if *Phil has a child.*

The above 'only if' sentence is closest in meaning to which of the following representable sentences?

> *It is false that Phil has a daughter.*
> *If Phil has a daughter, then Phil has a child.*
> *Phil has a daughter, or Phil has a child.*
> *Phil has a daughter, and Phil has a child.*

The '_____' sentence.

if then

5-91 *Phil has a daughter only if Phil has a child.*

To assert the above sentence amounts to saying that Phil's having a child is a necessary condition for Phil's having a daughter. For if having a child is a necessary condition for having a daughter, then knowing that Phil has a daughter we know without question that Phil has a child. In other words, an 'only if' sentence has as a related representable sentence an 'if then' sentence such that a sentence like the sentence following the 'only if' in the unrepresentable sentence follows the '_____' in the related 'if then' sentence.

then

5-92 The following two sentences are close in meaning:

> *Bob has a dollar only if Bob has at least a dime.*
> *If Bob has a* _____, *then Bob has at least a* _____.

dollar
dime

5-93 *Dixon is a U.S. Senator only if Dixon is a U.S. citizen.*

If we know that Dixon is a U.S. citizen, we do not necessarily know that Dixon is a U.S. Senator. For there are many citizens who are not _____.

senators

5-94 *Dixon is a U.S. Senator only if Dixon is a U.S. citizen.*

To which of the following 'if then' sentences is the above 'only if' sentence closer in meaning?

> (1) *If Dixon is a U.S. citizen, then Dixon is a U.S. Senator.*
> (2) *If Dixon is a U.S. Senator, then Dixon is a U.S. citizen.*

Sentence _____.

2

5-95 In other words, an 'only if' sentence has as a related representable sentence an '_____' sentence such that the sentence following the 'then' in the representable sentence is like the sentence following the '_____' in the unrepresentable sentence.

5-96 Another unrepresentable connecting word is 'if and only if.' This connecting word is related to a complex of representable connecting words. Before agreeing on the appropriate relatedness, we articulate first our understanding of 'if then' sentences and of 'and' sentences, and then take advantage of our understanding of 'only if' sentences.

5-97 *(1) If the rain stopped, then the game was played.*
(2) If the game was played, then the rain stopped.

Given sentence 1, if we know the rain stopped do we necessarily know the game was played? _____ Given sentence 2, if we know the game was played, do we necessarily know the rain stopped? _____

5-98 *(1) If the rain stopped, then the game was played.*
(2) If the game was played, then the rain stopped.

Given sentence 1 and knowing that the game was played, we do not necessarily know that the rain stopped. For perhaps the game was played in spite of the _____ . Given sentence 2 and knowing that the rain stopped, we do not necessarily know that the game was played. For perhaps the rain stopped but the field was too wet for the _____ to be played.

5-99 *If the rain stopped, then the game was played; and if the game was played, then the rain stopped.*

The above sentence is two 'if then' sentences joined by a connecting word '_____.' Given the above sentence, then if we know the rain stopped do we necessarily know the game was played? _____ Given the above sentence, then if we know the game was played do we necessarily know the rain stopped? _____

5-100   *The game was played* only if *the rain stopped.*

Now notice that the above 'only if' sentence is close in meaning to the following representable sentence.

> _____ *the game was played,* _____ *the rain*   If; then
> *stopped.*

5-101   (1) If *the game was played,* then *the rain stopped.*
(2) *The game was played* only if *the rain stopped.*

The above two sentences are close in meaning. So the following two sentences are close in meaning:

> (3) *If the rain stopped, then the game was played; and
> if the game was played,* then *the rain stopped.*
> (4) *If the rain stopped, then the game was played; and
> the game was played* _____ *the rain stopped.*   only if

5-102   *If the rain stopped, then the game was played; and if the
game was played, then the rain stopped.*

The above 'if then and if then' sentence is close in meaning to the following sentence:

> *If the rain stopped, then the game was played; and the
> game was played* _____ *the rain stopped.*   only if

5-103   *The game was played* if and only if *the rain stopped.*

The above 'if and only if' sentence is close in meaning to the following sentence:

> _____ *the rain stopped,* _____ *the game*   If; then
> *was played;* _____ *the game was played* only if   and
> *the rain stopped.*

5-104   If *the rain stopped,* then *the game was played;* and *the
game was played* only if *the rain stopped.*

The above sentence is close in meaning to the following sentence:

> *The game was played* _____ _____ _____   if and only
> _____ *the rain stopped.*   if

5-105 *The game was played if and only if the rain stopped.*

Given the above sentence, then if we know the rain stopped do we know necessarily that the game was played? _____   yes
Given the above sentence, then if we know the game was played do we know necessarily that the rain stopped? _____   yes

5-106 An 'if and only if' sentence is close in meaning to a representable sentence which is two '_____' sentences   if then
joined by a connecting word '_____.'   and

5-107 (1) *The game was played if and only if the rain stopped.*
(2) *If the rain stopped, then the game was played.*
(3) *If the game was played, then the rain stopped.*

To assert sentence 1 amounts to saying that knowing that the rain stopped is a sufficient condition for knowing that the game was played and, moreover, that knowing that the game was played is a sufficient condition for knowing that the rain stopped. Another way of looking at the matter is this: To assert sentence 1 amounts to saying that knowing that the game was played is a necessary condition for knowing that the rain stopped and conversely that knowing that the rain stopped is a necessary condition for knowing that the game was played. Or more simply, to assert sentence 1 amounts to asserting both sentence 2 and sentence 3—that is, amounts to saying that knowing that the rain stopped is both a sufficient and a necessary condition for knowing that the game was played. In yet other words, an 'if and only if' sentence has as a related representable sentence a sentence which is two 'if then' sentences joined by a connecting word 'and' and such that a sentence like the sentence following the 'if and only if' in the unrepresentable sentence follows the
'_____' in the first 'if then' sentence and follows the   if
'_____' in the second 'if then' sentence.   then

5-108 *The triangle is isosceles if and only if the triangle has two equal sides.*

The above 'if and only if' sentence is close in meaning to the following sentence:

_____ *the triangle has two equal sides,* _____   If; then
the triangle is isosceles; _____ *the triangle is*   and
isosceles only if the triangle has two equal sides.

5-109   *If the triangle has two equal sides, then the triangle is isosceles; and if the triangle is isosceles, then the triangle has two equal sides.*

The above sentence is close in meaning to the following sentence:

> *The triangle is isosceles* _____ _____   if and
> _____ _____ *the triangle has two equal*   only if
> *sides.*

5-110   *The triangle is isosceles* if and only if *the triangle has two equal sides.*

Given the above sentence, then if we know the triangle has two equal sides do we necessarily know the triangle is isosceles? _____ Given the above sentence, then if we   yes
know the triangle is isosceles do we necessarily know the triangle has two equal sides? _____   yes

5-111   *The animal is a mammal* if and only if *the animal is warm-blooded.*

The above 'if and only if' sentence is unrepresentable and is close in meaning to the *unrepresentable* sentence

> *If the animal is warm-blooded, then the animal is a mammal; and the animal is a mammal* only if *the animal is warm-blooded.*

But this unrepresentable sentence is close in meaning to the representable sentence

> _____ *the animal is warm-blooded,* _____   If; then
> *the animal is a mammal;* _____ _____ *the*   and if
> *animal is a mammal,* _____ *the animal is warm-*   then
> *blooded.*

5-112   *The animal is a mammal if and only if the animal is warm-blooded.*

The above 'if and only if' sentence has the following as a related representable sentence:

> _____ *the animal is warm-blooded,* _____   If; then
> *the animal is a mammal;* _____ _____ *the*   and if
> *animal is a mammal,* _____ *the animal is warm-*   then
> *blooded.*

5-113 An 'if and only if' sentence has as a related representable sentence a sentence which is two '_____'   *if then*
sentences joined by a connecting word '_____,' and   *and*
such that a sentence like the sentence preceding the 'if and only if' in the unrepresentable sentence follows the
'_____' in the first 'if then' sentence and follows the   *then*
'_____' in the second 'if then' sentence.   *if*

5-114 In terms now of our understanding of 'if and only if' we can see how connecting words like

unless   except if   or but not both

can be related to _____ connecting words.   *representable*

5-115 *Dixon will be President unless Dixon lost in Ohio.*

Given the above 'unless' sentence, consider these questions:

First

> If we know Dixon will be President, do we necessarily know Dixon lost in Ohio? _____   *no*
> If we know Dixon will be President, do we necessarily know it is false that Dixon lost in Ohio? _____   *yes*

Then

> If we know it is false that Dixon lost in Ohio, do we necessarily know it is false that Dixon will be President? _____   *no*
> If we know it is false that Dixon lost in Ohio, do we necessarily know that Dixon will be President?
> _____   *yes*

5-116 *Dixon will be President if and only if it is false that Dixon lost in Ohio.*

In the light of our understanding of 'if and only if' sentences, consider these questions: Given the above 'if and only if' sentence

> If we know Dixon will be President, do we necessarily know it is false that Dixon lost in Ohio? _____   *yes*
> If we know it is false that Dixon lost in Ohio, do we necessarily know Dixon will be President?
> _____   *yes*

5-117   *Dixon will be President* unless *Dixon lost in Ohio.*
Dixon will be President if and only if it is false that *Dixon lost in Ohio.*

From exploring our understanding of sentences like these two we see that an 'unless' sentence is very close in meaning to an '_____ _____ _____ _____ _____ _____ _____ _____' sentence.

if and only if it is false that

5-118   *The daffodils bloomed in April if and only if it is false that March was very severe.*

The above sentence is close in meaning to the shorter but also unrepresentable sentence

> *The daffodils bloomed in April unless*
> _____ .

March was very severe

5-119   The unrepresentable sentence

> *Unless baritones were needed, Dan sang bass.*

is close in meaning to the also unrepresentable sentence

> _____ *unless*
> _____ .

Dan sang bass
baritones were needed

which in turn is close in meaning to the still unrepresentable sentence

> *Dan sang bass* _____ *it is false that baritones were needed.*

if and only if

5-120   *Napoleon was defeated at Waterloo unless history deceives us.*

has as a related representable sentence

> _____ _____ _____ _____ _____
> *history deceives us,* _____ *Napoleon was defeated at Waterloo;* _____ _____ *Napoleon was de-*
> *feated at Waterloo,* _____ _____ _____
> _____ _____ *history deceives us.*

If it is false that
then
and if
then it is
false that

5-121   *Phil was guilty except if the witness lied.*
Phil was guilty unless the witness lied.

It seems hard to deny that the above 'except if' sentence is close in meaning to the 'unless' sentence. Both sentences are close in meaning, then, to the still unrepresentable sentence

> *Phil was guilty if and only if* _____ *the witness lied.*

   it is false that

and so the 'except if' sentence has as a related representable sentence

> _____ _____ _____ _____ _____
> *the witness lied,* _____ *Phil was guilty;* _____
> _____ *Phil was guilty,* _____ _____
> _____ _____ _____ *the witness lied.*

   If it is false that
then; and
if; then it
is false that

5-122   *The corporations will merge except if profits increase.*

This 'except if' sentence has as a related representable sentence:

> *If it is false that* _____ , *then* _____ ;
> _____ *the corporations will merge,* _____
> *profits increase.*

   profits increase; the
corporations will merge
and if; then it is false that

5-123   *Hegel was discussed* or *Hume was discussed* but not both.
Hegel was discussed except if *Hume was discussed.*
Hegel was discussed unless *Hume was discussed.*
Hegel was discussed if and only if it is false that *Hume was discussed.*

It seems difficult to deny that the 'or but not both' sentence is very close in meaning to the 'except if' sentence, to the '_____' sentence, and to the '_____' sentence. So the 'or but not both' sentence has as a related representable sentence

   unless; if and only if it is
false that

> *If it is false that* _____ , *then* _____ ;
> _____ *Hegel was discussed,* _____ *Hume was discussed.*

   Hume was discussed;
Hegel was discussed
and if; then it is false that

5-124 Copy those of the following that are representable connecting words:

and	though	because
but	although	for
whereas	even though	since

or
either or

if then	assuming that then
provided then	in the event that then
on condition that then	in case that then

it is false that	it is not true that
it is not the case that	not

and
or
if then
it is false that

5-125

but	though	because
whereas	although	for
	even though	since

Each of the above connecting words is unrepresentable and is related to a representable connecting word '_____,' which is represented by a '_____.'

and
K

5-126 either or

The above connecting word is unrepresentable and is related to a representable connecting word '_____,' which is represented by an '_____.'

or
A

5-127

provided then	in the event that then
on condition that then	in case that then
assuming that then	

Each of the above connecting words is unrepresentable and is related to a representable connecting word '_____,' which is represented by a '_____.'

if then
C

5-128 it is not the case that
it is not true that
not

Each of the above connecting words is unrepresentable and
is related to a representable connecting word '_____,' it is false that
which is represented by an '_____.' N

5-129 How many of the following are representable connecting words?

      only if   if and only if   unless

                            except if

                            or but not both

_____ none

5-130 *France was victorious only if Spain was conquered.*

The above 'only if' sentence has as a related representable
sentence which of the following:

      (1) If France was victorious, then Spain was conquered.
      (2) If Spain was conquered, then France was victorious.

Sentence _____. 1

5-131 *Adams won only if Jackson lost.*

For the above 'only if' sentence, write a related representable
sentence.

_____ If Adams won, then
Jackson lost.

5-132 *France was victorious if and only if Spain was conquered.*

The above 'if and only if' sentence has which of the following
as a related representable sentence?

      (1) If France was victorious, then Spain was conquered.
      (2) If Spain was conquered, then France was victorious.
      (3) If Spain was conquered, then France was victorious;
      and if France was victorious, then Spain was conquered.

Sentence _____. 3

5-133 An 'if and only if' sentence is close in meaning to a sentence which is two '_____' sentences joined by a connecting word '_____.'

5-134 *The group disbanded unless a strong leader emerged.*

The above 'unless' sentence has as a related sentence which of the following sentences?

> (1) *If the group disbanded, then it is false that a strong leader emerged.*
> (2) *If it is false that a strong leader emerged, then the group disbanded.*
> (3) *If it is false that a strong leader emerged, then the group disbanded; and if the group disbanded, then it is false that a strong leader emerged.*

Sentence _____ .

5-135 (1) *Fear persists unless help arrives.*
(2) *Fear persists except if help arrives.*
(3) *Fear persists or help arrives but not both.*
(4) *If it is false that help arrives then fear persists, and if fear persists then it is false that help arrives.*
(5) *Fear persists if and only if it is false that help arrives.*

How many of the above sentences are close in meaning? _____ Which of the above sentences is representable? Sentence _____ .

5-136 *If it is false that deceit flourishes, then truth is respected; and if truth is respected, then it is false that deceit flourishes.*

The above sentence is representable but unpleasing and cumbersome. If we wanted a shorter, more inviting sentence expressing much the same meaning, we might use an '_____' sentence, an '_____' sentence, an '_____' sentence, or an '_____' sentence.

5-137 Chopin wrote only piano music, whereas Wagner wrote operas.

Wagner wrote operas, because Wagner thought music without drama incomplete.

Therefore, Chopin wrote only piano music, though Wagner thought music without drama incomplete.

The above unrepresentable argument has as a related representable argument the following:

Chopin wrote only piano music, _____ Wagner wrote operas.   and

Wagner wrote operas, _____ Wagner thought music without drama incomplete.   and

Therefore, Chopin wrote only piano music, _____ Wagner thought music without drama incomplete.   and

5-138 Bismarck attacked France in 1870, for war alone could have unified Germany.

Napoleon III was totally unprepared for war, even though France was a great power.

Therefore, Bismarck attacked France in 1870, but Napoleon III was totally unprepared for war.

The above unrepresentable argument has as a related representable argument the following:

Bismarck attacked France in 1870, _____ war alone could have unified Germany.   and

Napoleon III was totally unprepared for war, _____ France was a great power.   and

Therefore, Bismarck attacked France in 1870, _____ Napoleon III was totally unprepared for war.   and

5-139 John Brown was an Abolitionist hero, since Brown fought militantly against slavery.

John Brown was hanged, because Brown fought militantly against slavery.

Therefore, John Brown was hanged, although John Brown was an Abolitionist hero.

The above argument has as a related representable argument the following:

John Brown was an Abolitionist hero, _____   and
Brown fought militantly against slavery.
John Brown was hanged, _____ Brown fought   and
militantly against slavery.
Therefore, John Brown was hanged, _____ John   and
Brown was an Abolitionist hero.

5-140 Some unrepresentable connecting words are related
to one of the representable connecting words

     _____   and
     _____   or
     _____   if then
     _____   it is false that

Other unrepresentable connecting words are related to some
combination of the representable connecting words

     _____   and
     _____   or
     _____   if then
     _____   it is false that

5-141 Bill's policy was in force unless a minor was driving.
Peter was just seventeen, but Peter was licensed to drive.
Assuming that Peter was driving, then a minor was
driving.
Therefore, in the event that Peter was driving then Bill's
policy was not in force, even though Peter was licensed
to drive.

This argument is unrepresentable but has as a related representable argument the following:

_____ _____ _____ _____ _____   If it is false that
a minor was driving, _____ Bill's policy was in   then
force; _____ _____ Bill's policy was in force,   and if
_____ _____ _____ _____ _____   then it is false that
a minor was driving.
Peter was just seventeen, _____ Peter was licensed   and
to drive.
_____ Peter was driving, _____ a minor was   If; then
driving.
Therefore, _____ Peter was driving _____   if; then
_____ _____ _____ _____ Bill's policy   it is false that
was in force, _____ Peter was licensed to drive.   and

5-142 *If laws are passed for man's good, then laws can be repealed.*
If laws can be repealed, then it is false that laws are unchangeable.
Laws are unchangeable, or laws can change with time.
Therefore, if laws are passed for man's good, then laws can change with time.

Is the above argument representable? _____

yes

5-143 *The Benton will sail on Friday if and only if the cargo is complete.*
The Bismarck sailed on Tuesday or the Elsa sailed on Tuesday but not both.
Either the Bismarck sailed on Tuesday or the cargo is not complete, since the Bismarck carried goods for the Benton.
Therefore, in case that the Elsa sailed on Tuesday, then it is not true that the Benton will sail on Friday.

The above argument has as a related representable argument the following:

_____ *the cargo is complete* _____ *the Benton will sail on Friday,* _____ _____ *the Benton will sail on Friday* _____ *the cargo is complete.*
_____ _____ _____ _____ _____
the Elsa sailed on Tuesday _____ *the Bismarck sailed on Tuesday,* _____ _____ *the Bismarck sailed on Tuesday* _____ _____ _____
_____ _____ *the Elsa sailed on Tuesday.*
The Bismarck sailed on Tuesday _____ _____
_____ _____ _____ *the cargo is complete,*
_____ *the Bismarck carried goods for the Benton.*
Therefore, _____ *the Elsa sailed on Tuesday,*
_____ _____ _____ _____ _____
the Benton will sail on Friday.

If; then
and if
then
If it is false that
then
and if
then it is
false that
or it
is false that
and
if
then it is false that

5-144 *Integration can succeed only if living standards can be raised.*

Our economy is basically faulty except if living standards can be raised.

Therefore, provided integration can succeed, then our economy is not basically faulty.

The above unrepresentable argument has as a related representable argument the following:

_____ *integration can succeed,* _____ *living standards can be raised.*

If; then

_____ _____ _____ _____ _____
living standards can be raised _____ *our economy is basically faulty,* _____ _____ *our economy is basically faulty* _____ _____ _____ _____ _____ *living standards can be raised.*
Therefore, _____ *integration can succeed,* _____ _____ _____ _____ _____ *our economy is basically faulty.*

If it is false that
then
and if
then it is
false that
if; then
it is false that

5-145 *Alaska was called Seward's Icebox because Secretary of State Seward purchased Alaska from Russia in 1867, although the purchase was deemed a folly.*

Alaska has proved itself a great asset, for natural resources abound in Alaska.

Therefore, Alaska has proved itself a great asset, whereas the purchase was deemed a folly.

The above unrepresentable argument has as a related representable argument the following:

Alaska was called Seward's Icebox _____
Secretary of State Seward purchased Alaska from Russia in 1867, _____ *the purchase was deemed a folly.*
Alaska has proved itself a great asset, _____
natural resources abound in Alaska.
Therefore, Alaska has proved itself a great asset, _____ *the purchase was deemed a folly.*

and

and

and

and

5-146 Given an unrepresentable argument, we write a related _____ argument. Then if we can use system F to show that the related representable argument is valid, we will claim that the unrepresentable argument is also _____ .

representable

valid

B Unrepresentable Words Indicating Premiss or Conclusion

5-147 How do we distinguish an argument from a sequence of sentences that is not an argument? That is, how do we know that one sentence of a sequence is _____ _____ _____ from the other sentences of the sequence?

said
to follow

5-148 *If we can represent arguments, then we can formalize arguments.*
We can represent arguments.
Therefore, we can formalize arguments.

In the above argument we could tell that the third sentence was said to follow from the first two because a 'therefore' precedes the third sentence. We saw that often the conclusion of an argument was preceded by a '_____ .'

therefore

5-149 *If we can represent arguments, then we can formalize arguments.*
We can represent arguments.
Thus, we can formalize arguments.

The conclusion of the above argument is preceded by a '_____ .'

thus

5-150 *If we can represent arguments, then we can formalize arguments.*
We can represent arguments.
Hence, we can formalize arguments.

The conclusion of the above argument is preceded by a '_____ .'

hence

5-151 *If we can represent arguments, then we can formalize arguments.*
We can represent arguments.
So, we can formalize arguments.

The conclusion of the above argument is preceded by a '_____ .'

so

5-152   *If we can represent arguments, then we can formalize
arguments.
We can represent arguments.
Consequently, we can formalize arguments.*

The conclusion of the above argument is preceded by a
'_____.'

consequently

5-153   *If we can represent arguments, then we can formalize
arguments.
We can represent arguments.
Wherefore, we can formalize arguments.*

The conclusion of the above argument is preceded by a
'_____.'

wherefore

5-154   *If we can represent arguments, then we can formalize
arguments.
We can represent arguments.
Whence, we can formalize arguments.*

A 'whence' precedes the _____ of the above argument.

conclusion

5-155   *If we can represent arguments, then we can formalize
arguments.
We can represent arguments.
Ergo, we can formalize arguments.*

The conclusion of the above argument is preceded by an
'_____.'

ergo

5-156   *If we can represent arguments, then we can formalize
arguments.
We can represent arguments.
Accordingly, we can formalize arguments.*

The conclusion of the above argument is preceded by an
'_____.'

accordingly

5-157   *If we can represent arguments, then we can formalize
arguments.
We can represent arguments.
As a result, we can formalize arguments.*

The conclusion of the above argument is preceded by an
'_____.'

as a result

5-158   *If we can represent arguments, then we can formalize*
arguments.
We can represent arguments.
For that reason, we can formalize arguments.

The conclusion of the above argument is preceded by a
'_____.'

for that reason

5-159   therefore   consequently   accordingly
thus   wherefore   as a result
hence   whence   for that reason
so   ergo

How many of the above words are used to precede the conclusion of an argument—that is, to indicate that a given sentence of a sequence is said to follow from the other sentences
of that sequence? _____

eleven

5-160   *If we can represent arguments, then we can formalize*
arguments.
We can represent arguments.
Therefore, we can formalize arguments

Suppose we represent the above argument by

$$\begin{array}{|l} CPQ \\ P \\ \hline Q \end{array}$$

Then the '⊢' represents a word '_____.'

therefore

5-161   We call a '⊢' a 'therefore' indicator because a '⊢'
represents a '_____.'

therefore

5-162   thus   wherefore   as a result
hence   whence   for that reason
so   accordingly
consequently   ergo

A '⊢' represents a 'therefore.' How many of the above words
can be represented by a '⊢'? _____

5-163   *If we can represent arguments, then we can formalize*
            arguments.
            We can represent arguments.
            Thus, we can formalize arguments.

We cannot represent the above argument by a

> | CPQ
> | P
> ─────
> | Q

because a 'thus' is not just like a 'therefore' and so a 'Ⱶ' does
not represent a '_____.'

thus

5-164   Given an argument we cannot represent because the
conclusion of the argument is preceded, not by a 'therefore,'
but by a word we cannot represent, what do we do? We write
as a related representable argument an argument just like
the given argument except that a '_____' precedes the
conclusion of the representable argument.

therefore

5-165   *If we can represent arguments, then we can formalize*
            arguments.
            We can represent arguments.
            Thus, we can formalize arguments.

The unrepresentable argument has as a related representable argument the following:

> *If we can represent arguments, then we can formalize*
> *arguments.*
> *We can represent arguments.*
> _____, *we can formalize arguments.*

therefore

5-166   thus   wherefore   as a result
            hence   whence   for that reason
            so   ergo
            consequently   accordingly

Given an argument whose conclusion is preceded by one of
the above words, we write as a related representable argument an argument just like the given argument except that
a '_____' precedes the conclusion.

therefore

5-167 An argument is a sequence of sentences in which the conclusion is said to follow from the premisses. In all the arguments we have looked at, the conclusion comes not before or between the premisses but _____ the premisses.

after

5-168 In all the arguments we have looked at, the conclusion comes after the premisses. Moreover, in all the arguments we have looked at, a 'therefore' or a word related to a 'therefore' preceded the _____ of the argument.

conclusion

5-169 But it is false that in every argument the conclusion comes _____ the premisses. And it is false that a conclusion is always preceded by a 'therefore' or by a word related to a '_____.'

after

therefore

5-170 Frequently enough the conclusion of an argument comes before or between the premisses of the argument. And in these arguments where the conclusion does not come *after* the premisses, often some word precedes—not the conclusion—but the _____ of the argument.

premisses

5-171 *An argument has a conclusion, and an argument has premisses.*
Therefore, an argument has premisses.

The conclusion of the above argument is:

_____

An argument has premisses.

5-172 *An argument has premisses.*
For, an argument has a conclusion, and an argument has premisses.

The conclusion of the above argument is:

_____

An argument has premisses.

5-173 *An argument has premisses.*
For, an argument has a conclusion, and an argument has premisses.

No 'therefore' or related word precedes the conclusion of the above argument. But a word '_____' precedes the premiss of the argument.

for

5-174 *An argument has premisses.*
For, an argument has a conclusion, and an argument
has premisses.

The above unrepresentable argument has as a related representable argument

    _____ *argument has a conclusion, and an argu-*   An
ment has premisses.
    _____ *, an argument has premisses.*   Therefore

5-175 A word 'for' often precedes the premisses of an argument in which the conclusion comes before the premisses.
Similarly, in an argument whose conclusion comes before the
premisses, words like

    since   in so far as
    because   for the reason that
    inasmuch as

are often used to precede the _____ of an argument.   premisses

5-176   for   Inasmuch as   ergo
        since   in so far as   hence
        because   for the reason that   thus

How many of the above words are used to precede the premisses of an argument whose conclusion comes before the
premisses? _____   six

5-177   therefore   consequently   accordingly
        thus   wherefore   as a result
        hence   whence   for that reason
        so   ergo

How many of the above words are used to precede the conclusion of an argument whose conclusion comes after the
premisses? _____   eleven

5-178   Any word used to precede the conclusion of an argument whose conclusion comes after the premisses may be
related to a 'therefore.' Any word used to precede the premisses of an argument whose conclusion comes before the
premisses may be related to a 'therefore.' So how many of the
following words may be related to a 'therefore'?

thus	wherefore	as a result
hence	whence	for that reason
so	ergo	
consequently	accordingly	
for	inasmuch as	
since	in so far as	
because	for the reason that	

_____   sixteen

5-179   *It is false that* in every argument

1. The conclusion comes _____ the premisses, and the   after
conclusion is preceded by a word '_____.'   therefore

5-180   But given an argument in which the conclusion does
not come *after* the premisses or an argument in which the
conclusion is *not* preceded by a 'therefore,' we write a related
representable argument in which

1. The conclusion comes _____ the premisses, and   after
2. The conclusion is preceded by a word '_____.'   therefore

Scope of System F Validity

5-181 We saw that the system F definition of valid argument did not always call valid every argument which by immediate inspection seems undeniably valid according to the following-from definition; and so to extend system F's use in commenting on the validity of arguments while still providing an agreed-upon procedure for establishing validity, we have been recording some agreements as to how unrepresentable connecting words are to be related to representable ones.

5-182 We know for many unrepresentable connecting words how they are to be related to the representable connecting words

_____	and
_____	or
_____	if then
_____	it is false that

Similarly, we know that words which point out the conclusion or premises of an argument are to be related to the representable word '_____.'   therefore

5-183 Not *every* connecting word has been discussed. Nor have we considered *all* the words that might be related to a 'therefore.' Nor, again, have we discussed *all* the reasons why we might not be able to represent an expression. Even so, we can say in general how we should proceed, given an expression we cannot _____ .   represent

5-184 Given an expression we cannot represent, we write a related representable expression. In general, we choose as a related representable expression

1. An expression as close as possible in _____ to the unrepresentable expression, but   meaning
2. An expression which we can _____ .   represent

5-185 Given an argument we cannot represent, we write a _____ _____ argument. Then if we can use system F to show the _____ _____ argument valid, we claim that the _____ argument is also valid.

5-186 But now consider the argument

> *All primates are mammals.*
> *All mammals are vertebrates.*
> *Therefore, all primates are vertebrates.*

On inspection it is hard to deny that the conclusion does follow from the premisses. But would system F call the argument valid—even if we resorted to our agreement about nonrepresentable connecting words? Notice that the argument contains no connecting words; hence no unrepresentable ones. So, following our conventions for representing we might represent the argument by

P
Q
_____

Any capital other than a 'P,' a 'Q,' a 'K,' an 'A,' a 'C,' or an 'N.'

5-187 If we represent the argument

> *All primates are mammals.*
> *All mammals are vertebrates.*
> *Therefore, all primates are vertebrates.*

by, say, a

P
Q
R

then we can formalize the argument by the AF

p
q
r

If system F is to show the argument valid we must find a proof that corresponds to the AF. But we can know without bothering to search that no such proof will be found. For there are no connectives in the AF and so if in the sequence

$$
\begin{array}{c|c}
1 & p \\
2 & q \\
\hline
\text{last} & r
\end{array}
$$

we are to give a good reason for the 'r' our only hope would be to try a rep LAF. But neither of the available items is an 'r.' So we know that system F will not show this argument about mammals valid—though the conclusion seems undeniably to follow from the premises.

Nor is there an arrangement, parallel to the one we made for unrepresentable connecting word, sufficient to allow system F even indirectly to call this argument valid. For except for arguments that can be shown valid by a proof using nothing but rep LAFs, the only arguments system F can call valid—directly or indirectly—are arguments containing connecting words. And what is revealed by consideration of the obvious validity of the mammal argument—which has no connecting words—is that though connecting words impart argumentive force to language, connecting words are not the only source of argumentive force.

To have the convenience of an agreed-upon procedure for showing valid those arguments whose validity depends not on mere repetition nor on force imparted by connecting words but rather on the internal structure of the sentences system F would take as elementary (since they contain no connecting words) requires the use of a formal system beyond the limits of system F. (Traditionally, syllogistic systems, or more currently and more comprehensively, systems of functional or predicate calculus have been proposed to serve this use.[1]

5-188 That system F can comment on the validity of only those nontrivial arguments whose validity depends on logical form imparted by connecting words is no adverse criticism of system F. And that system F can—strictly speaking—show valid only representable arguments offers no inconvenience, given our agreements about how to deal with unrepresent-

---

[1] Treatments of such systems will be found in *Symbolic Logic and Systems*, forthcoming, by James Dickoff and Patricia James. See also *Symbolic Logic* by F. B. Fitch for a natural-deduction treatment of functional calculus.

able connecting words and argument signs. But consider the argument

> *Molasses is sticky.*
> *Therefore, Socrates drank hemlock or it is false that Socrates drank hemlock.*

In this argument we are not inclined to say that the conclusion does follow from the premiss. But what does system F say as to the argument's validity? We can represent the argument by a

P
AQNQ

and so formalize the argument by an AF

p
AqNq

and this AF corresponds to the proof

1	p		hyp
2	2.1	NAqNq	hyp
	2.2	2.2.1	Nq	hyp
		2.2.2	AqNq	2.2.1, Ai
		2.2.3	KAqNqNAqNq	2.2.2, 2.1, Ki
	2.3	q	2.2, No
	2.4	AqNq	2.3, Ai
	2.5	KAqNqNAqNq	2.4, 2.1, Ki
3	AqNq		2, No

So system F would call the argument valid. This may seem odd, but now look at the conclusion of the argument shown valid. Though we are not inclined to say that the conclusion follows from the premiss, we might well be inclined to accept the conclusion as established quite independently of any premiss. For just as we find any contradiction—that is, a sentence that can be formalized by a 'KpNp'—absurd and hence reject not only it but any assumption that has a contradiction as a consequence, so any sentence (as for example the conclusion in question) that can be formalized by an 'ApNp' it seems to us absurd not to accept, given only our understanding of connecting words like 'or' and 'it is false that.' And in the same category as sentences of a form 'ApNp' are many other sentences which share with the conclusion of the argument in question this characteristic: In virtue simply of our understanding of the connecting words in the sentence and quite apart from any other content of the sentence we find it absurd to reject the sentence. Any argument which has such a sentence as a conclusion system F will show valid; but in essence to call such an argument valid can be looked on as making the innocuous comment that this conclusion can be regarded as following from this premiss since the conclusion would follow from any other premiss or could be established without any appeal to premisses for support.

5-189   Moreover, consider this argument:

> *Lessing pioneered, and it is false that Lessing pioneered. Therefore, avocadoes are appetizing.*

We would perhaps not be inclined to say that the conclusion follows from the premiss; but we could represent the argument by a

> | KPNP
> ─
> | Q

and hence formalize the argument by an AF

> | KpNp
> ─
> | q

and since this AF corresponds to the proof

1	KpNp		hyp
2	2.1	Nq	hyp
	2.2	KpNp	1, rep
3	q		2, No

system F would call this argument valid. But notice that the premiss of the argument is a contradiction; and calling such an argument valid amounts to making the fairly innocuous comment that if we are going to grant a contradiction as premiss we might as well grant anything at all as conclusion. Furthermore, system F will show valid any argument which shares with this argument the following characteristic: The premisses of the argument are such that from like premisses a contradiction follows; or in other words, some premiss of the argument is a contradiction or the premisses taken together are mutually contradictory.

5-190   System F shares with all systems of so-called "classical" sentential or propositional calculus these two features:
When the systems are used to comment on validity, a sufficient condition (though of course not a necessary condition)
for calling an argument valid (even when there seems to be no
"connection" between premises and conclusion) is that the
conclusion be a sentence of a form such that to reject the
conclusion would be absurd, or else that the premises be
such that like premises would establish a contradiction—
that is, an absurdity.[1] That these two really are sufficient
conditions for validity is not wholly unplausible, and at the
very least such systems will never call an argument valid if in
effect the argument would lead us from true premises to a
false conclusion.[2]

---

[1] See Appendix B for two further examples of "classical" sentential logic—an axiomatic
treatment and a truth-table formulation.

[2] Modal logics or logics of "strict" implication or of entailment have been suggested as
providing systems which can comment more suitably on validity and inference than can
the classical systems or systems involving only "material implication" (cf. frame 4-346)—
which permits inferences which parallel the two noted "oddities" of system F. But such
proposed systems have their own peculiarities—sometimes referred to as the "paradoxes
of strict implication." For one of the earliest formal systems of this logic of strict implication, see Lewis and Langford, *Symbolic Logic*, especially appendix 2.

Inherent Gains and Losses in Taking Symbols—or Even Words—at Face Value

5-191 We have been looking at system F with an eye to appreciating some of the features, advantages, and limitations of the system. After noting that system F could deal directly with only representable arguments, agreements were recorded to extend the usefulness of system F. But since unrepresentable expressions were related to representable ones, why bother to distinguish what is representable from what is not? Depending on the intention of the user, the expression

> *ruler*

may be similar in meaning to

> *king*

or to

> *measure*

But whatever the intention of the user, the expression

> *ruler*

is like in shape to only an expression '_____.' Similarly, we can decide whether two expressions are like simply by looking at them—with no need to know the user's meaning. For instance, the expression

ruler

> *baragouin*

is like an expression '_____.' Moreover, two expressions have like representations if and only if the expressions are like expressions.

baragouin

5-192 Representing always on the basis of an expression's shape—that is, taking into account only the expression's "face" value—rather than on the basis of meaning has two advantages:

1. Given any representation, we know the shape of the expression represented.
2. Two expressions can have like representations provided only the expressions are of the same shape.

But representing on the basis of shape has two further consequences:

1. Expressions with the same meaning will not be given like representations unless the expressions are like in shape.
2. Expressions with different meanings will be given like representations provided only the expressions are like in shape.

So though

> *The land's foreign policy is creatively brilliant.*
> *The land's foreign policy is at a new low.*

would be given unlike representations, the expressions

> *The land's foreign policy is unparalleled in history.*
> *The land's foreign policy is unparalleled in history.*

are given like representations whether or not the expressions are like in _____ .

meaning

5-193 Because we represent on the basis of shape and formalize on the basis of representation, we can always agree upon the formalization of a given argument; and given a formalization of an argument and a discovered proof in system F, we can agree whether or not the AF corresponds to the proof; and if the formalization does correspond to the proof, then we have shown both for ourselves and other people that the argument is a valid argument according to the system F definition of validity. Essential to our use of system F as an agreed-upon procedure for establishing validity was our agreement to represent not on the basis of an expression's _____ but on the basis of an expression's _____ .

meaning; shape

5-194 Representing on the basis of shape is essential to a dependable use of system F—or any other formal system—as a calculating device for showing arguments valid. But just as we saw that the system F definition of validity had its limitations, so—conversely—exercise in *applying* the system F definition of validity has certain advantages beyond deciding validity. Because the connecting words

> and   if then
> or   it is false that

are represented by the connectives in system F, manipulation within system F may well increase appreciation of the logical force of these connecting words; moreover, the practice of relating unrepresentable connecting words to this small selection of representable ones may suggest at the very least a technique for analyzing complex or novel connections in terms of those more basic or familiar.

Representing strictly on the basis of shape emphasizes too that although the same meaning may be expressed in more than one way, that similarity may go unnoticed unless the similarity of meaning expressed is reflected in likeness of expression used. But to represent on the basis of shape stresses too that expressed or intended difference in meaning may not be sensed if not reflected by perceptible difference in expression.

Concentration on assessing validity as imparted by connecting words was calculated to increase awareness of the argumentive force of language. But attempts to isolate logical or argumentive force probably made obvious too that language has considerable force other than argumentive. The connecting words

> and   even though

are not like expressions, and though the words have much the same logical force, they are far from identical in *all* their functions. To note that language—not only connecting words but all expressions—may have argumentive force is important; but similarly important is the realization that language has many other important functions.

If we are aware of language's ambiguity, we may detect and remove ambiguity in language whose primary aim is to communicate information correctly. But when language functions poetically, humorously, persuasively, or even diplomatically, the very ambiguity of language is a rich resource.

Just as we noted that considering system F and its relation to arguments was an appropriate basic step in preparation for considering sources of argumentive force other than connecting words, so too we suggest that the concentration on the *argumentive* force of *representable* language is the appropriate basic step toward a fuller appreciation of those dimensions of language which impart to language its beauty, variety, style, subtlety, and emotional or persuasive impact. Quite apart from any skills or knowledge imparted to a reader, this book will count itself not unsuccessful if at the very least the reader is a bit more aware of the limitless problems, possibilities, and wonders of linguistic communication.

Exercises for Part 5

1 **a** For none of the following connecting words have we a convention for representing or an agreement as to relation to representable connecting words. For each word, suggest an appropriate relation to a representable connecting word or some complex of representable connecting words.

(1) accordingly as
(2) while
(3) whether or not
(4) granting that then
(5) in the circumstance that then
(6) so long as
(7) albeit
(8) whilst
(9) despite that
(10) no sooner than
(11) before
(12) as soon as
(13) after
(14) when
(15) until
(16) neither nor

b Pick a newspaper article or a page from some textbook or novel. Record all the distinct kinds of connecting words you find, and for any unrepresentable ones suggest a relation to representable connecting words if this relation has not already been specified.

2 **a** Consider the connecting words

    and   if then

    or   it is false that

Do such words ever have, in addition to their argumentive force, also some commentorial meaning? Consider, for example, how an 'and' functions in narration and compare the function of 'and' there with the function 'and' would seem to have, given that system F would show valid an argument formalized by the following AF

    |Kpq
    |Kqp

b In English a "bare" 'or' sometimes has the weight of 'at least one but not both' (exclusive 'or') as opposed to simply 'at least one.' Given that system F would show valid *any* argument formalizable by the Ai LAF

    |p
    |Apq

English prose where the 'or' has only the exclusive sense should be considered as are arguments whose conclusions are not explicitly indicated to be conclusions; and before representing and formalizing we should write a new prose in which any 'or' meant to bear the exclusive sense has been replaced by the complex of representable connecting words related to 'or but not both.' What other unrepresentable connecting words have the same meaning as the exclusive 'or'?

c How would you deal with these sentences:

(1) *The number is odd or the number is even.*

(2) *The number is odd or even.*

3 The 'or but not both' sentence

    Socrates taught or Plato lied but not both.

is very close in meaning to the representable sentence

    If it is false that Plato lied then Socrates taught, and if

    Socrates taught then it is false that Plato lied.

which could be formalized by, say,

    KCNpqCqNp

But the 'or but not both' sentence is similarly close in meaning to the representable sentence that could be formalized by, say,

    AKpNqKNpq

or to a representable sentence that could be formalized by, say,

    KApqNKpq

Show that to analyze an 'or but not both' sentence (or an 'unless' sentence or an 'except if' sentence) in any one of these three ways amounts to the same thing as far as showing validity in terms of system F by finding in system F for each of the following AFs a proof that corresponds to that AF:

a | AKpNqKNpq |KCNpqCqNp
     | KCNpqCqNp |AKpNqKNpq

b | KApqNKpq |KCNpqCqNp
     | KCNpqCqNp |KApqNKpq

c | AKpNqKNpq |KApqNKpq
     | KApqNKpq |AKpNqKNpq

4 For each of the following prose passages, write a representable argument you deem to have the same argumentive force as does the passage. Then use system F to show the representable argument valid.

a Apparently Lucian did not cast a vote. For provided Lucian is still a member, then he cast a vote only if he paid his dues; and, moreover, he is still a member though he hasn't paid his dues.

b Either free speech is maintained or else justice is cruelly mocked. But it is similarly undeniable that either individuals do not respect their own dignity or free speech is not maintained. So without doubt it follows that either individuals fail to respect their own dignity or leaders fail to honor their own leadership, for either it is false that justice is mocked or it is false that leaders honor their own leadership.

c Unless art works have some significance other than as modes of self-expression, surely then art is purely subjective. Therefore, neither is art purely subjective nor is the artist an oddity in a healthy society. For admittedly, if art has failed to communicate, then art is purely subjective; and conversely, if the artist is an oddity in a healthy society, then art has failed to communicate. But it must be granted that neither is it false that art works have some significance other than as modes of self-expression nor does the artist abandon an attempt to communicate even though he aims at originality and wants self-expression.

d   Assuming that Kant is a pedant, then even if he urges his distinctions as important the distinctions are, nonetheless, academic. On the other hand, Kant is filled with "important" distinctions; but without question in philosophic circles Kant's distinctions would hardly be called academic. Consequently, no matter how tedious and involved are Kant's elaborated distinctions, he cannot be charged with pedantry.

e   So long as the immediate pictorial presentation lacks its own integrity a movie is somehow imperfect; but then again criticism is out of place except if a movie is somehow imperfect. Admittedly even though pictorial integrity is present and even is enhanced by symbolic overtones, oftentimes still a movie is somehow imperfect. It must be the case, then, that pictorial integrity is not the only demand made of a movie; for either criticism is out of place or the immediate pictorial presentation fails to lack its own integrity, assuming, of course, that pictorial integrity is the only demand made of a movie.

f   Surely Claire is innocent. For Joe perjured himself only if Claire did not leave the key with Francis's wife; and despite Francis's being out with Joe on the evening of the sixteenth and even though Marsha despised Claire, still Claire left the key with Francis's estranged wife Marsha. Joe's having an alibi implies that either Claire is innocent or that Joe perjured himself. But Joe is without an alibi if and only if he wasn't out with Francis on the evening of the sixteenth.

g   When the working force are good consumers prices go down; but it is true too that prices go down only if production efficiency goes up; and that if—and only if—the labor force is in good supply then does production efficiency go up. So, ironically, it must be the case that the labor force is in good supply whether or not they are good consumers.

h   Provided the prediction is confirmed and the analysis is correct, then the previous recordings are not reliable. Moreover, the prediction is confirmed if either the delta test is positive or the observed velocity decreases. Therefore, the analysis is not correct, or the delta test is not positive, or the observed velocity does not decrease, or else we must admit that the previous recordings are not reliable.

i   More educators should be recruited even though the cost is prohibitive if teachers are scarce, or alternatively, if teachers are scarce entrance requirements should be raised, whether or not this move works a hardship on the less talented. Consequently, it is clear that either teachers are not scarce or else either entrance requirements should be raised or more teachers recruited.

j   Existence is absurd unless life has a purpose, or alternatively, man has some hope of determining his own life except if he relinquishes his capacity for regulating action in accordance with knowledge. So, either man has some hope of determining his own life only if life has some purpose or else existence is absurd only if man relinquishes his capacity for regulating action in accordance with knowledge; for we cannot deny that existence is absurd only if it is false that man has some hope for determining his own life.

5 For each of the following AFs write an argument that has the same argumentive force as a representable argument that could be formalized by the AF. Make the argument as colloquial, convincing, and stylish as possible. For each AF find in system F a proof that corresponds to the AF.

a | NArNCpq   b | CKpqr   c | CCpqCpr   d | KNNpt   e | KCpqCqp
   | KCpqNr | KNrt | NANpr | CNsNr | KCrNsCNsr
                     | Ctq | NANpq | AKprCps | KCrNpp
                     | p | Kst | s
                     | AsCNtNq

6 An enthymeme is a sequence of sentences which has argumentive force despite the suppression of a premiss or sometimes even of a conclusion. Consider each of the following as an enthymeme and supply premiss and conclusion as needed.

a Slips of the tongue have nothing to do with illness, since they occur in all healthy people.
b A cure for cancer would prolong human life. Therefore, the government should support cancer research.
c All burdens or depressants to the economy should be removed, and excessive corporation tax is clearly a depressant.
d Because education broadens the mind, you should get a good education.
e Crime does not pay, but graft is very lucrative.
f I was one and twenty: no use to speak to me. (A. E. Housman, *A Shropshire Lad*)

7 Choose a newspaper editorial. Then write one or more representable arguments which you deem have the same argumentive force as does the editorial.

8 In English an 'only if' is at times quite obviously said in place of an intended 'if and only if.' An 'only if' found in a prose context should be carefully considered and a decision made as to whether the stronger 'if and only if' is meant; if so, then, in writing a related representable prose passage this stronger connection should be made explicit. For each of the following sentences write a related representable sentence:

a The number is even only if divisible by two.
b Tom is a man only if Tom is an animal.

Achievement Test for Part 5

1 Put a check ($\sqrt{}$) in front of each of the following statements which is true, and put a cross ($\times$) in front of each of the following statements which is false.

a _____ We can represent a sentence only if we can formalize that sentence.

b _____ We can formalize a sentence only if we cannot represent that sentence.

c _____ We cannot formalize a sentence unless we can represent that sentence.

d _____ We can formalize a sentence if and only if we can represent that sentence.

2 Put a check ($\sqrt{}$) in front of each of the following statements which is true, and put a cross ($\times$) in front of each of the following statements which is false.

a _____ If we can represent an argument, then we can use system F to show that argument valid.

b _____ If we cannot represent an argument, then we cannot, strictly speaking, use system F to show that argument valid.

c _____ If we can formalize an argument, then we can use system F to show that argument valid.

d _____ If we cannot formalize an argument, then we cannot, strictly speaking, use system F to show that argument valid.

3 Given an unrepresentable expression, we choose as a related representable expression an expression which we can represent and which is as close as possible in _____ to the unrepresentable expression.

4 For each of the following expressions write a related representable expression.

a _____ either or

b _____ provided then

c _____ since

d _____ whereas

e _____ even though

f _____ in case that then

g _____ not

h _____ but

i _____ although

j _____ on condition that then

k _____ it is not true that

l _____ for

m _____ assuming that then

n _____ though

o _____ because

p _____ in the event that then

q _____ it is not the case that

5 What word precedes the conclusion of every representable argument? _____

6 In every representable argument, do the premises come before or after the conclusion? _____

7 Put a check ($\sqrt{}$) in front of each of the following expressions which can be used to precede a conclusion of an argument. Put a cross ($\times$) in front of each of the following which can be used to precede the premises of an argument.

a	_____ thus	j	_____ whence
b	_____ for	k	_____ in so far as
c	_____ ergo	l	_____ for the reason that
d	_____ because	m	_____ in as much as
e	_____ hence	n	_____ therefore
f	_____ as a result	o	_____ for that reason
g	_____ since	p	_____ consequently
h	_____ so	q	_____ accordingly
i	_____ wherefore		

8 therefore   therefore   thus

   a There are how many words just above? _____

   b There are how many like words just above? _____

9 Write two words each of which can be represented by a 'F'. _____ _____

10 The 'only if' sentence

The murderer escapes only if the burglar escapes.

has as a related representable sentence which of the following:

    (1) If the burglar escapes, then the murderer escapes.

    (2) If the murderer escapes, then the burglar escapes.

Sentence _____

11 *Tom goes if and only if Mary goes.*

The above sentence is unrepresentable; write a related representable sentence.

12 *If it is false that Mary goes then Tom goes, and if Tom goes then it is false that Mary goes.*

The above sentence is representable. Put a check (√) in front of each of the following sentences which, though unrepresentable, would have much the same force in an argument as would the above representable sentence.

   a _____ Tom goes only if Mary goes.

   b _____ Tom goes unless Mary goes.

   c _____ Tom goes if and only if Mary goes.

   d _____ Tom goes except if Mary goes.

   e _____ Tom goes or Mary goes but not both.

13 Put a check (√) in front of each of the following sentences which is true. Put a cross (×) in front of each of the following sentences which is false.

   a _____ We cannot, strictly speaking, use system F to show an unrepresentable argument to be valid.

   b _____ We claim an unrepresentable argument is valid if we can use system F to show a related representable argument to be valid.

   c _____ We claim an unrepresentable argument is valid if there is a related representable argument which can be formalized by an AF that corresponds to a proof in system F.

14 *Mary came after John came.*

The above sentence is unrepresentable. Write a related representable sentence.

15 *Not only Mary came but also John came.*

The above sentence is unrepresentable. Write a related representable sentence.

16 K K K A C N
  a How many connectives are just above? _____
  b How many like connectives are just above? _____
  c Write two connectives each of which represents a connecting word 'and'.

  _____ _____

  d How many connectives can represent a connecting word 'but'? _____

17 *(1) Magnesium is used in missiles.*
  (2) Magnesium has a high melting point.
  Write a sentence that states the two facts just above and in addition indicates that magnesium's melting point makes the metal appropriate for missile construction.

18 *(1) Bears hibernate.*
  (2) Coyotes hunt all winter.
  Write a sentence that states the two facts just above and in addition emphasizes that the habits of bears differ from the habits of coyotes.

19 *(1) The Greeks conquered the Persians.*
  (2) The Persians outnumbered the Greeks.
  Write a sentence that states the two facts just above and in addition emphasizes that the Greeks were victorious despite the Persians' strength of numbers.

20 For each of the following arguments:
  (1) Write a related representable argument,
  (2) Write an AF that could formalize that argument, and then
  (3) Find in system F a proof that corresponds to the AF.

  a Apparently we can conclude that Dos Passos wrote *Moby Dick*. For Melville is acknowledged as great even though if universal acclaim is required for greatness then Melville is not so acknowledged. Moreover, democratic principles are not everywhere respected, although universal acclaim is required for greatness.

  b Assuming that Ted bought the gun, then Carlo fired the shot. Consequently, it cannot be the case that both Roger is innocent although Fred is culpable and Roger is not innocent provided that Fred is culpable. For admittedly Mary was blackmailed only if Carlo fired the shot.

  c Either state primaries are of some worth or else politicians are not more perceptive than formerly. But on the other hand, politicians are more perceptive than formerly provided that income is some indication of merit. So, assuming that some convention delegates are selected through primaries, then if in the event that voters are more discriminating then politicians are more perceptive than formerly, then income is some indication of worth only if state primaries are of some worth.

  d Freedom from poverty is just around the corner unless some persons merit special privileges. Hence, freedom from poverty is just around the corner or America is not a land of promise. For in the event that some people merit special privileges, then equality for all has been discarded as the land's hallmark. But there is no question but that it is false that equality for all has been discarded as America's hallmark.

e If you are willing to exert energy toward a goal, then truly you hold it dear. Moreover, if you pay mere lip service to a goal, then clearly you fail to act to reach that goal. So, if you are willing to exert energy towards a goal, then obviously you do not pay mere lip service to that goal. For either you don't hold a goal dear or else you don't fail to act to reach that goal.

Appendix **A**

Summary Specification of System F—A Natural-deduction Formulation of Classical Sentential Calculus

System F is called, following Gentzen's usage,[1] a system of natural deduction. Its "naturalness" stems from specification of proofs in terms of argument forms that parallel the kinds of arguments we are *naturally* inclined to call valid and from allowing a proof to have hypotheses—again paralleling the practice of *natural* reason to establish a conclusion, not necessarily categorically, but rather on the basis of premiss or hypothesis. We specify system F by specifying

1. The symbols in system F,
2. The WFFs in system F,
3. The LAFs in system F, and
4. The proofs in system F.

1 SYMBOLS IN F

The symbols in F are of three kinds—sentence variables, connectives, and 'therefore' indicators.

1. Any 'p,' 'q,' 'r,' 's,' or 't' is a sentence variable in F. (To provide an unlimited number of distinct kinds of sentence variables and as a trivial extension of F, we can allow also that any 'p,' 'q,' 'r,' 's,' or 't' primed one or more times is a sentence variable in F.)
2. Any 'K,' 'A,' 'C,' or 'N' is a connective in F.
3. Any '⊢' is a 'therefore' indicator in F.

---

[1] See Gerhard Gentzen, "Untersuchungen über das logische Schliessen," *Mathematische Zeitschrift*, 39:176–210, 405–431, 1934.

2 WFFS (WELL-FORMED FORMULAS) IN F

The WFFs in system F are of five kinds and are fully specified by the following five statements:

1. Any sentence variable is a WFF.
2. Any 'K' followed by two WFFs is a WFF.
3. Any 'A' followed by two WFFs is a WFF.
4. Any 'C' followed by two WFFs is a WFF.
5. Any 'N' followed by one WFF is a WFF.

3 LAFS (LOGICAL ARGUMENT FORMULAS) IN F

The LAFs in system F are of nine kinds:

K-in LAFs	K-out LAFs
A-in LAFs	A-out LAFs
C-in LAFs	C-out LAFs
N-in LAFs	N-out LAFs
repetition LAFs	

1. K-IN LAF

```
1│ p
2│ q
3│ Kpq      1, 2, Ki
```

Every Ki (for 'K-in' we write 'Ki'; for 'K-out' we write 'Ko'; and so on) LAF has three items, all of them WFF items; and the last item is a 'K' followed by two WFFs, the first of which is just like item 1 of the LAF and the second of which is just like item 2 of the LAF.

2. K-OUT LAF

```
1│ Kpq                    1│ Kpq
2│ p       1, Ko          2│ q       1, Ko
```

Every Ko LAF has two items, both of them WFF items; and the first item is a 'K' followed by two WFFs, one of which is just like the last item of the LAF.

3. A-IN LAF

```
1│ p                      1│ p
2│ Apq      1, Ai         2│ Aqp      1, Ai
```

Every Ai LAF has two items, both WFF items; and the last item is an 'A' followed by two WFFs, one of which is just like item 1 of the LAF.

4. A-OUT LAF

```
1 | AKpqKrq
2 | 2.1 | Kpq
    | 2.2 | q        2.1, Ko
3 | 3.1 | Krq
    | 3.2 | q        3.1, Ko
4 | q               1, 2, 3, Ao
```

Every Ao LAF has four items—two WFF items and two tail items.

Item 1 is a WFF item beginning with an 'A';

Item 2 is a tail item whose only item above its 'Ⱶ' is a WFF like the first WFF following the 'A' in item 1 and whose last item is a WFF like item 4; and further, tail item 2 must be so constructed that each item of item 2 can be given a good reason;

Item 3 is a tail item whose only item above its 'Ⱶ' is a WFF like the second WFF following the 'A' in item 1 and whose last item is a WFF like item 4; and further, tail item 3 must be so constructed that each of its items can be given a good reason;

Item 4 is a WFF like the last item of tail item 2 and tail item 3.

5. C-IN LAF

```
1 | 1.1 | Kpq
    | 1.2 | p        1.1, Ko
    | 1.3 | Apr      1.2, Ai
2 | CKpqApr          1, Ci
```

Every Ci LAF has two items—one WFF item and one tail item.

Item 1 is a tail item whose only item above its 'Ⱶ' is a WFF like the first WFF following the 'C' in item 2 and whose last item is a WFF like the second WFF following the 'C' in item 2; and further, tail item 1 is so constructed that each of its items can be given a good reason;

Item 2 is a WFF item beginning with a 'C' which is followed by two WFFs the first of which is like the only WFF above the 'Ⱶ' for item 1 and the second of which is like the last item of item 1.

6. C-OUT LAF

```
1 | Cpq
2 | p
3 | q          1, 2, Co
```

Every Co LAF has three items, all of them WFF items.

Item 1 is a WFF item beginning with a 'C';

Item 2 is a WFF like the first WFF following the 'C';

Item 3 is a WFF like the second WFF following the 'C' in item 1.

7. N-IN LAF

```
1│ 1.1│ KqKpNp
 │ 1.2│ KpNp        1.1, Ko
2│ NKqKpNp         1, Ni
```

Every Ni LAF has two items—one WFF item and one tail item.

Item 1 is a tail item whose only item above its '⊢' is a WFF like the WFF following the 'N' in item 2 and whose last item is a contradictory WFF; and further, tail item 1 must be so constructed that each of its items can be given a good reason;

Item 2 is an 'N' followed by a WFF like the only WFF above the '⊢' for item 1.

8. N-OUT LAF

```
1│ 1.1│ NCKpqp
 │ 1.2│ 1.2.1│ Kpq
 │    │ 1.2.2│ p        1.2.1, Ko
 │ 1.3│ CKpqp          1.2, Ci
 │ 1.4│ KCKpqpNCKpqp   1.3, 1.1, Ki
2│ CKpqp              1, No
```

Every No LAF has two items—one WFF item and one tail item.

Item 1 is a tail item whose only item above its '⊢' is an 'N' followed by a WFF like item 2 and whose last item is a contradictory WFF; and further, tail item 1 must be so constructed that each of its items can be given a good reason; Item 2 is a WFF item just like the WFF following the 'N' in the only item above the '⊢' for item 1.

9. REPETITION LAF

```
1│ p
2│ p        1, rep
```

Every rep LAF has two items, and item 1 is just like item 2.

4 PROOFS IN F

A proof is a sequence of items each of which has a good reason. Items are of two kinds—WFF items and tail items, where a WFF item is simply a WFF and a tail item is a sequence of items. A WFF item of a sequence has a good reason if

1. The item is above the '⊢' for the sequence and so has a 'hyp' as a good reason, or

2. The item is below the '⊢' for the sequence and can be thought of as the last item of a LAF whose preceding items are

   a   preceding item of the same sequence, or

   b   preceding items in the same sequence of which the *sequence* (tail item) is an item.

A tail item has a good reason if each of its items has a good reason.

Valid argument = $_{df}$. An argument that can be formalized by an AF (argument formula) that corresponds to a proof in system F. An AF (argument formula) is a sequence of items with exactly one '⊢' and exactly one item below the '⊢' and that item is a WFF item. An AF corresponds to a proof in system F if and only if there can be constructed a proof in system F such that the only hypotheses of the proof are just like the items above the '⊢' for the AF and such that the last item in the proof is just like the only item below the '⊢' for the AF. So, according to the system F definition, an argument is valid if there is in system F a proof whose only hypotheses formalize the premisses of the argument and such that the last item of the proof formalizes the argument's conclusion.

Specifications of a Truth-table Formulation (System T) and Then of an Axiomatic Formulation (System X) of Classical Sentential Calculus and Comments on Relations to System F

System T

System T is a truth-table formulation of classical sentential calculus (cf. Ludwig Wittgenstein, *Tractatus Logico-philosophicus*, p. 93ff). We specify system T by specifying

1. The symbols in T,
2. The WFFs in T,
3. The truth specifications for T, and
4. The theorems in T.

1 SYMBOLS IN T

The symbols in T are of three kinds—sentence variables, connectives, and parentheses (used for punctuation).

 1. Any lowercase letter is a sentence variable in T.
 2. Any '&,' '∨,' '⊃,' or '∼' is a connective in T.

2 WFFS IN T
 1. Any sentence variable is a WFF.
 2. Any expression which is an '&' between two WFFs each of which is enclosed in parentheses is a WFF; and the main connective of such WFFs is an '&.'
 3. Any expression which is a '∨' between two WFFs each of which is enclosed in parentheses is a WFF; and the main connective of such WFFs is a '∨.'

4. Any expression which is a '⊃' between two WFFs each of which is enclosed in parentheses is a WFF; and the main connective of such WFFs is a '⊃.'
5. Any expression which is a '∼' preceding a WFF which is enclosed in parentheses is a WFF; and the main connective of such WFFs is a '∼.'

We further adopt the convention that an expression remains a WFF if parentheses around single sentence variables are omitted.

3 SPECIFICATION OF TRUTH VALUES FOR SENTENCES FORMALIZED BY WFFS IN T
1. A sentence formalized by a WFF whose main connective is an '&' is true if and only if the sentences formalized by the two WFFs joined by the '&' are both true.
2. A sentence formalized by a WFF whose main connective is a '∨' is true if and only if at least one of the sentences formalized by the two WFFs joined by the '∨' is true.
3. A sentence formalized by a WFF whose main connective is a '⊃' is true *unless* the sentence formalized by the WFF preceding the '⊃' is true and the sentence formalized by the WFF following the '⊃' is false.
4. A sentence formalized by a WFF whose main connective is a '∼' is true if and only if the sentence formalized by the WFF following the '∼' is false.

The specification of truth values for sentences formalized by WFFs in T in terms of the truth values of sentences formalized by sentence variables in T is exemplified by tabulation in *truth tables* as follows, where we adopt the convention that a column label, say 'p,' can be used in place of the more cumbersome but more nearly adequate label 'sentence formalized by a 'p' true' and where a '1' stands for a 'yes' and a '0' for a 'no.'

	p	q	p & q	p ∨ q	p ⊃ q	∼p
Case 1	1	1	1	1	1	0
Case 2	1	0	0	1	0	0
Case 3	0	1	0	1	1	1
Case 4	0	0	0	0	1	1

4 THEOREMS IN T
An expression is a theorem in T if and only if the expression is a WFF in T and is tautological with respect to T. An expression is *tautological with respect to T* if and only if *any* and *every* sentence formalized by that expression is true according to the determination of truth values in accord with the specifications for T.

DEFINITION OF VALID ARGUMENT IN TERMS OF SYSTEM T
Valid argument = $_{df.}$ An argument that can be formalized by an AF that corresponds to a theorem in system T. Let the symbols in T be (trivially) extended to include 'therefore' indicators ('⊢'). Then an AF or argument formula is a sequence of WFFs with exactly one '⊢' and exactly one WFF below the '⊢.' An AF corresponds to an expression in T if and only if that expression is a WFF that results from joining

by '&'s (conjoining) WFFs like those above the 'Ⱶ' for the AF and letting this WFF be the antecedent of a '⊃' expression whose consequent is a WFF like the WFF below the 'Ⱶ' for the AF. For example, the AF

$$\begin{array}{|l}
p \\
p \supset q \\
(\sim q) \vee (\sim r) \\
\hline
\sim r
\end{array}$$

corresponds to the expression

$$((p \,\&\, (p \supset q)) \,\&\, ((\sim q) \vee (\sim r))) \supset (\sim r)$$

To determine if according to the system T definition the argument formalized by the AF is valid, we determine whether the corresponding expression is a theorem in T by constructing a truth table, which in essence is a device for a systematic consideration of all possible combinations of truth and falsity of sentences formalized here by a 'p,' 'q,' 'r,' that we may ascertain if the sentence formalized by the expression in question is true according to T for every possible combination. To determine whether or not the expression corresponding to the AF is tautological —and so to determine whether an argument formalized by the AF is valid according to system T's definition of validity, we would construct the following truth table:

p	q	r	p ⊃ q	p & (p ⊃ q)	~q	~r	(~q) ∨ (~r)	(p & (p ⊃ q)) & ((~q) ∨ (~r))	((p & (p ⊃ q)) & ((~q) ∨ (~r))) ⊃ (~r)
1	1	1	1	1	0	0	0	0	1
1	1	0	1	1	0	1	1	1	1
1	0	1	0	0	1	0	1	0	1
1	0	0	0	0	1	1	1	0	1
0	1	1	1	0	0	0	0	0	1
0	1	0	1	0	0	1	1	0	1
0	0	1	1	0	1	0	1	0	1
0	0	0	1	0	1	1	1	0	1

Since in the column corresponding to the expression which corresponds to the AF we find all '1's we know the questioned expression is tautological with respect to T, for the table shows that any sentence formalized by that expression would be true according to the truth specifications for T. So according to system T's definition, the argument formalized by the AF would be a valid argument.

System X

System X is an axiomatic formulation of classical sentential calculus (cf. Jan Lukasiewicz's 1929 formulation). We specify system X by specifying

1. The symbols in X,
2. The WFFs in X,

3. The axioms in X,
4. The rules in X,
5. The definitional equivalences in X,
6. The proofs in X, and
7. The theorems in X.

1 SYMBOLS IN X

The symbols in X are of two kinds—sentence variables and connectives.
1. Any lowercase letter is a sentence variable in X.
2. Any 'K,' 'A,' 'C,' or 'N' is a connective in X.

2 WFFS IN X

1. Any sentence variable is a WFF.
2. Any expression which is a 'K' followed by two WFFs is a WFF.
3. Any expression which is an 'A' followed by two WFFs is a WFF.
4. Any expression which is a 'C' followed by two WFFs is a WFF.
5. Any expression which is an 'N' followed by one WFF is a WFF.

3 AXIOMS IN X

Axiom 1. CCpqCCqrCpr   (or any like WFF)
Axiom 2. CCNppp   (or any like WFF)
Axiom 3. CpCNpq   (or any like WFF)

4 RULES IN X

These rules are variably called either rules of deduction, rules of consequence, rules of inference, or transformation rules.

1. RULE OF DETACHMENT. If a proof has two items, one of which is a 'C' followed by two WFFs, and another of which is a WFF like the first WFF following the 'C,' then we can write as a subsequent item of the proof a WFF just like the second WFF following the 'C.'
2. RULE OF SUBSTITUTION. If a proof has as an item some WFF, then we can add as a subsequent item of the proof a WFF which is just like the given WFF except that for a given kind of sentence variable in the given WFF we have substituted throughout the subsequent item WFFs of a specified kind.
3. RULE OF REPLACEMENT. If a proof has as an item some WFF, then we can add as a subsequent item of the proof a WFF just like the given WFF except that in the subsequent item some part of the given WFF has been replaced by an expression which is equivalent by definition to the part replaced.

5 DEFINITIONAL EQUIVALENCES IN X

1. Apq $=_{df}$ CNpq
   (And any WFF like an 'Apq' is definitionally equivalent to any WFF just like a 'CNpq.')
2. Kpq $=_{df}$ NCpNq
   (And any WFF like a 'Kpq' is definitionally equivalent to any WFF just like an 'NCpNq.')

6 PROOFS IN X

A proof in X is a sequence of WFFs in X such that every WFF in the sequence is an axiom in X or follows from preceding WFFs in the sequence by the rule of detachment, the rule of substitution, or the rule of replacement.

7 THEOREMS IN X

An expression is a theorem in X if and only if the expression is a WFF in X and can be the last WFF of a proof in X.

DEFINITION OF VALID ARGUMENT IN TERMS OF SYSTEM X

Valid argument $=_{df}$. An argument that can be formalized by an AF that corresponds to a theorem in system X. Let the symbols in X be (trivially) extended to include 'therefore' indicators ('⊢'). Then an AF or argument formula is a sequence of WFFs with exactly one '⊢' and exactly one WFF below the '⊢.' An AF corresponds to an expression in X if and only if that expression is a WFF that results from joining by 'K's WFFs like those above the '⊢' for the AF (or simply a WFF like the only WFF above the '⊢' if there be but one) and letting this WFF be the first WFF of an expression beginning with a 'C' in which the second WFF following the 'C' is a WFF like the WFF below the '⊢' for the AF. For example, the AF

$$\begin{array}{|l} p \\ \hline p \end{array}$$

corresponds to the expression

    Cpp

To determine if according to X the argument formalized by the AF is valid, we try to determine whether the corresponding expression is a theorem in X by trying to construct a proof in X whose last item is a WFF like the expression corresponding to the AF. That is, we try to determine if the expression corresponding to the AF is an axiom in X or is the last item of a sequence whose first item is an axiom and whose other items either are axioms or follow from preceding items solely by use of the rules of detachment, substitution, or replacement.

For example, the sequence

1.	CCpqCCqrCpr	axiom 1
2.	CCpCNpqCCCNpqrCpr	1, substitution, q/CNpq
		(that is, from 1 by virtue of Rule of Substitution where for a 'q' in 1 we substitute in 2 a 'CNpq')
3.	CpCNpq	axiom 3
4.	CCCNpqrCpr	2, 3, detachment
5.	CCCNpprCpr	4, substitution, q/p
6.	CCCNpppCpp	5, substitution, r/p
7.	CCNppp	axiom 3
8.	Cpp	6, 7, detachment

is a proof in X since every item is a WFF which is an axiom or follows from preceding items by one of the rules in X. Since a 'Cpp' is the last item of the proof, a 'Cpp' is a theorem in X. And since a 'Cpp' corresponds to an AF

$$\frac{p}{p}$$

according to the system X definition of validity, any argument formalized by that AF is a valid argument.

Three systems—F, T, and X—have been specified, and we have seen examples of calculations in each of the systems. Moreover, roughly speaking, what is provable in the one system is provable in each of the others. Still the systems have obvious differences. Systematic differences in notation, though perhaps striking, are nonetheless trivial. The intended correspondence between the *Principia*-like notation of T and the parenthesis-free Lukasiewicz notation of X and F is indicated in this table:*

Lukasiewicz notation of F and X	Principia-like notation of T
K	&
A	$\vee$
C	$\supset$
N	$\sim$
Kpq	p & q
Apq	p $\vee$ q
Cpq	p $\supset$ q
Np	$\sim$p
KKpqr	(p & q) & r
AKpqr	(p & q) $\vee$ r
CKpqr	(p & q) $\supset$ r
NKpq	$\sim$(p & q)
KKpqKpr	(p & q) & (p & r)
KpKKpqKrs	p & ((p & q) & (r & s))

More interesting are the differences in the systems' modes of specification. That systems F, T, and X differ in mode of specification reflects the different systematic analysis each makes of validity. Roughly speaking, system F analyzes validity as based on nine patterns of inference (LAFs) such that each pattern has considerable plausibility as a legitimate passing from suppositions to consequence of suppositions. System T stipulates how the truth of a sentence depends on the connecting words (represented by connectives) in the sentence and then considers an inference pattern legitimate provided only that the pattern would not allow passage from truth to falsity.

---

* See Part 1, especially Unit 4, for comments on the history and advantages of the two notations.

System X stipulates a very restricted selection of sentence patterns as axiomatic—that is, as being worthy of acceptance as conveying truth on a sentence—and then calls an inference legitimate if its inference pattern is related to an axiomatic sentence pattern or else to a sentence pattern arrivable at from an axiomatic pattern by using only moves allowed by X's three rules of passage (sometimes called transformation rules). These differences are indicated in the following table:

Systems of classical sentential calculus

System F (natural-deduction formulation)	System T (truth-table formulation)	System X (axiomatic formulation)
Symbols	Symbols	Symbols
WFFs	WFFs	WFFs
LAFs	Truth specifications	Axioms
		Rules
		Definitions
Proofs		Proofs
	Theorems	Theorems

Exercises for Appendix B

1   For each of these axioms in X
    a CCpqCCqrCpr   **b** CCNppp   **c** CpCNpq
    write the corresponding expression in *Principia* notation and show by truth tables
    that the expression is tautological with respect to T.

2   For each of the following AFs find in system F a proof that corresponds to that AF:
    a (cf. axiom 1 in X)   **b** (Cf. axiom 2 in X)   **c** (Cf. axiom 3 in X)

    |t |t |t
    |CCpqCCqrCpr |CCNppp |CpCNpq

3   For each of the following expressions write the corresponding expression in
    Principia notation and then show by truth tables that the expression is tautological
    with respect to T.
    a (Cf. first definitional equivalence in X)
           KCApqCNpqCCNpqApq
    b (Cf. second definitional equivalence in X)
           KCKpqNCpNqCNCpNqKpq

4   For each of the following AFs find in system F a proof that corresponds to that AF.
    a (Cf. first definitional equivalence in X)

    |t
    |KCApqCNpqCCNpqApq
    b (Cf. second definitional equivalence in X)

    |t
    |KCKpqNCpNqCNCpNqKpq

5   The rule of detachment in X reflects what kind of LAF in system F?

6   For each of the following WFFs in F write a corresponding expression in *Principia*
    notation and use truth tables to determine whether or not the expression is
    tautological with respect to T.
    a CKpqKpq   **b** CKpqp   **c** CpApq
           (Cf. Ki LAF)   (Cf. Ko LAF)   (Cf. Ai LAF)
    d CKKAKpqKrqCKpqAqsCKrqAqsAqs   **e** CApqCNpq   **f** CKCpqpq
           (Cf. Ao LAF)   (Cf. Ci LAF)   (Cf. Co LAF)
    g NKpCpNp   **h** ApNp   **i** Cpp
           (Cf. Ni LAF)   (Cf. No LAF)   (Cf. rep LAF)

*7 In general it is not easy to find in system X a proof whose last item is a specified WFF—that is, it is not easy to say for a given WFF in X whether or not that WFF is a theorem in X. One reasonably easy theorem to establish is the following: Cpp. (See Appendix B, specification of system X, for a proof of which a 'Cpp' is the last item.) For exercise in proof finding in system X, take any expression tautological with respect to T and write a corresponding expression in Lukasiewicz notation. Any such expression should be a theorem in X—but that is not to say it will be easy to find a proof establishing the expression as a theorem.

Answers to Achievement Tests

Part 1
1. CPQ
2. N
3. if then
4. a content; sentence
   b logical form; sentence
5. Hawaii is a state and Alaska is a state.
6. A; sentence
7.

a	×	d	√	g	×	j	×	m	√
b	√	e	√	h	√	k	√	n	×
c	√	f	×	i	×	l	√	o	×

8. Charles I capitulated.
9. K
10. if then
11. connectives; sentence
12. and
13. A
14. N
15. it is false that
16. or
17. C
18. indicates; isolates
19. China is in Africa.
20. p (or any other sentence variable)
21.

a	√	d	√	g	√	j	√
b	×	e	√	h	×	k	√
c	×	f	√	i	×	l	√

22. well-formed formula; WFF
23. none; five
24. none; four or more than four
25. none
26. *They are like sentences (have same form and same content). (A '*' preceding an answer indicates that a correct answer need not be precisely like the answer suggested.)
27. *They share a logical form.
28. none
29. If Socrates survived, then Socrates survived.
30. words
31. connectives and sentence variables (or symbols)
32. none
33. none
34. a $(p \,\&\, q) \supset (p \vee q)$ c $(p \vee s) \,\&\, (\sim(p \vee s))$
    b $\sim((\sim p) \,\&\, (\sim q))$ d $(p \supset q) \vee (\sim((\sim t) \supset r))$
35. a AKpqKNpNq c CNCNpqKNpNq
    b CKApKqtNpKqt d NNCANpKtqs

Part 2

1 said to follow
2 therefore; premisses; conclusion
3 |KSR
  ‾|R
4 Smith lost the election.
5 r; s; p; q
6 form; form
7 argument; AF
8 yes; no
9 sentences
10 *In valid arguments a conclusion is not only said to follow, but actually does follow, from premisses. In invalid arguments a conclusion is said to follow, but does not follow, from premisses.
11 none
12 *like arguments (arguments have the same content, the same logical form)
13 *share a logical form (have the same logical form)
14 the sentence that is said to follow from the premisses
15 *the sentence formalized by a 'q'—but we don't know what sentence that might be, nor do we know its content
16 premisses of the argument formalized by the AF
17 conclusion of the argument formalized by the AF
18 none
19 none
20 one
21 yes
22 representations; sentences
23 yes
24 a |$p \supset q$ b |$p \supset (q \supset t)$ c |$((t \,\&\, p) \lor q) \supset r$
    |$q \supset r$ ‾|$(p \,\&\, q) \supset t$ ‾|$(\sim r) \supset (((\sim p) \lor (\sim t)) \,\&\, (\sim q))$
    |$p \supset t$
    ‾|$r \lor t$
25 a |CrKtp   b |Apq   c |CpCqNt
    ‾|CNtNr |Np |Kqt
                 ‾|Nq   ‾|Np

Part 3

1 a; c
2 symbols; WFFs; LAFs; proofs
3 connective; sentence variable; therefore
4 a ×   c ×   e ×   g ×   i √
   b √   d ×   f √   h ×   j √
5 a ×   c ×   e √   g √   i ×
   b √   d ×   f ×   h √   j ×
6 a √   c √   e √   g √   i √
   b √   d √   f √   h √   j √
7 a √   c √   e ×   g ×   i ×   k ×
   b √   d √   f √   h √   j ×   l √

8 Ki LAFs   Ko LAFs
      Ai LAFs   Ao LAFs
      Ci LAFs   Co LAFs
      Ni LAFs   No LAFs
              rep LAFs

9 **a** none
     b Ko, Ai, Ci, Ni, No, rep
     c Ki, Co
     d Ao
     e none
     f Ki, Ko, Ai, Co, rep
     g Ci, Ni, No
     h Ao
     i none
     j Ni, No
     k Ki, Ko, Ao, Co, No, rep
     l Ki, Ci, Ni
     m Ki, Ai, Co, rep (Ni is not strictly correct; the first item of the first item could begin with a 'C')
     n Ko, Ao, Ci, Co, Ni, No

10 sentences; items

11 b; d

12 *a Not a sequence of items; a 'CPQ' is neither a WFF item nor a tail item.
      *b Item 2 cannot be given a good reason because one of its items—the 't'—cannot be given a good reason.

13 **a** √   **c** ×   **e** √
      b √   **d** √   **f** √

14 **a** 1, 2, Ki   **f** 1, 2, Co
      b 1, Ko   **g** 1, No
      c 1, 2, 3, Ao   **h** 1, Ni
      d 1, Ai   **i** 1, rep
      e 1, Ci   **j** 1, rep

15 **a** ×   **b** √   **c** √   **d** ×   **e** ×

16 **a**

17 **a** 1; 2; 5   **b** 3; 4   **c** no

18 **a** hyp   **b** hyp
          hyp   hyp
          2, 1, Co   hyp
          3, Ko   2, Ko
                                 4, 1, Ki
                                 3, 5, Co

19 **a** hyp   **b** last

20 tail; hyp

21 **a** tail   **b** item

22 **a** hyp   **b** (italic portions only)
          hyp
          Ki | 1 | p | *hyp* |
          2, Ci | 2 | CApqt | *hyp* |
          1, 3, Co | 3 | *Apq* | 1, *Ai* |
                                 | 4 | t | 2, 3, *Co* |

23 **a** ×   **b** √   **c** √   **d** –   **e** –

24 b; c

25 a; c

Part 4

1   **b**

2   **a**   ✗
    b   ✗
    c   √

3   corresponds

4   *1 | Cpr   hyp
    2 | 2.1 | p   hyp
       | 2.2 | r   1, 2.1, Co
       | 2.3 | Ars   2.2, Ai
    3 | CpArs   2, Ci

5   *1 | Ktr   hyp
    2 | Kqs   hyp
    3 | r   1, Ko
    4 | s   2, Ko
    5 | Krs   3, 4, Ki

6   *1 | CpKqNq   hyp
    2 | 2.1 | p   hyp
       | 2.2 | KqNq   1, 2.1, Co
    3 | Np   2, Ni

7   *1 | Ars   hyp
    2 | Csr   hyp
    3 | 3.1 | r   hyp
       | 3.2 | r   3.1, rep
    4 | 4.1 | s   hyp
       | 4.2 | r   2, 4.1, Co
    5 | r   1, 3, 4, Ao

8   *1 | CNps   hyp
    2 | Ns   hyp
    3 | 3.1 | Np   hyp
       | 3.2 | s   1, 3.1, Co
       | 3.3 | KsNs   3.2, 2, Ki
    4 | p   3, No

9   **a**   If it is false that Adams won, then Jackson won.
        It is false that Jackson won.
        Therefore, Adams won.
    b   yes

10   formalized

11   *1 | s   hyp
    2 | 2.1 | p   hyp
       | 2.2 | s   1, rep
       | 2.3 | 2.3.1 | q   hyp
       | | 2.3.2 | s   2.2, rep
       | | 2.3.3 | 2.3.3.1 | r   hyp
       | | | 2.3.3.2 | s   2.3.2, rep
       | | 2.3.4 | Crs   2.3.3, Ci
       | 2.4 | CqCrs   2.3, Ci
    3 | CpCqCrs   2, Ci

12
*1	Cts		hyp
2	2.1	KtNs	hyp
	2.2	t	2.1, Ko
	2.3	s	1, 2.2, Co
	2.4	Ns	2.1, Ko
	2.5	KsNs	2.3, 2.4, Ki
3	NKtNs		2, Ni

13 **a** If Jackson won, then Adams lost.
Therefore, it is false that (Jackson won and it is false that Adams lost).

    b yes

14 above; last

15
*1	CNpq			hyp
2	2.1	NApq		hyp
	2.2	CNpq		1, rep
	2.3	2.3.1	Np	hyp
		2.3.2	q	2.2, 2.3.1, Co
		2.3.3	Apq	2.3.2, Ai
		2.3.4	KApqNApq	2.3.3, 2.1, Ki
	2.4	p		2.3, No
	2.5	Apq		2.4, Ai
	2.6	KApqNApq		2.5, 2.1, Ki
3	Apq			2, No

16 *the sentence which is formalized by an 'r'

17
*1	CApqNp			hyp
2	2.1	p		hyp
	2.2	Apq		2.1, Ai
	2.3	Np		1, 2.2, Co
	2.4	2.4.1	q	hyp
		2.4.2	KpNp	2.1, 2.3, Ki
	2.5	Nq		2.4, Ni
3	CpNq			2, Ci

18
*1	CrAqp		hyp
2	Krt		hyp
3	Cqp		hyp
4	r		2, Ko
5	Aqp		1, 4, Co
6	6.1	q	hyp
	6.2	p	3, 6.1, Co
7	7.1	p	hyp
	7.2	p	7.1, rep
8	p		5, 6, 7, Ao

19
*1	q			hyp
2	2.1	NAArsNArs		hyp
	2.2	2.2.1	NArs	hyp
		2.2.2	AArsNArs	2.2.1, Ai
		2.2.3	KAArsNArsNAArsNArs	2.2.2, 2.1, Ki
	2.3	Ars		2.2, No
	2.4	AArsNArs		2.3, Ai
	2.5	KAArsNArsNAArsNArs		2.4, 2.1, Ki
3	AArsNArs			2, No

*1	CqArs				hyp
2	Ctp				hyp
3	ANArsNp				hyp
4	4.1	NArs			hyp
	4.2	CqArs			1, rep
	4.3	4.3.1	NANqNt		hyp
		4.3.2	4.3.2.1	Nq	hyp
			4.3.2.2	ANqNt	4.3.2.1, Ai
			4.3.2.3	KANqNtNANqNt	4.3.2.2, 4.3.1, Ki
		4.3.3	q		4.3.2, No
		4.3.4	Ars		4.2, 4.3.3, Co
		4.3.5	KArsNArs		4.3.4, 4.1, Ki
	4.4	ANqNt			4.3, No
5	5.1	Np			hyp
	5.2	Ctp			2, rep
	5.3	5.3.1	NANqNt		hyp
		5.3.2	5.3.2.1	Nt	hyp
			5.3.2.2	ANqNt	5.3.2.1, Ai
			5.3.2.3	KANqNtNANqNt	5.3.2.2, 5.3.1, Ki
		5.3.3	t		5.3.2, No
		5.3.4	p		5.2, 5.3.3, Co
		5.3.5	KpNp		5.3.4, 5.1, Ki
	5.4	ANqNt			5.3, No
6	ANqNt				3, 4, 5, Ao

Part 5

1 a √ b × c √ d √
2 a × b √ c × d √
3 meaning
4 a or   g it is false that   m if then
   b if then   h and   n and
   c and   i and   o and
   d and   j if then   p if then
   e and   k it is false that q it is false that
   f if then   l and
5 therefore
6 before
7 a √ d × g × j √ m × p √
   b × e √ h √ k × n √ q √
   c √ f √ i √ l × o √
8 a three   b two
9 therefore; therefore
10 (2)
11 If Mary goes then Tom goes, and if Tom goes then Mary goes.
12 a – b √ c – d √ e √
13 a √ b √ c √
14 Mary came, and John came.
15 Mary came, and John came.
16 a six   b three   c K; K   d none
17 A sentence like any of these three:
    1. Magnesium is used in missiles, because magnesium has a high melting point.

2. Magnesium is used in missiles, since magnesium has a high melting point.
3. Magnesium is used in missiles, for magnesium has a high melting point.

18 A sentence like any of these four:
1. Bears hibernate, but coyotes hunt all winter.
2. Bears hibernate, whereas coyotes hunt all winter.
3. Coyotes hunt all winter, whereas bears hibernate.
4. Coyotes hunt all winter, but bears hibernate.

19 A sentence like any of these three:
1. The Greeks conquered the Persians, though the Persians outnumbered the Greeks.
2. The Greeks conquered the Persians, although the Persians outnumbered the Greeks.
3. The Greeks conquered the Persians, even though the Persians outnumbered the Greeks.

20 ***a** 1. Melville is acknowledged as great, and if universal acclaim is required for greatness then it is false that Melville is acknowledged as great. It is false that democratic principles are everywhere respected, and universal acclaim is required for greatness.
Therefore, Dos Passos wrote *Moby Dick*.

2. | KpCqNp
| KNrq
| s

3. 1 | KpCqNp   hyp
   2 | KNrq   hyp
   3 | 3.1 | Ns   hyp
     | 3.2 | q   2, Ko
     | 3.3 | p   1, Ko
     | 3.4 | CqNp   1, Ko
     | 3.5 | 3.5.1 | Nr   hyp
     | | 3.5.2 | Np   3.4, 3.2, Co
     | | 3.5.3 | KpNp   3.3, 3.5.2, Ki
     | 3.6 | r   3.5, No
     | 3.7 | Nr   2, Ko
     | 3.8 | KrNr   3.6, 3.7, Ki
   4 | s   3, No

*b 1. If Ted bought the gun, then Carlo fired the shot.
If Mary was blackmailed, then Carlo fired the shot.
Therefore, it is false that (Roger is innocent and Fred is culpable and if Fred is culpable then it is false that Roger is innocent).

2. | Cpq
| Crq
| NKKstCtNs

3. 1 | Cpq   hyp
   2 | Crq   hyp
   3 | 3.1 | KKstCtNs   hyp
     | 3.2 | Kst   3.1, Ko
     | 3.3 | CtNs   3.1, Ko
     | 3.4 | s   3.2, Ko
     | 3.5 | t   3.2, Ko
     | 3.6 | Ns   3.3, 3.5, Co
     | 3.7 | KsNs   3.4, 3.6, Ki
   4 | NKKstCtNs   3, Ni

*c 1. State primaries are of some worth, or it is false that politicians are more perceptive than formerly.

If income is some indication of worth, then politicians are more perceptive than formerly.

Therefore, if some convention delegates are selected through primaries, then if if voters are more discriminating then politicians are more perceptive than formerly, then if income is some indication of worth then state primaries are of some worth.

2. |ApNq
  |Crq
  |CsCCtqCrp

3.

1 | ApNq — hyp
2 | Crq — hyp
3 | 3.1 | s — hyp
    3.2 | ApNq — 1, rep
    3.3 | Crq — 2, rep
    3.4 | 3.4.1 | Ctq — hyp
        3.4.2 | ApNq — 3.2, rep
        3.4.3 | Crq — 3.3, rep
        3.4.4 | 3.4.4.1 | r — hyp
                3.4.4.2 | q — 3.4.3, 3.4.4.1, Co
                3.4.4.3 | 3.4.4.3.1 | p — hyp
                        3.4.4.3.2 | p — 3.4.4.3.1, rep
                3.4.4.4 | 3.4.4.4.1 | Nq — hyp
                        3.4.4.4.2 | q — 3.4.2, rep
                        3.4.4.4.3 | 3.4.4.4.3.1 | Np — hyp
                                3.4.4.4.3.2 | KqNq — 3.4.4.2, 3.4.4.4.1, Ki
                        3.4.4.4.4 | p — 3.4.4.4.3, No
                3.4.4.5 | p — 3.4.2, 3.4.4.3, 3.4.4.4, Ao
        3.4.5 | Crp — 3.4.4, Ci
    3.5 | CCtqCrp — 3.4, Ci
4 | CsCCtqCrp — 3, Ci

*d 1. If it is false that some persons merit special privileges, then freedom from poverty is just around the corner; and if freedom from poverty is just around the corner, then it is false that some persons merit special privileges.

If some persons merit special privileges, then equality for all has been discarded as the land's hallmark.

It is false that equality for all has been discarded as the land's hallmark.

Therefore, freedom from poverty is just around the corner, or it is false that America is a land of promise.

2. |KCNpqCqNp
  |Cpr
  |Nr
  |AqNs

3. 1 | KCNpqCqNp   hyp
   2 | Cpr   hyp
   3 | Nr   hyp
   4 | 4.1 | NAqNs   hyp
       4.2 | CNpq   1, Ko
       4.3 | 4.3.1 | Np   hyp
            4.3.2 | q   4.2, 4.3.1, Co
            4.3.3 | AqNs   4.3.2, Ai
            4.3.4 | KAqNsNAqNs   4.3.3, 4.1, Ki
       4.4 | p   4.3, No
       4.5 | r   2, 4.4, Co
       4.6 | KrNr   4.5, 3, Ki
   5 | AqNs   4, No

*e 1. If you are willing to exert energy towards a goal, then you hold a goal dear.

If you pay mere lip service to a goal, then you fail to act to reach a goal. It is false that you hold a goal dear, or it is false that you fail to act to reach a goal

Therefore, if you are willing to exert energy towards a goal, then it is false that you pay mere lip service to a goal.

2. | Cpq
| Crs
| ANqNs
| CpNr

3. 1 | Cpq   hyp
   2 | Crs   hyp
   3 | ΛNqNs   hyp
   4 | 4.1 | p   hyp
       4.2 | Cpq   1, rep
       4.3 | 4.3.1 | Nq   hyp
            4.3.2 | q   4.2, 4.1, Co
            4.3.3 | 4.3.3.1 | r   hyp
                    4.3.3.2 | KqNq   4.3.2, 4.3.1, Ki
            4.3.4 | Nr   4.3.3, Ni
       4.4 | Crs   2, rep
       4.5 | 4.5.1 | Ns   hyp
            4.5.2 | Crs   4.4, rep
            4.5.3 | 4.5.3.1 | r   hyp
                    4.5.3.2 | s   4.5.2, 4.5.3.1, Co
                    4.5.3.3 | KsNs   4.5.3.2, 4.5.1, Ki
            4.5.4 | Nr   4.5.3, Ni
       4.6 | Nr   3, 4.3, 4.5, Ao
   5 | CpNr   4, Ci

Glossary

1   *AF:* Abbreviation of 'argument formula' (which see).
2   *Argument:* An argument is a sequence of sentences in which one sentence, called the conclusion, is said to follow from the other sentences, called the premises; so in the defined sense an argument is an expression, rather than a meaning.
3   *Argument formula:* **a.** An argument formula is a formalization of an argument, a symbolic expression that isolates a logical form of an argument. For example, a

> CNpq
> Nq
> p

is an argument formula that isolates a logical form—formalizes—for instance an argument

> *If it is false that language is ambiguous, then stipulative definitions are useless.*
> *It is false that stipulative definitions are useless.*
> *Therefore, language is ambiguous.*

b. In terms of system F an AF can be defined as a sequence of WFFs [well-formed formula (which see)], one 'therefore'-indicator ('Ⱶ') (which see), and exactly one WFF below the 'Ⱶ'.

4   *'and' sentence:* Two sentences connected by an 'and.' (And an 'unless' sentence is two sentences connected by an 'unless'; and so on for other connecting words.)
5   *Connecting word:* A connecting word is a word which when placed before one sentence yields another sentence or when placed between two sentences yields another sentence. ("Sentential connecting word" might be a more descriptive terminology.)
6   *Connective:* **a.** A connective is a symbolic representation of a connecting word. **b.** In system F 'connective' is defined by an enumeration of the kinds of symbols that qualify as connectives in system F: 'K's, 'A's, 'C's, and 'N's.
7   *Conclusion:* The conclusion is that sentence in an argument which is said to follow from the premises; in a representable argument (see representable language), the last sentence of the argument; in nonrepresentable arguments, any sentence in the sequence may be the conclusion.
8   *Contradiction:* **a.** A contradiction is a logical or other kind of absurdity; an assertion that a thing both is and is not the case. **b.** In terms of system F, any sentence that can be formalized by a contradictory WFF (which see) is a contradiction.
9   *Contradictory WFF:* **a.** A sentence which can be formalized by a contradictory WFF is a contradiction. **b.** In terms of system F a contradictory WFF is any WFF which is a 'K' followed by two WFFs, the second of which is an 'N' followed by a WFF just like the first WFF following the 'K.' For example, a

> KpNp

and a

> KApNpNApNp

are both contradictory WFFs. And the sentence

> *Language communicates and it is false that language communicates.*

is a contradiction, since the sentence could be formalized by the contradictory WFF

> KpNp

(Note that a 'KNpp' is not a contradictory WFF; so to restrict contradictory WFFs is admittedly but harmlessly arbitrary, and the restriction yields considerable simplicity and uniformity.)

10 *Corresponding AF (or corresponding proof):* **a.** If an AF corresponds to a proof (which see) then the proof has as its only hypotheses (which see) formalizations (which see) of the formalized argument's premises and the proof has as last item a formalization of the conclusion of the argument formalized by the AF. **b.** In terms of system F an AF corresponds to a proof if and only if the only items above the 'therefore' indicator ('⊢') for the AF are just like the items above the '⊢' for the proof and the only item below the '⊢' for the AF is an item just like the last item of the proof.

11 *Formalization:* **a.** A symbolic expression which isolates a logical form of a linguistic expression—sentence, argument, or even a more extended piece of prose. **b.** In terms of system F, a formalization is an expression composed of nothing but sentence variables (which see), connectives, and perhaps 'therefore' indicators. For example, a

    CNpq

is a formalization (and also a WFF); and a

    |CCpqr
    |Nr
    |ANpq

is a formalization (and also an AF).

12 *Good reason:* In terms of system F, having a good reason is a property an item (which see) (expression) possesses in virtue of its own shape and the relation of the expression to certain other expressions in the context of a sequence, such that the given expression can be regarded as in a certain specified relation by a person wanting to justify the placing of that expression in the context of a sequence. Also, derivately, we call 'good reason' an expression indicating how a WFF item can be justified within a sequence of items that is a proof.

13 *Hypothesis:* **a.** An hypothesis is an assumption entertained to discover its consequences. **b.** In terms of system F, any WFF item above a 'therefore' indicator can be justified as an hypothesis; or in other words, any such item has 'hypothesis' as a good reason.

14 *Item:* In terms of system F, an item is a unit of a sequence; items are of two kinds —WFFs items and tail items (which see); a WFF item is simply a WFF considered as a unit of a sequence; a tail item is a sequence of items considered as a unit of a sequence.

15 *'it is false that' sentence:* A sentence which is one sentence preceded by an 'it is false that' is an 'it is false that' sentence.

16 *'if then' sentence:* An 'if then' sentence is a sentence which is two sentences properly connected by an 'if then.'

17 *LAF:* Abbreviation of 'logical argument formula' (which see).

18 *Like expressions:* Two expressions are like expressions if and only if the expressions are similar with respect to shape. For example, the expression

    match

is like the expression

    match

but unlike the expression

    lighter

Note that like expressions are not necessarily like in meaning.

19 *Logical argument formula:* **a.** Part 2 reflects intuitions and defines 'logical argu-

ment formula' as an argument formula or AF such that every argument that could be formalized by that AF is a valid argument (which see). **b.** Part 3 gives an economic and systematic treatment of LAF and defines 'logical argument formula' by an enumeration of kinds: An argument formula is a LAF in system F if and only if the AF is an expression of one of these nine kinds:

K-in LAF	K-out LAF
A-in LAF	A-out LAF
C-in LAF	C-out LAF
N-in LAF	N-out LAF
repetition LAF	

where each of these kinds of LAFs is defined in terms of the relative shape and placing of the expressions occurring as items within the AF.

20 *Lukasiewicz notation:* Lukasiewicz notation is a notation which prefixes connectives, needs no signs of punctuation, and uses as connectives 'K's, 'A's, 'C's, and 'N's; sometimes called "Polish notation."

21 *Premisses:* The premisses are those sentences in an argument from which the conclusion is said to follow; in a representable argument, all the premisses precede the conclusion; in a nonrepresentable argument, any sentence in the sequence may be a premiss.

22 Principia-*like notation:* Principia-like notation is a notation closely related to that of *Principia Mathematica* and a notation, moreover, which infixes connectives, uses '&'s, '∨'s, '⊃'s, and '∼'s as connectives, and has some device for punctuation—dots or parentheses, for example—to eliminate ambiguity in well-formed formulas.

23 *Proof:* In terms of system F, a proof is a sequence of items each of which has a good reason, but see also Appendix B.

24 *Related representable argument:* A related representable argument is an argument as close in meaning as possible to some given argument but an argument written in a representable language (which see).

25 *Representable language:* **a.** Language whose very shape makes explicit the relevant logical or argumentive force of the language. **b.** In terms of system F, representable language is language whose only connecting words are 'and's, 'or's, 'if then's, and 'it is false that's, and such that any argument in that language has premisses before conclusion and a 'therefore' preceding the conclusion.

26 *Representable connecting word:* **a.** A connecting word for which a convention for representing has been established (see under *Representation*). **b.** In terms of system F, a representable connecting word is one that notation conventions and representing conventions allow to be represented by a connective in system F.

27 *Representation:* **a.** A symbolic expression, each symbol of which corresponds in a known way to the represented expression; and the known way in which the symbols correspond to represented expressions is specified by conventions—that is, by agreeing on a notation. The specification of conventions for representing and then for writing a formalization given a representation can be regarded as an interpretation of a formal system, where the formalizations are expressions within that formal system. **b.** The representing conventions set down for use with system F are as follows:

1. Sentences containing no connecting words are represented by capitals other than 'K's, 'A's, 'C's, and 'N's.
2. Connecting words are represented as follows:
   a. A 'K' represents an 'and',

b. An 'A' represents an 'or',

c. A 'C' represents an 'if then', and

d. An 'N' represents an 'it is false that'.

3. When sentences that contain connecting words are represented, the symbol representing the connecting word precedes the symbols representing the sentences joined by the connecting word.

4. A 'Ͱ' represents a 'therefore.'

5. When arguments are represented, the representations of the premises go above the horizontal line of the 'therefore' indicator, and the representation of the conclusion goes below the horizontal line of the 'therefore' indicator.

28 *Single quotation marks:* In the usage of this book, an expression enclosed in single quotation marks is used to name any expression like the one enclosed between the quotes. For example, a 'K' names

K

as well as

K

A 'Cpq' names

Cpq

and a "Cpq" names

'Cpq'

and so on.

29 *Sentence variable:* **a.** A sentence variable is a symbolic expression which isolates a logical form of a sentence and such that the only form isolated is that of being a sentence. **b.** In terms of system F, a sentence variable is a 'p,' 'q,' 'r,' 's,' or 't.'

30 *Sound argument:* A sound argument is a valid argument with true premises.

31 *Tail item:* **a.** Tail items are a device of system F (and there is some parallel device in any system of natural deduction—sometimes called "subordinate proofs" or "conditional proofs") that parallels our practice in "argument" of making assumptions and exploring their consequences—whether or not we assert the assumption. **b.** In terms of system F a tail item is a sequence of items considered as a single item of another sequence of items.

32 *'therefore' indicator:* **a.** A 'therefore' indicator is a word or sign signaling the conclusion of an argument. **b.** In terms of system F, any 'Ͱ' is a 'therefore' indicator.

33 *Valid argument:* **a.** Intuitively, a valid argument is an argument in which the conclusion is not only said to, but actually does, follow from the premises. **b.** In terms of system F, a valid argument is an argument that can be formalized by an AF that corresponds to a proof in system F.

34 *Well-formed formula (WFF):* **a.** A well-formed formula is a formalization of a sentence. **b.** In terms of system F a WFF is defined recursively as follows:

1. Any sentence variable in system F is a WFF in system F.

2. Any 'K,' 'A,' or 'C' followed by two WFFs in system F is a WFF in system F.

3. Any 'N' followed by one WFF in system F is a WFF in system F.

4. An expression is a WFF in system F if and only if it can be seen to be a WFF by statements 1 to 3.

35 *WFF:* Abbreviation of 'well-formed formula' (which see).